Making Gluten-Free Living Easy!

D1397315

Cecelia's Marketplace
Kalamazoo, Michigan

www.CeceliasMarketplace.com

Gluten/Casein/Soy Free

GROCERY SHOPPING
GUIDE

2011/2012 EDITION

Dr. Mara Matison
Dainis Matison

khP
Kal-Haven Publishing

Cecelia's Marketplace
Gluten/Casein/Soy Free Grocery Shopping Guide

by Dr. Mara Matison & Dainis Matison

khP

Kal-Haven Publishing
P.O. Box 20383
Kalamazoo, MI 49019 U.S.A.

ISBN 978-0-9831659-0-3

2011 / 2012 Edition

Printed in the United States of America
Cover illustration: Lilita Austrins

CONTENTS

About the Authors

The co-author of this book, Dr. Mara Matison, received her Doctor of Dental Surgery degree from University of Detroit Mercy, and her Bachelor of Arts degree in Psychology from Villanova University. Her husband and co-author, Dainis Matison, received his Master of Science degree in Information Technology and Bachelor of Arts degree in Finance from Ball State University. They are both members of Celiac Disease Foundation, Celiac Sprue Association, Gluten Intolerance Group, and supporters of Talk About Curing Autism and Generation Rescue. These are nationwide organizations that support people with celiac disease, gluten intolerance, gluten sensitivity and autism.

Cecelia's Marketplace was established by both Mara and Dainis in 2006, soon after Mara was diagnosed with celiac disease. The couple struggled with Mara's huge lifestyle change, which included adhering to a strict gluten-free diet. Shopping trips to the grocery store were very frustrating. Spending time calling food manufacturers to find out if products were gluten-free seemed like a daily routine. They knew there had to be an easier way, so they decided to compile a gluten-free grocery shopping guide. Since then, Mara has also been diagnosed with a casein and soy intolerance, which brought about the need for the *Gluten/Casein Free Grocery Shopping Guide* and the *Gluten/Casein/Soy Free Grocery Shopping Guide*. Her latest achievement is the newly released *Cecelia's Marketplace International Classics Gluten-Free Mexican* cookbook.

Thanks to all three of Cecelia's Marketplace Grocery Shopping Guides and the Gluten-Free Mexican cookbook, gluten-free living has now become easier not only for the authors, but also their families, friends and thousands of celiacs nationwide.

Preface - Note to the Reader

Cecelia's Marketplace Gluten/Casein/Soy Free Grocery Shopping Guide has been written to help people that are in search of gluten-free, casein-free and soy-free (GFCFSF) products. Whether you are on a GFCFSF diet, prepare GFCFSF meals for yourself or others, or just enjoy eating GFCFSF foods, this book is for you. It will help guide you to easy grocery shopping and eliminate the frustration and headaches that you've experienced trying to find GFCFSF products. This guide is also great for restaurant owners, chefs, dieticians, family members, husbands, wives, friends, and others who shop for, or prepare GFCFSF foods. For those that are not familiar with GFCFSF cooking or GFCFSF dining out, we have included three sections in the front of the book: *What is Gluten Casein & Soy, Clean Kitchen Tips,* and *Gluten/Casein/Soy Free Dining Out.*

We have alphabetized our *Gluten/Casein/Soy Free Grocery Shopping Guide* to help you quickly find brand names of the GFCFSF products. The guide is easy to use: just pick a product, look it up, and you'll have GFCFSF brands at your fingertips. This book is small enough so that it can be carried with you to the grocery store when searching for products. Use it anytime, anywhere. In addition to the grocery shopping guide, there is a section in the back of the book that lists GFCFSF over the counter (OTC) medications. GFCFSF shopping has never been easier. Treasure this book and enjoy all the GFCFSF foods that are available!

Due to periodic changes in ingredients and new products being released, *Cecelia's Marketplace Gluten/Casein/Soy Free Grocery Shopping Guide* will be updated annually. Look for the new edition every year.

A percentage of our proceeds are donated to nationwide nonprofit organizations that support people with celiac disease, gluten intolerance, autism, and other food sensitivities.

Dr. Mara Matison & Dainis Matison

Acknowledgments

There are many people that have contributed to the creation of this book. The support from our family and friends has made this journey more enjoyable. Lilita A. for editing, cover illustration, and all the gluten-free meals that kept us going; Mik for editing, critiquing and successful business strategies; Ray for the reference materials and guidance to becoming successful entrepreneurs; Ligita for supporting us and all the delicious gluten-free recipes along the way; Lija for marketing & advertising; Lilita M. for showing us 'The Secret'; Liana, Velta, Ilga, Ryan and Matiss for believing in us; Our meticulous data collection and editing team of Annette Hensley, Caroline Aasen, Jessica Hensley, Jessica Rector, Jessica Schmidt, John Williamson, Lauma Matison, Melissa Al-Azzawi and Sarah Gregor; Jonnie Bryant for all the publishing advice and knowledge; Dr. Heidi Gjersoe for the diagnosis and support; Tracy Clupper for data entry & document styling; Natural Health Center for the wonderful gluten-free book signing events; Dr. Arnis Pone, Dr. Jason Ham, Kal-Haven Publishing, McNaughton & Gunn, and all our fellow "celiacs" for all the support.

Warning - Disclaimer

This book has been prepared for the gluten-free, casein-free and soy-free (GFCFSF) consumer in order to make GFCFSF grocery shopping easier.

This book should be used as an aide to guide the GFCFSF consumer in the right direction when trying to find GFCFSF products. The content of this book is not medical advice, nor is it the advice of medical professionals. The authors, Cecelia's Marketplace, and Kal-Haven Publishing shall have neither liability, nor responsibility to any person or entity with respect to gluten, casein or soy ingestion or any health consequence.

Every effort has been made to make this gluten/casein/soy free grocery shopping guide as complete and accurate as possible. However, there may be errors, both typographical and in content. Therefore, this guide should be used only as a general guide, not as the ultimate source for GFCFSF information. Food companies and manufacturers indicate that product ingredients may change periodically; therefore, the consumer needs to always check the ingredients on the manufacturers' labels before consuming their products. For specific questions or further information on a gluten/casein/soy free diet, please consult your physician.

If you do not wish to be bound by the above, you may return this book to the publisher within 30 days of purchase for a full refund (minus any shipping fees).

What is Gluten, Casein & Soy ?

Gluten is a special type of protein that is most commonly found in wheat, rye, and barley. It is comprised of two main protein groups: gliadins, and gluteins. People who have celiac disease, gluten intolerance, or gluten sensitivity may suffer from chronic digestive problems when ingesting foods that contain gluten. Gluten is found in most cereals, breads, pastas, soups, and pizza crusts. It may also be hidden in foods such as seasonings, salad dressings, sauces, additives and natural flavors.

Casein is a protein found in milk. It is a phosphoprotein, which is a collection of proteins bound to phosphoric acid. Casein is found in products containing milk, such as cheese, butter, cream, yogurt, ice cream and any other derivative of milk. Many people suffering from celiac disease or casein intolerance cannot properly digest this protein.

Soy is derived from the soybean, also called the soya bean. Common forms of soy include soy meal, soy flour, soy milk, soy sauce, tofu, textured vegetable protein, tempeh, soy lecithin and soybean oil. Various studies show that most soy allergic individuals may safely eat products that contain soy lecithin and soybean oil, since they do not contain the soy protein. On the contrary, other studies show that any form of soy should be avoided for those individuals with either a soy intolerance or soy allergy.

Maintaining a strict gluten/casein/soy free diet has shown to greatly improve the symptoms of celiac disease, and gluten/casein/soy intolerance. After gluten, casein and soy are eliminated from the diet, the digestive tract begins to heal and the symptoms normally start to disappear after a few weeks[1].

---

1. http://www.mayoclinic.com/health/celiac-disease/DS00319/DSECTION=treatments-and-drugs

Clean Kitchen Tips

It is very important prior to preparing a gluten/casein/soy free (GFCFSF) meal, to clean the surrounding area including, pots, pans, utensils and any other items being used. Bread crumbs, flour particles or other gluten, casein or soy containing foods left in the cooking area can potentially contaminate a GFCFSF meal.

Here are some tips to help prevent gluten, casein and soy contamination:

- Use an uncontaminated sponge to wash all working surfaces with soap and water.

- Clean and inspect pots, pans, utensils, cutting boards and other kitchenware for gluten, casein or soy residue.

- Use clean kitchen hand towels.

- If grilling, place aluminum foil over the grilling surface.

- Use squeeze bottle mustard, ketchup, peanut butter, jelly/jam, or other condiments to prevent cross-contamination.

- Avoid using wooden utensils. Gluten, casein and/or soy residue can stay embedded in wooden utensils and cutting boards.

- Use a separate toaster for GFCFSF bread, rice cakes, etc..

- Do not deep fry foods in contaminated oil (e.g. from breaded chicken wings, breaded chicken tenders, mozzarella sticks).

- In commercial kitchens, if using latex/rubber gloves, make sure the gloves are not coated with powder (starch).

Our Data Collection

The product information in this book was collected between August 2010 - November 2010. The information was received from product manufacturers and major supermarkets via internet, e-mail, phone, mail, or product labels.

The Food and Drug Administration (FDA) has proposed to define the term "gluten-free" as containing less than 20 parts per million (ppm) gluten. A final rule on this proposal will be issued no later than four years after the law's enactment date of August 2008. For further information on this regulation please visit www.fda.gov.

Some food manufacturers test their products for the presence of gluten. Those products that have not passed this test have been excluded from this book. Currently, not all companies test their products, therefore, we cannot guarantee that all the products listed in our book are less than 20 ppm gluten.

Casein is the protein found in milk products. Milk is one of the top eight allergens recognized by the FDA. Products containing any form of milk have been excluded from this guide. This includes casein, caseinate, lactose, and any other milk derivative.

Soy is also one of the top eight allergens recognized by the FDA. Products containing any form of soy have been omitted from this guide, as well as soy lecithin and soybean oil.

Those products that have been manufactured in the same facility or on shared equipment with gluten, casein or soy, but follow strict cross-contamination control guidelines, have been included. We have tried our best not to include products from manufacturers that do not take measures to prevent cross-contamination.

For more information on our data collection and up to date product alerts, please visit our website www.CeceliasMarketplace.com.

Symbols

There are some companies that manufacture their products in a dedicated gluten-free facility or environment. Some products also go through strict guidelines and vigorous testing by either the Celiac Sprue Association (CSA) Recognition Seal Program or the Gluten Intolerance Group (GIG) Gluten-Free Certification Organization to be verified as gluten-free. In this guide we have marked these manufacturers and products with the following symbols:

▲ - manufactured in a dedicated gluten-free facility or environment
● - verfied, tested, or certified gluten-free by either the CSA Recognition Seal Program or the GIG Gluten-Free Certification Organization

Celiac Spruce Association®

There are also some manufacturers that label their gluten-free, casein-free and/or soy-free products as being manufactured in the same facility or on shared equipment with gluten, casein and/or soy. In this guide we have labeled those products with following symbols:

! - manufactured in the same facility as other products containing gluten, casein and/or soy

!! - manufactured on shared equipment as other products containing gluten, casein and/or soy

Gluten/Casein/Soy Free Dining Out

Nationwide restaurant chains offering *gluten-free menus:

Austin Grill
Bertucci's Italian Restaurant
Biaggi's Ristorante Italiano
Bonefish Grill
Bugaboo Creek Steak House
Carino's Italian
Carrabba's Italian Grill
Charlie Brown's Steakhouse
Cheeseburger In Paradise Bar & Grill
Claim Jumper Restaurants
Daily Grill
Fire Bowl Café
Fleming's Prime Steakhouse & Wine Bar
Garlic Jim's Famous Gourmet Pizza
Lee Roy Selmon's
Legal Sea Foods Restaurant & Oyster Bar
Mama Fu's Asian House
Mitchell's Fish Market
Ninety Nine 99
Old Spaghetti Factory
Outback Steakhouse
P.F. Chang's China Bistro
Pei Wei Asian Diner
Pizza Fusion
The Melting Pot
Village Tavern
Weber Grill Restaurant
Wildfire Steaks, Chops & Seafood
Z' Tejas Southwestern Grill

*These menus are only gluten-free. Please explain to the wait staff that the meal needs to be gluten-free, casein-free and soy-free.

Other Products Available
by Cecelia's Marketplace

<u>Grocery Shopping Guides:</u>
Gluten-Free
Gluten/Casein Free

<u>Cookbooks:</u>
Gluten-Free Mexican

<u>Other Products:</u>
Gluten-Free Dining Out Cards

<u>FREE Email Newsletter:</u>
Gluten-Free Product of the Day

For **Product Alerts** or more information about our products please visit us online:

www.CeceliasMarketplace.com

This book is dedicated to:

All those in search of gluten/casein/soy free products.

Gluten/Casein/Soy Free Grocery Shopping Guide (A-Z)

A A

Almond Beverages... see Nut Beverages
Almonds... see Nuts
Amaranth
  Arrowhead Mills - Whole Grain
  Bob's Red Mill▲ - Organic Flour
  Gluty Free - Organic●
  Nu-World Foods▲ -
    Amaranth Side Serve (Garlic Herb●, Savory Herb●,
      Spanish Tomato●)
    Bread Crumbs●
    Flour●
    Pre Gel Powder●
    Puffed●
    Seed●
    Starch●
    Toasted Bran Flour●
Anchovies
  Crown Prince -
    Flat In Olive Oil
    Natural (Anchovy Paste, Fillets Of Anchovies In Olive Oil)
    Rolled w/Capers In Olive Oil
Angel Hair Pasta... see Pasta
Animal Crackers... see Cookies
Apple Butter
  Eden Organic - Apple, Apple Cherry, Cherry
  Fischer & Wieser - Pecan
  Lucky Leaf
  Musselman's
Apple Cider... see Cider/Cider Mix
Apple Cider Vinegar... see Vinegar
Apple Rings
  Lucky Leaf - Spiced
  Musselman's - Spiced

A

Apples
... *All Fresh Apples Are Gluten/Casein/Soy Free

Dole - All Fruits Bowls *(Except Fruit Crisps)*

Earthbound Farm - Organic Sliced

Gluty Free - Dried (Cinnamon●, Organic●, Regular●)

Lucky Leaf - Fried, Sliced

Musselman's - Sliced

Nuts Online - Dried Apples (Cinnamon Wedges●, Diced Fuji●, Dried●, Infused Dried Wedges●, Organic Chips●, Organic Dried●, Simply Organic●)

Applesauce

Albertsons - Cinnamon, Natural, Original

Apple Time - Regular

Beech-Nut - Applesauce (Stage 1 Fruits, Stage 2 Fruits)

Eden Organic - Organic Apple (Cherry, Cinnamon, Regular, Strawberry)

Full Circle - Organic (No Sugar Added, Sweetened)

Great Value Brand (Wal-Mart) -
Applesauce Glass Jar (Cinnamon, Regular, Unsweetened)
Applesauce Plastic Cups (Cinnamon, Light, Natural, No Sugar Added, Regular, Strawberry)

Hy-Vee - Applesauce, Cinnamon, Light (w/Mixed Berry, w/ Strawberry), Natural, Unsweetened

Kroger Brand - Flavored, Plain

Lucky Leaf - Cherry Fruit 'N Sauce, Cinnamon, Natural, Regular, Strawberry Fruit 'N Sauce

Meijer Brand - Chunky, Cinnamon, Mixed Berry, Natural, Organic (Cinnamon, Sweetened, Unsweetened), Original, Regular, Strawberry

Midwest Country Fare - Home Style, Natural w/(Cinnamon, Peaches, Raspberries, Strawberries)

Momma's Old-Fashioned Applesauce - No Sugar Added, Original Flavor

Mott's - Chunky, Cinnamon, Homestyle, Natural No Sugar Added, Original

A **Musselman's -**
  Chunky
  Cinnamon (Lite, Regular)
  Golden Delicious
  Granny Smith
  Healthy Picks (Blueberry Pomegranate, Cupucacu Key Lime,
    Raspberry Acai)
  Homestyle (Cinnamon, Regular)
  Lite Fruit 'N Sauce (Cherry, Grape, Orange Mango, Peach,
    Raspberry, Strawberry)
  McIntosh Apple
  Organic (Regular, Unsweetened)
  Regular
  Totally Fruit (Apple, Mixed Berry, Peach, Strawberry)
  Unsweetened
Nature's Goodness Baby Food - Stage I, Stage 2
O Organics
Publix - Chunky, Cinnamon, Old Fashioned, Unsweetened
Publix GreenWise Market - Organic Unsweetened
Safeway Brand - Cups, Natural, Sweetened
Santa Cruz - Fruit Sauces (All Varieties)
Spartan Brand - Cinnamon, Natural, Peach, Raspberry, Regular,
  Strawberry
Stop & Shop Brand - Chunky, Cinnamon, Mixed Berry, Natural,
  Strawberry
Tree Top - Cinnamon, Naturally Sweetened, No Sugar Added
  Natural, Organic, Raspberry, Strawberry
Wegmans Brand -
  Chunky
  Cinnamon
  McIntosh
  Mixed Berry
  Natural (Chunky, No Sugar Added)
  No Sugar Added

Peach Mango

Regular

Winn Dixie - Cinnamon, Sweetened, Unsweetened

Woodstock Farms - Organic (Apricot, Blueberry, Cinnamon, Mango, Regular)

Apricots

... *All Fresh Apricots Are Gluten/Casein/Soy Free*

Albertsons - Canned

Del Monte - Canned/Jarred Fruit (All Varieties), Fruit Snack Cups (Metal, Plastic)

Gluty Free - Dried (California●, Diced●, Organic Turkish●, Pluots●, Turkish●)

Hy-Vee - Lite Unpeeled Halves Sweetened w/Splenda, Unpeeled Halves

Nuts Online - Dried Fruit (California●, Diced●, Dried●, Organic California●, Organic Turkish●, Pluots●)

Publix - Canned Halves Unpeeled (In Heavy Syrup, Water & Artificial Sweetener)

S&W - All Canned/Jarred Fruits

Stop & Shop Brand - Heavy Syrup, Island Apricots In Light Syrup, w/Splenda

Winn Dixie - Unpeeled Halves In Heavy Syrup

Artichokes

... *All Fresh Artichokes Are Gluten/Casein/Soy Free*

Birds Eye - All Plain Frozen Artichokes

C & W - All Plain Frozen Artichokes

Cara Mia - In Water, Marinated

Kirkland Signature - Hearts

Mezzetta - Grilled

Native Forest - Artichoke Hearts (Marinated, Quartered, Whole)

Reese - Hearts (Extra Small, Medium, Large, Quartered Small)

Safeway Select - Marinated Artichoke

Spartan Brand - Hearts

A

B

Trader Joe's - Artichoke Antipasto**!!**, Artichoke Hearts In Water,
Artichoke Red Pepper Tapenade**!!**

Wegmans Brand - Artichoke Hearts (Halves & Quarters, In Brine,
Marinated Quartered)

Asparagus

... *All Fresh Asparagus Is Gluten/Casein/Soy Free*

Albertsons - Cuts & Tips, No Salt Spears, Whole Spears

Birds Eye - All Plain Frozen Asparagus

Del Monte - All Canned Asparagus

Great Value Brand (Wal-Mart) - Canned (All Green Asparagus
Spears, Extra Long)

Green Giant - Canned Spears, Cut Asparagus

Hannaford Brand - Cuts & Tips, Whole Tall

Hy-Vee - Cut Spears

Kroger Brand - All Plain Asparagus (Canned, Frozen)

Meijer Brand - Canned Cuts & Tips

Native Forest - Green (Cuts & Tips, Spears)

Nuts Online - Simply Asparagus Freeze Dried Vegetables●

S&W - All Canned Asparagus

Safeway Brand - Canned Cut

Spartan Brand - Cut

Stop & Shop Brand - Asparagus (Spears, Tips & Cuts)

Trader Joe's - Frozen Spears (Grilled, Regular)

Wegmans Brand - Cleaned & Cut Tips, Cut Spears & Tips

Woodstock Farms - Organic Frozen Whole Baby Asparagus

Avocado

... *All Fresh Avocados Are Gluten/Casein/Soy Free*

Avocado Dip... see Guacamole and/or Dip/Dip Mix

B

Baby Food

Baby Mum-Mum▲ - Rice Rusks (Banana, Organic Original)

baby food

B

Beech-Nut -
  Rice Cereal
  Stage 1 Fruits (Applesauce, Chiquita Bananas, Peaches, Pears)
  Stage 1 Meats (Beef & Beef Broth, Chicken & Chicken Broth, Turkey & Turkey Broth)
  Stage 1 Vegetables (Butternut Squash, Tender Golden Sweet Potatoes, Tender Sweet Carrots, Tender Sweet Peas, Tender Young Green Beans)
  Stage 2 Desserts DHA Plus Apple Delight
  Stage 2 Dinners (Apples & Chicken, Chicken & Rice, Chicken Noodle, Macaroni & Beef w/Vegetables, Pineapple Glazed Ham, Sweet Potatoes & Chicken, Turkey Rice, Vegetables & Chicken)
  Stage 2 Dinners Good Evening (Ham & Pineapple & Rice, Sweet Potato & Turkey)
  Stage 2 Fruits (Apples & Bananas, Apples & Blueberries, Apples & Cherries, Apples Mango & Kiwi, Apples Pears & Bananas, Applesauce, Apricots w/Pears & Apples, Chiquita Bananas, Chiquita Bananas & Strawberries, DHA Plus Apple Delight, DHA Plus Apple w/Pomegranate Juice, DHA Plus Banana Supreme, Mango, Peaches, Pears, Pears & Pineapples, Pears & Raspberries)
  Stage 2 Rice Cereal Apples w/Cinnamon
  Stage 2 Vegetables (Butternut Squash, Corn & Sweet Potatoes, Country Garden Vegetables, DHA Plus Butternut Squash w/ Corn, DHA Plus Sweet Potatoes, Mixed Vegetables, Sweet Corn Casserole, Sweet Potatoes & Apples, Tender (Sweet Carrots, Sweet Peas, Young Green Beans), Tender Golden Sweet Potatoes)
  Stage 3 Dinners (Country Vegetables & Chicken, Turkey Rice)
  Stage 3 Fruits (Apples & Bananas, Chiquita Bananas, Homestyle Apples Cherries Plums, Homestyle Cinnamon Raisins & Pears, Homestyle Peaches Apples & Bananas, Homestyle Pears & Blueberries)

B

Stage 3 Rice Cereal & Pears

Stage 3 Vegetables (Green Beans Corn & Rice, Sweet Potatoes)

Earth's Best Organic Baby Food -

1st Foods (Apples, Bananas, Carrots, Pears, Peas, Prunes, Squash, Sweet Potatoes)

2nd Antioxidant Blends (Apple Butternut Squash, Banana Mango, Carrot Tomato, Sweet Potato Apricot)

2nd Dinners (Rice & Lentil, Summer Vegetable, Sweet Potatoes & Chicken)

2nd Fruits (Apples, Apples & Apricots, Apples & Bananas, Apples & Blueberries, Apples & Plums, Bananas, Bananas Peaches & Raspberries, Pears, Pears & Mangos, Pears & Raspberries, Plum Banana Brown Rice Fruit & Whole Grain Combination)

2nd Gourmet Meals (Creamy Chicken Apple Compote, Sweet Pea Turkey Wild Rice)

2nd Seasonal Harvest (Pumpkin Apple, Sweet Potato Cinnamon)

2nd Vegetables (Carrots, Corn & Butternut Squash, Garden Vegetables, Green Beans & Rice, Peas & Brown Rice, Sweet Potatoes, Winter Squash)

3rd Dinners (Vegetable Beef Pilaf)

3rd Fruits (Banana & Strawberries, Chunky Orchard Fruit)

3rd Vegetable Medley (Sweet Corn & Carrot)

Whole Grain Rice Cereal (Apples)

Ella's Kitchen -

Smoothie Fruits (The Green One, The Purple One, The Red One, The Yellow One)

Stage 1 Baby Food (Apples & Bananas, Broccoli Pears & Peas, Butternut Squash Carrots Apples & Prunes, Carrots Apples & Parsnips, Peaches & Bananas, Spinach Apples & Rutabaga, Strawberries & Apples, Sweet Potatoes Pumpkin Apples & Blueberries)

Gerber Baby Food -

1st Foods Fruits & Vegetables (Applesauce, Bananas, Carrots,

Green Beans, Peaches, Pears, Peas, Prunes, Squash, Sweet
Potatoes)

2nd Foods Dinners (Apples & Chicken, Beef & Beef Gravy,
Chicken & Chicken Gravy, Chicken & Rice, Ham & Ham Gravy,
Sweet Potatoes & Turkey, Turkey & Turkey Gravy, Veal & Veal
Gravy, Vegetable Beef, Vegetable Chicken)

2nd Foods Fruits & Vegetables (Apple Blueberry, Apple Strawberry
Banana, Apples & Cherries, Applesauce, Apricots w/Mixed Fruit,
Banana Mixed Berry, Banana Orange Medley, Banana Plum
Grape, Banana w/Apples & Pears, Bananas, Butternut Squash
& Corn, Carrots, Green Beans, Peaches, Pear Pineapples, Pears,
Peas, Prunes w/Apples, Sweet Potatoes)

2nd Foods Smoothies (Fruit Medley, Mango, Peach Cobbler)

3rd Foods Dinners (Mixed Vegetables & Beef, Mixed Vegetables &
Chicken, Mixed Vegetables & Turkey, Turkey Rice & Vegetables)

3rd Foods Fruits & Vegetables (Apples, Banana Strawberry,
Bananas, Green Beans w/Rice, Peaches, Pears, Squash, Sweet
Potatoes)

3rd Foods Smoothies (Fruit Medley)

Graduates Fruit (Diced Apples)

Graduates Fruit Splashers (Grape, Strawberry Kiwi, Tropical Fruit),

Graduates Fruit Strips (Strawberry, Wildberry)

Graduates Fruit Twists (Apple & Strawberry, Cherry Berry,
Strawberry & Grape)

Graduates Lil Entrees (White Turkey Stew w/Rice & Vegetables)

Graduates Mini Fruit Snacks (Apple)

Graduates Vegetables (Diced Carrots)

Gerber Organic Baby Food -

1st Foods (Applesauce, Bananas, Carrots, Pears, Sweet Peas,
Sweet Potatoes)

2nd Foods (Apple Strawberry, Applesauce, Bananas, Butternut
Squash & Carrots, Butternut Squash & Corn, Carrots, Corn,
Green Beans, Pear & Wildberry, Sweet Potatoes)

B

Homemade Baby - Baby Tex Mex●, Just (Apples●, Green Beans●, Pears●, Peas●, Squash●, Sweet Potatoes●), Piwi●, Squapples●, Yummy Yammies●

Meijer Brand - Little Fruit (Apple, Strawberry/Banana), Little Veggies Corn

Nature's Goodness Baby Food -

Stage 1 Fruits & Vegetables (Applesauce, Bananas, Carrots, Green Beans, Peaches, Pears, Peas, Prunes, Squash, Sweet Potatoes)

Stage 2 Desserts (Banana Pudding, Dutch Apple, Fruit Dessert, Tutti Frutti)

Stage 2 Dinners (Apples & Chicken, Apples & Ham, Broccoli & Chicken, Green Beans & Turkey, Sweet Potato & Turkey, Turkey Rice Dinner, Vegetable Dinner (Chicken, Ham))

Stage 2 Fruits & Vegetables (Apples & Blueberries, Apples & Pears, Apples Strawberries & Bananas, Applesauce, Apricots w/Pears & Apples, Bananas, Bananas w/Apples & Pears, Bananas w/Mixed Berries, Carrots, Corn & Sweet Potatoes, Green Beans, Mixed Vegetables, Peaches, Pears, Plums w/Apples, Pumpkins w/Pears, Squash, Sweet Peas, Sweet Potatoes)

Stage 2 Rice Cereal (w/Applesauce, w/Peaches & Bananas)

Stage 3 Desserts (Bananas & Strawberries w/Tapioca, Bananas w/Tapioca)

Stage 3 Dinners (Green Beans & Rice, Turkey Rice)

Stage 3 Rice Cereal w/Apples & Bananas

Stage 3 Vegetable Sweet Potatoes

O Organics -

Stage 1 (Applesauce, Bananas, Carrots, Pears, Peas, Sweet Potatoes)

Stage 2 (Apple Apricot, Apple Banana, Apple Wild Blueberry, Applesauce, Bananas, Carrots, Mixed Vegetables, Peach Rice Banana, Pear Raspberry, Pears, Peas and Brown Rice, Prunes, Squash, Summer Vegetables, Sweet Potatoes)

Stage 3 (Sweet Potato Chicken Dinner, Vegetable Chicken Dinner, Vegetable Lentil Dinner)

Baby Formula
    Hy-Vee - Pediatric Electrolyte (Fruit, Grape, Regular)
    Kroger Brand - Comforts For Baby Pediatric Electrolyte
    Neocate - Junior (Chocolate, Tropical, Unflavored, w/Prebiotics),
        One +

Bacon
    Applegate Farms - Natural (Canadian, Dry Cured, Peppered,
        Sunday, Turkey), Organic (Sunday, Turkey)
    Busseto - Pancetta, Prosciutto
    Butcher's Cut - Hickory Smoked (Regular Sliced, Sliced Center
        Cut, Thick Sliced)
    Butterball - Turkey Bacon (Lower Sodium, Regular, Thin & Crispy)
    Dietz & Watson▲ - Canadian Style●, Gourmet Imported●
    Eckrich -
        Fresh Hickory Smoked Bacon
        Fully Cooked Ready To Crisp Bacon
    Farmer John - Classic, Old Fashion Maple Table Brand, Premium
        (Applewood, Low Sodium, Old Fashioned Maple, Thick Cut)
    Garrett County Farms - Classic Sliced (Dry Rubbed!, Turkey!),
        Sliced (Applewood!, Canadian Style!), Thick Sliced Dry Rubbed!,
        Turkey Peppered!
    Global Gourmet - Irish Bacon
    Great Value Brand (Wal-Mart) - Hickory Smoked, Low Sodium
    Hannaford Brand - Fully Cooked, Lower Sodium, Maple Flavored,
        Premium Cut, Regular
    Hertel's - All Varieties
    Honeysuckle White - Smoked Turkey Bacon
    Hormel - Black Label Bacon (Center Cut, Lower Sodium, Maple,
        Mesquite, Original), Canadian Style, Fully Cooked, Microwave,
        Natural Choice (Canadian, Original)
    Hy-Vee - Double Smoked, Fully Cooked Turkey Bacon, Hickory,
        Hickory Smoked Fully Cooked, Lower Sodium
    Jennie-O Turkey Store - Bacon (Extra Lean Turkey, Turkey)

B

Jimmy Dean - Fully Cooked Slices Thick Sliced Hickory Smoked ,
Premium Bacon (Lower Sodium, Original, Thick Slice)

Jones Dairy Farm -
Canadian●
Cherry Hardwood Smoked Regular ●
Sliced●
Old Fashioned Slab●
Sliced (Regular●, Thick●)

Kirkland Signature - Bacon, Crumbled

Kroger Brand - Canadian, Hardwood Smoked (No Sugar, Sugar
Cured), Hickory Smoked, Turkey

Kroger Value - Hickory Smoked

Meijer Brand - Lower Sodium, Regular

Old Smokehouse - Applewood, Maple Peppered, Original

Organic Prairie - Hardwood Smoked Turkey Bacon**!!**

Oscar Mayer -
America's Favorite
Center Cut
Fully Cooked (Bacon, Thick Cut)
Hearty Thick Cut
Lower Sodium
Natural Smoked Uncured

Publix - All Varieties

Pure Market Express▲ - Bac'un●

Range Brand

Safeway Brand - Fully Cooked, Hickory Smoked

Safeway Select - 40% Less Sodium, Regular Sliced, Thick Sliced

Smithfield -
Brown Sugar
Center Cut 40% Lower Fat
Cracked Peppercorn
Maple
Natural Hickory Smoked
Natural Hickory Smoked Thick Sliced

Tom & Ted's - Thick Sliced Sugar Cured
Trader Joe's - Turkey, Uncured
Wegmans Brand - Fully Cooked Naturally Smoked
Wellshire Farms - Bacon (Applewood Smoked!!, Beef!!, Bulk Maple Dry Rubbed!, Classic Sliced Dry Rubbed!, Classic Sliced Turkey!, Dry Rubbed Applewood!!, Fully Cooked Hickory Smoked!!, Natural!!, Sliced Canadian Brand Turkey!!, Sliced Canadian Style!!, Sliced Dry Rubbed!!, Sliced Maple!!, Sliced Panchetta!!, Sliced Peppered Dry Rubbed!!, Thick Sliced Dry Rubbed!!, Whole Panchetta!!)
Wellshire Organic - Organic Bacon (Dry Rubbed, Turkey)
Winn Dixie - Hickory Sweet Sliced Bacon (Hardwood Smoked, Lower Sodium, Thick, Thin, Turkey)

Bacon Bits
Garrett County Farms - Salt Cured Bacon Bits!
Great Value Brand (Wal-Mart) - Real Bacon Pieces
Hormel - Bacon (Bits, Crumbles, Pieces)
Oscar Mayer - Real Bacon Bits
Publix - Bits, Pieces
Wellshire Farms - Salt Cured Bacon Bits!!

Bagels
Enjoy Life▲ - Bagels (Cinnamon Raisin●, Classic Original●)
Gluten-Free Creations▲ - Berry●, Cinnamon Raisin●, Everything●, Onion●, Plain●
Kinnikinnick▲ - Tapioca Rice (Cinnamon Raisin, New York Style Plain, Sesame)
Trader Joe's - Gluten Free Bagels
Udi's Gluten Free Foods▲ - Gluten Free (Cinnamon Raisin, Plain, Whole Grain)

Baked Apples
Lucky Leaf - Dutch
Musselman's - Dutch

Baking Bars
Baker's - Unsweetened!!

B Baking Chips
    Ener-G▲ - Chocolate Chips
    Enjoy Life▲ - Semi Sweet Chocolate Chips●
  Baking Cocoa
    Hy-Vee
    Kroger Brand
    Spartan Brand
    Watkins
  Baking Decorations & Frostings
    Betty Crocker -
      Cookie Icing (Blue, Green)
      Decorating Decors (All Sugars, Nonpareils)
      Decorating Gels (All Colors)
    Cake Mate - Decorating Gels All Colors!!
    Cherrybrook Kitchen - Gluten Free Frosting Mix *(Box Must Say
      Gluten Free)* (Chocolate, Vanilla), Ready To Spread Vanilla
      Frosting
    Earthly Treats▲ - Sugar Sprinkles●
    Food-Tek Fast & Fresh▲ - Dairy Free Chocolate Flavored Icing, Dairy
      Free Vanilla Flavored Icing
    Gluten-Free Creations▲ - Frosting Mix (Chocolate●, White●)
    Gluten-Free Essentials▲ - Frosting Mix (Lemon Glaze●, Supreme
      Chocolate●, Vanilla Royal●)
    Kinnikinnick▲ - Icing Sugar
    Kroger Brand - Sugar Sprinkles
    Let's Do...Sprinkelz - Carnival, Chocolatey, Confetti
    Namaste Foods▲ - Frosting Mix (Chocolate Fudge, Toffee Vanilla)
    Nuts Online -
      Butterscotch Crunch●
      Filling (Almond●, Chocolate●, Cinnamon●, Poppy Seed●)
      Macaroon Crunch●
      Marzipan●
      Nutty Crunch●
      Paste (Hazelnut Praline●, Pistachio Nut●)

Pamela's Products▲ - Frosting Mix (Confetti, Dark Chocolate, Vanilla)

Baking Mix... see Bread Mix

Baking Powder

Barkat

Bob's Red Mill▲

Cause You're Special▲ - Double Acting Baking Powder

Clabber Girl

Davis

Durkee

Ener-G▲ - Double Acting, Regular

Ginger Evans - Regular

Hain Pure Foods

Hannaford Brand

Hearth Club

Hy-Vee - Double Acting

KC

Kinnikinnick▲ - KinnActive

Kraft - Calumet

Kroger Brand

Nuts Online - Double Active●

Really Great Food Company▲ - Baking Powder Aluminum Free/ Double Acting

Royal

Rumford

Safeway Brand

Spartan Brand

Spice Islands

Tones

Watkins

Wegmans Brand - Double Acting

Baking Soda

Albertsons

Arm & Hammer

B

Bob's Red Mill▲
Durkee
Ener-G▲ - Calcium Carbonate Baking Soda Substitute
Ginger Evans - Regular
Hannaford Brand
Hy-Vee
Kroger Brand
Meijer Brand
Nuts Online - Arm & Hammer Baking Soda●
Spartan Brand
Spice Islands
Tones

Bamboo Shoots
... *All Fresh Bamboo Shoots Are Gluten/Casein/Soy Free*
Native Forest - Organic Sliced

Banana Chips
Brothers All Natural▲ - Crisps (Banana, Strawberry Banana)
Full Circle - Sweetened
Gluty Free - Chips●, Freeze Dried●, Organic Chips●
Nuts Online - Dried Fruit (Chips●, Organic Chips●)
Woodstock Farms - Regular, Sweetened

Bananas
... *All Fresh Bananas Are Gluten/Casein/Soy Free*
Chiquita
Dole
Nuts Online - Dried Fruit (Organic Simply●, Simply●)
Woodstock Farms - Organic Frozen Bananas

Barbeque Sauce
Albertsons - Hickory, Original
Annie's Naturals - Organic Sweet & Spicy**!!**
Bone Suckin' Sauce - Habanero, Original
Cattlemen's - Kansas City Classic, Memphis Sweet, Mississippi
Honey BBQ

barbeque sauce

B

Daddy Sam's - Bar B Que Sawce (Medium Ginger Jalapeno, Original)

Fischer & Wieser - Elly May's Wild Mountain Honey, Plum Chipotle Grilling Sauce

Frontera - Original Sweet & Smoky, Roasted Chipotle Pineapple, Texas Black Pepper

Hannaford Brand - Honey, Kansas City Style, Original, Sweet & Zesty

Hy-Vee - Hickory, Honey Smoke, Original

Jack Daniel's - Hickory Brown Sugar, Honey Smokehouse, Original No. 7 Recipe, Rich Honey, Smooth Original

Kurtz - Hickory, Honey, KC Style, Original

Midwest Country Fare - Hickory, Honey, Original

Mr. Spice Organic - Honey BBQ

Organicville - Organic BBQ Sauce (Original●, Tangy●)

Publix - Hickory, Honey, Original

Royal Food Products -
Garden Fresh
Gourmet Choice (Baby Back Rib, South Texas)
Royal Deluxe (Santa Fe, Texas Style)

Safeway Brand - Hickory Smoked, Honey (Mustard, Smoked)

Saz's - Original, Sassy, Vidalia Onion

Spartan Brand - Hickory & Brown Sugar, Honey, Original

Stubb's - Bar-B-Q Sauce (Hickory Bourbon●, Honey Pecan●, Mild●, Original●, Smokey Mesquite●, Spicy●)

Sweet Baby Ray's - Hickory & Brown Sugar, Honey, Honey Chipotle, Original, Sweet 'N Spicy, Sweet Vadalia Onion

Taste Of Inspiration - Maple Chipotle!, Spicy Mango!, Wild Maine Blueberry!

Trader Joe's - All Natural, Kansas City!!

Walden Farms - Hickory Smoked, Honey, Original, Thick & Spicy

Wegmans Brand - Brown Sugar, Kansas City Style, Memphis Style

Winn Dixie - Hickory, Honey, Original

B Bars

... (includes Breakfast, Energy, Fruit, Protein, etc.)

1-2-3 Gluten Free▲ - Sweet Goodness Pan Bars●

AllerEnergy▲ - Nutrition Bars (Apple Cinnamon, Cherry Blossom, Chocolate Chip, Wild Blueberry)

Alpsnack - Apricots & Cranberries, Coconut/Mango & Pineapple, Plums & Currants

Arico - Cookie Bars (Almond Cranberry, Peanut Butter)

Attune Foods - Chocolate Probiotic Wellness Chocolate Crisp●

Boomi Bar -
  Apricot Cashew
  Cashew Almond
  Cranberry Apple
  Fruit & Nut
  Healthy Hazel
  Macadamia Paradise
  Maple Pecan
  Perfect Pumpkin
  Pineapple Ginger
  Pistachio Pineapple
  Walnut Date

Breakaway Bakery▲ - Organic Lemon Bar Dough & Topping●, Shortbread Crumble & Bar Dough●

Bumble Bar -
  Awesome Apricot
  Chai w/Almonds
  Chunky Cherry
  Original Flavor
  Original Flavor w/(Almonds, Cashews, Hazelnuts, Mixed Nuts)
  Tasty Tropical

Clif Nectar - Organic (Cherry Pomegranate, Cranberry Apricot Almond, Dark Chocolate Walnut, Lemon Vanilla Cashew)

Crenu - Nutrition Bars (Almond, Banana Nut, Blueberry, Cherry, Cherry Chocolate, Lemon Chia, Orange Cranberry)

B

Eat Natural -
  100% Organic Brazils Hazelnuts & Sultans
  Blackcurrants Walnuts Mango & Dark Chocolate
  Brazils Sultanas Almonds & Hazelnuts
  Dark 70% Chocolate Brazils & Apricots
  Dates Walnuts & Pumpkin Seeds
  Macadamias Brazils & Apricots
  Peanuts Almonds & Hazelnuts
Ener-G▲ - Snack Bar Chocolate Chip
Enjoy Life▲ -
  Boom Choco Boom
    Dairy Free Rice Milk Bar●
    Dairy Free Rice Milk w/Crispy Rice Bar●
    Dark Chocolate Bar●
  Caramel Apple●
  Cocoa Loco●
  Sunbutter Crunch●
  Very Berry●
Glenny's - Cashew & Almond ●, Classic Fruit & Nut ●, Classic Nut
  Mix ●, Cranberry & Almond ●
Gluten Free Cafe - Cinnamon Sesame●
Gopal's -
  Happy Herb w/Maca
  Rawma (Apple Delicious, Carob Quinoa, Pineapple Nut,
    Pumpkin Agave, Sesame Mango, Walnut Fig)
Goraw▲ - Organic (Banana Bread Flax●, Live Granola●, Live
  Pumpkin●, Real Live Flax●, Spirulina Energy●)
Gorge Delights▲ -
  Acai Fruit Bars (Acai Apple Cherry, Acai Apple Raspberry, Acai
    Pear Cranberry, Acai Pear Strawberry)
  Just Fruit Bar (Apple, Apple Blueberry, Apple Cherry, Apple
    Raspberry, Blueberry Pear, Pear, Pear Cranberry, Pear
    Strawberry)

B

Jennies▲ - Omega 3 Energy Bar (Coconut, Coconut Almond, Coconut Chocolate)

Larabar -
  Apple Pie●
  Banana Bread●
  Carrot Cake●
  Cashew Cookie●
  Cherry Pie●
  Chocolate Chip Brownie●
  Chocolate Chip Cookie Dough●
  Chocolate Coconut●
  Cinnamon Roll●
  Coconut Cream Pie●
  Ginger Snap●
  Jocalat
    Chocolate●
    Chocolate Cherry●
    Chocolate Coffee●
    Chocolate Hazelnut●
    Chocolate Mint●
    Chocolate Orange●
    German Chocolate Cake●
  Key Lime Pie●
  Lemon Bar●
  Peanut Butter & Jelly●
  Peanut Butter Chocolate Chip●
  Peanut Butter Cookie●
  Pecan Pie●
  Tropical Fruit Tart●

Mareblu Naturals▲ -
  Crunch (Almond●, Cashew●)
  Trail Mix Crunch (BlueCran Pomegranate●, Mango Pomegranate●, Pistachio●, Strawberry Pomegranate●)

Mixes From The Heartland▲ - Coffee Bars Mix (Apple Cinnamon●, Cranberry●, Tropical●)

Mrs. May's Naturals - Trio (Blueberry●, Cranberry●, Strawberry●, Tropical●)

NuGO Free - Gluten Free Bars (Carrot Cake●, Dark Chocolate Crunch●, Dark Chocolate Trail Mix●)

Nutiva - Organic (Flax & Raisin, Flax Chocolate, Hempseed Original)

Omega Smart Bars▲ - Banana Chocolate Chip, Pomegranate Strawberry Colada, Pumpkin Spice

Organic Food Bar -
Organic Food Bar (Active Greens, Active Greens Chocolate, Cranberry, Omega 3 Flax, Original, Protein, Vegan, Wild Blueberry)
Organic Food Bar Kids Keerunch (Chocolate Brownie Crunch)
Raw Organic Food Bar Cinnamon Raisin

Oskri Organics -
Coconut Bar
  Almond
  Cherry
  Mango
  Original
  Pineapple
  Strawberry
Date Fruit
Fiber Bar
  Almond Cranberry
  Cashew Cranberry
  Pecan Raisin
Fig Fruit
Honey Bar
  Cashew
  Desert Date
  Flaxseed
  Granola
  Mixed Nuts
  Muesli
  Turkish Delight

B

Mini Bars
  Coconut Original
  Date
  Fiber w/Almonds & Cranberries
  Fig
  Honey Cashew
  Honey Desert Date
  Honey Muesli
  Quinoa
  Sesame w/Date Syrup
Sesame Bar
  Black Sesame
  Date Syrup & (Black Cumin, Fennel, Regular)
  Molasses & (Black Cumin, Fennel, Regular)
  Quinoa
Prana -
  Apricot Goji
  Apricot Pumpkin
  Cashew Almond
  Cinnamon Apple
  Coconut Acai
  Pear Ginseng
  Supercharger (Blueberry Coconut, Goldenberry Goji, Mango
    Maca, Raspberry Pomegranate)
Private Selections - Frozen Premium Fruit Bars (Regular, Sugar Free)
PURE Bar - Organic (Apple Cinnamon●, Cherry Cashew●,
  Chocolate Brownie●, Cranberry Orange●, Trail Mix●, Wild
  Blueberry●)
Raw Revolution▲ -
  Apple Cinnamon
  Cashews & Agave
  Chocolate & Cashews
  Chocolate & Coconut
  Coconut & Agave

Hazelnut & Chocolate
Raisin & Chocolate
Raspberry & Chocolate
Spirulina & Cashew
Tropical Mango
Ruth's Hemp Power -
Cranberry Trail HempPower
CranNut Flax Power
Ginger Almond MacaPower
Hemp & Trail HempPower
VeryBerry Flax Power
Vote Hemp/Blueberry Bar
Salba - Whole Fruit Bars (Cranberry Nut●, Mixed Berry●,
Tropical Fruit●)
Seitenbacher - Xtra Fiber
Shakti Bar - Organic (Blueberry Chia, Goldenberry Goji,
Mango Maca)
Taste Of Nature -
Exotics
Caribbean Ginger Island●
Himalayan Goji Summit●
Persian Pomegranate Garden●
Regular
Argentina Peanut Plains●
Brazilian Nut Fiesta●
California Almond Valley●
Niagara Apple Country●
Nova Scotia Blueberry Fields●
Quebec Cranberry Carnival●
Wegmans Brand - Fruit Flats (Cherry, Grape, Raspberry, Strawberry)
Basmati Rice... see Rice
Bean Dip... see Dip/Dip Mix

B Beans
... *All Fresh Beans Are Gluten/Casein/Soy Free* **(Except Soybeans)**

Albertsons -
All Dried *(Except Soybeans)*
Canned
Black
Blackeyed
Chili
Dark Red Kidney
Garbanzo
Great Northern
Green (Cut, French Style, Whole)
Pinto
Refried Fat Free

Amy's -
Organic Light In Sodium (Black**!**, Traditional**!**)
Organic Refried Beans (Black**!**, Traditional**!**, w/Green Chiles**!**)
Organic Vegetarian Baked**!**

Arrowhead Mills - Adzuki, Anasazi, Garbanzo Chickpeas, Green Split Peas, Lentils (Green, Red), Pinto

B&M Baked Beans - All Varieties

Birds Eye - All Plain Frozen Vegetables *(Except Edamame)*

Bush's Best -
Baked Beans (Bold & Spicy, Boston Recipe, Country Style, Homestyle, Honey, Maple Cured Bacon, Onion, Original, Vegetarian)
Black
Butter (Baby, Large, Speckled)
Cannellini
Chili Beans (Hot - *Must Be NEW Recipe*, Medium - *Must Be NEW Recipe*, Mild - *Must Be NEW Recipe*)
Chili Magic Chili Starter (Texas Recipe *(Must Be NEW Recipe)*, Traditional Recipe *(Must Be NEW Recipe)*)
Garbanzo

Great Northern
Grillin' Beans (Black Bean Fiesta, Bourbon & Brown Sugar,
    Smokehouse Tradition, Southern Pit Barbecue, Steakhouse
    Recipe, Texas Ranchero)
Kidney (Dark Red, Light Red)
Microwaveable Cup Original
Navy
Pinto
Red
C & W - All Plain Frozen Vegetables *(Except Edamame)*
Del Monte - All Canned Vegetables *(Except Soybeans)*
Eden Organic -
Organic (Aduki, Baked w/Sorghum & Mustard, Black, Black
    Eyed Peas, Butter, Cannellini, Caribbean Black, Garbanzo, Great
    Northern, Kidney, Navy, Pinto, Small Red)
Organic Dried (Aduki, Black, Garbanzo, Green (Lentils, Split Peas),
    Kidney, Navy, Pinto, Small Red)
Refried (Black, Kidney, Pinto, Spicy Black, Spicy Pinto)
Rice & (Cajun Small Red, Caribbean Black, Garbanzo, Kidney,
    Lentils, Pinto)
Fantastic World Foods - Hummus Original, Instant (Black, Refried)
Freshlike - Frozen Plain Vegetables *(Except Edamame)*
Full Circle -
Canned Organic
    Baked Beans
    Baked Beans Maple & Onion
    Black
    Garbanzo
    Green Cut
    Organic Frozen Cut Beans
    Pinto
    Red Kidney
    Refried (Black, Green Chile & Lime, Vegetarian)
Dried (Kidney, Lentil, Lima, Navy, Pinto)

B

Gluty Free - Chickpeas (Salted (Golden●, White●), Unsalted (Golden●, White●)), Cranberry●, Green Bean Chips●, Organic Cannellini●

Grand Selections - Fancy (Cut Green, Whole Green), Frozen Whole Green

Great Value Brand (Wal-Mart) -
  Beans & Weiners
  Canned
    Cut Green
    No Salt Added (Cut Green, French Style Green)
    Whole Green
  Dried
    Baby Lima
    Black
    Garbanzo
    Great Northern
    Large Lima
    Light Red Kidney
    Pinto
    Small Red

Green Giant -
  Canned
    Cut Green (50% Less Sodium, Regular)
    French Style Green
    Kitchen Sliced Green
    Three Bean Salad
  Frozen
    Baby Lima
    Cut Green
    Green Beans & Almonds
    Select w/No Sauce Whole Green
    Simply Steam (Baby Lima, Green Beans & Almonds)
    Steamers Cut Green
    Valley Fresh Steamers (Cut Green Beans, Select Whole Green Beans)

Hannaford Brand - All Dried *(Except Soybeans)*, Black, Cannellini, Cut Green, Cut Wax, Dark Red Kidney, French Green, Great Northern, Light Red Kidney, No Salt Green (Cut, French), Pinto, Refried (Fat Free, Traditional), Whole Green

HealthMarket - Organic (Black, Cut Green, Dark Red Kidney, French Cut Green, Garbanzo, Pinto)

Heinz - Vegetarian Beans

Hy-Vee -

    Black (Refried, Regular)

    Blue Lake (Cut Green, French Style Green, Whole Green)

    Butter

    Chili (Beans, Style, Style In Chili Gravy)

    Country Style Baked

    Dark Red Kidney

    Diced Baby Lima

    Dried (Large Lima, Lentils, Mixed Soup, Navy)

    Fat Free Refried

    Frozen (Cut Green, French Cut Green)

    Garbanzo Beans

    Great Northern (Dried, Regular)

    Home Style Baked

    Large Lima

    Lentils

    Light Red Kidney

    Maple Cured Bacon Baked

    Navy

    Onion Baked

    Original Baked

    Pinto (Dried, Regular)

    Pork & Beans

    Red (Dried, Kidney, Regular)

    Spicy Refried

    Steam In A Bag Frozen Beans

    Traditional Refried

B

Joan Of Arc - Dark Red Kidney, Great Northern, Light Red Kidney
Kid's Kitchen - Beans & Wieners
Kirkland Signature - Green Beans
Kroger Brand -
    All Plain Vegetables (Canned, Frozen) *(Except Soybeans)*
    Baked (Country Style, Homestyle, Original)
    Pork & Beans (Regular, Veggie)
    Refried Mexican
    Unseasoned (Canned, Dry)
Lowes Foods Brand -
    Canned
        French
        Great Northern
        Green (Cut, French Style, Whole)
        Lima
        Pinto Regular
        Red Kidney Beans (Dark, Light)
        Refried (Fat Free, Regular)
        Whole Green
    Dry
        Baby Lima
        Black Eyed Peas
        Great Northern
        Lentil
        Lima
        Mixed
        Navy
        Pinto
    Frozen
        Deluxe Whole Green
        Green (Cut, French Cut, Regular)
        Lima (Baby, Deluxe Tiny, Regular)
Meijer Brand -
    Baked Beans Organic

Canned Beans
  Black (Organic, Regular)
  Butter
  Garbanzo (Organic, Regular)
  Great Northern
  Lima
  Mexican Style
  Pinto (Organic, Regular)
  Red Kidney (Dark, Dark Organic, Light, Regular)
  Refried (Fat Free, Regular, Vegetarian)
  Refried Organic (Black Bean, Black Bean Jalapeno, Roasted Chili Lime, Traditional)
  Wax Cut
Canned Green Beans Cut
  Blue Lake
  French Style (Blue Lake, No Salt, Organic, Veri Green)
  No Salt
  Organic
  Veri Green
Canned Green Beans Whole
Dry Beans
  Black
  Blackeyed
  Fordhook
  Great Northern
  Green Split Beans & Peas
  Lentil
  Lima Large
  Navy
  Pinto
  Pork & Beans
  Red Kidney
Frozen Baby Lima Beans
Frozen Green Beans (Cut, French Cut, Italian Cut)

B

Midwest Country Fare - Cut Green, French Style Green,
  Pork & Beans
Nielsen-Massey - Madagascar Bourbon Pure Vanilla Bean Paste●,
  Whole Vanilla Beans●
Nuts Online -
  Ceci Fava Mix●
  Chickpeas
    Roasted Golden (Salted●, Unsalted●)
    Roasted White (Salted●, Unsalted●)
  Cranberry Beans●
  Giant Fava Beans●
  Organic Cannellini Beans●
  Simply Green Beans Freeze Dried Vegetables●
O Organics - Canned (Black, Cut Green, Frozen Whole Green,
  Garbanzo, Kidney, Pinto)
Old El Paso - Refried Beans (Fat Free, Spicy Fat Free, Traditional,
  w/Green Chiles)
Ortega - Black, Refried (Fat Free, Regular)
Pictsweet - All Plain Frozen Vegetables *(Except Soybeans)*, Cracked
  Pepper Seasoned Green, Seasoned Corn & Black Beans
Private Selections - Frozen Green Beans
Publix -
  Canned
    Baked (Original, Veggie)
    Black Beans
    Garbanzo
    Green (French Cut, Italian Cut, Lima, Original, Veggi Green)
    Kidney (Dark, Light)
    Pinto
    Pork & Beans
  Dry
    Baby Lima
    Black
    Blackeyed Peas
    Garbanzo

    Great Northern
    Large Lima
    Lentils
    Light Red Kidney
    Navy
    Pinto
    Small Red
  Frozen
    Green (Cut, French Cut)
    Lima (Baby, Fordhook)
    Speckled Butter Beans
Publix GreenWise Market - Organic Canned (Black, Dark Red Kidney, Garbanzo, Green, Pinto)
S&W - All Canned Vegetables *(Except Soybeans)*
Safeway Brand -
  Canned
    Black (Eyed, Regular)
    Chick
    Dark Kidney
    Green (Cut, Cut No Salt, French Style, Whole)
    Light Kidney
    Lima
    Pinto
  Dried
    Baby Lima
    Black (Eyed, Regular)
    Great Northern
    Large Lima
    Lentils
    Light Red Kidney
    Navy
    Pink
    Pinto
    Small (Red, White)

B

Frozen
>Baby Lima
>Cut
>Fordbook Lima
>French Style
>Whole

Refried Beans (Fat Free, Traditional)

Safeway Select - Frozen Whole Green Beans

Spartan Brand -

Canned
>Baked (Homestyle, Regular, w/Bacon & Maple Flavor, w/
>>Onions)
>Black
>Butter
>Dark Red Kidney
>Garbanzo
>Great Northern
>Green (Cut, French Cut Style, Whole)
>Light Red Kidney
>Lima
>Pinto
>Pork & Beans
>Red
>Wax Cut

Dried
>Black
>Black Eyed
>Great Northern
>Kidney
>Lentil
>Lima (Baby, Large)
>Navy
>Pinto

Frozen
>Baby Lima

Fordhook Lima
Green (Cut, French Cut, Whole)

Stop & Shop Brand - Baby Lima, Black, Dark Red Kidney, Fordhook Lima, Garbanzo, Golden Cut Wax, Green Beans (Cut, French, No Added Salt, Whole), Kidney Light, Lima, Organic Green, Pinto, Red

Trader Joe's - All Canned Plain **!!** *(Except Soybeans)* All Plain Dried Varieties *(Except Soybeans)*, Frozen Haricot Vert Extra FIne Green Beans **!!**, Marinated Bean Salad **!!**

Wegmans Brand -
Baby Lima
Baked Beans (Original, Vegetarian)
Black
Canned (Black, Dark Red Kidney, Great Northern, Light Red Kidney, Pinto, Pork & Beans In Tomato Sauce, Red)
Cannellini Beans Italian Classics
Cut Green Beans (No Salt, Regular)
Dark Kidney
French Style Green Beans (No Salt, Regular)
Garbanzo Beans Italian Classics
Great Northern
Green (Cut, French Style, Italian Cut, Regular, Whole)
Light Red Kidney
Lima
Pinto
Pork & Beans In Tomato Sauce
Wax Cut

Westbrae - Green Beans (Cut, French Cut), Organic (Black, Chili, Garbanzo, Great Northern, Kidney, Lentils, Pinto, Red, Salad)

Winn Dixie -
All Dried *(Except Soybeans)*
Canned Beans (Baby White Lima, Dark Red Kidney, Garbanzo, Great Northern, Green & White Lima, Green Cut, Green French Style Sliced, Green Lima, Green No Salt Added, Green Whole, Light Red Kidney, Navy)

B

Frozen Green Beans (Butter Speckled, Cut, French Style Sliced, Italian, Organic Cut, Whole)

Frozen Lima Beans (Baby, Fordhook, Petite, Speckled)

Refried (Fat Free, Traditional)

Woodstock Farms - Dried Green Beans, Organic Frozen (Baby French Beans, Cut Green Beans, Lima)

Beef

*... *All Fresh Meat Is Gluten/Casein/Soy Free (Non-Marinated, Unseasoned)*

Applegate Farms -

Natural (Beef Hot Dogs, Roast Beef)

Organic (Frozen Beef Burger, Roast Beef)

Boar's Head - All Varieties *(Except Italian Roast Beef, Pesto Parmesan Italian Roast Beef)*

Butcher's Cut - Beef Salami, Bulk Wrapped Corned Beef Brisket, Corned Beef Brisket *(Without Seasoning Packet)*, Patties

Carl Buddig - Deli Cuts Roast Beef, Extra Thin Original Regular, Original Regular

Castle Wood Reserve - Deli Meat (Angus Corned Beef, Angus Roast Beef)

Coleman's Natural Foods - All Natural Uncured Hot Dog●

Dietz & Watson▲ -

Corned Beef (Brisket●, Flat●)

Dried Beef Classic Top Round●

Pastrami (Brisket●, Spiced Beef●)

Roast Beef (Extra Lean●, Oven Roasted All Natural Rare Whole●, Premium Angus●, USDA Pepper Choice●)

Seasoned Prime Rib w/Juices●

Eckrich - Deli Meat (Black Angus Roast Beef, Cooked Corned Beef, Lite Roast Beef)

Garrett County Farms -

Beef Franks (4 XL Big!, Old Fashioned!, Premium!)

Corned Beef Brisket (Half!, Whole!)

Sliced (Beef Bologna!, Beef Salami!, Corned Beef!, Roast Beef!)

Whole Roasted Beef!

B

Great Value Brand (Wal-Mart) - Frozen 100% Pure Beef Patties

Hillshire Farms - Deli Select Roast Beef, Deli Select Thin Sliced Corned Beef, Deli Select Ultra Thin Roast Beef

Hormel - Bread Ready Corned Beef, Corned Beef Hash, Deli Meat Natural Choice Roast Beef, Dried Beef, Fully Cooked Entrees Beef Roast Au Jus, Natural Choice Deli Counter (Corned Beef, Medium Roast, Rare Roast)

Hy-Vee - Deli Thin Sliced Roast Beef, Thin Sliced Regular

Jones Dairy Farm - Golden Brown All Natural Fully Cooked Beef Sausage Links●

Kayem - Roast Beef (Classic, Seasoned Garlic, Seasoned Original)

Kirkland Signature - Fresh (Brisket, NY Strip, Ribeye, Ribs, Roast, Steaks, Top Round), Frozen Lean Ground Beef, Ground Beef Patties

Kroger Brand - Sliced Dried

Meijer Brand - Ground Beef (Chuck Fine, Fine)

Organic Prairie -
Fresh Organic
Ground Beef 1 lb. (85% Lean, 90% Lean)
Sliced Roast Beef
Frozen Organic
Beef Liver Steak 12 oz.
Ground Beef 12 oz.
Ground Beef Patties 10.6 oz.
New York Strip Steak
Ribeye Steak

Oscar Mayer - Shaved Deli Fresh (French Dip Roast Beef, Slow Roasted Roast Beef)

Private Selections - Frozen Angus Patties Chuck, Frozen Charbroiled Burgers All Natural, Frozen Ground Sirloin Patties

Publix - Premium Certified Beef

Publix GreenWise Market -
Beef (Cubed Steak, For Stew)
Beef Back Ribs

B

Bottom Round (Regular, Steak)

Brisket Flat

Chuck (Eye Steak, Roast Boneless, Short Rib Boneless, Short Ribs, Steak Boneless)

Eye Round (Regular, Steak)

Flank Steak

Flap Meat

Flat Iron Steak

Ground (Chuck, Chuck For Chili, Chuck Patties, Round, Round Patties)

Porterhouse Steak

Rib Eye (Roast Boneless, Steak Bone In, Steak Boneless)

Rib Roast

Round Cubes

Rump Roast

Shoulder (Roast Boneless, Steak)

Sirloin (Flap Meat, For Kabobs, For Stir Fry, Tip Roast, Tip Side Steak, Tip Steak)

Skirt Steak (Inside, Outside)

Strip Steak Boneless

T Bone Steak

Tenderloin (Roast, Steak)

Top Blade (Roast Boneless, Steak)

Top Round (For Stir Fry, London Broil, Regular, Steak, Steak Thin Sliced)

Top Sirloin (Filet Steak, Steak Boneless)

Tri Tip (Roast, Steak)

Sara Lee - Deli Meat Slices Roast Beef

Spartan Brand - Corned Beef Hash

Sweet Bay - All Fresh Beef, All Fresh Veal

Trader Joe's - Fully Cooked & Seasoned Beef Prime Rib

Wellshire Farms - Roast Beef (Sliced!!, Whole!!)

Winn Dixie - Corned Beef Hash

Beef Jerky... see Jerky/Beef Sticks

Beef Sticks... see Jerky/Beef Sticks

Beer

    Anheuser - Busch - Redbridge

    Bard's - Bard's Gold

    Carlsberg Brewery (Finland) - Saxon Premium Lager

    Green's (England) - Discovery, Endeavor, Herald, Pathfinder,
        Premium Golden Apple, Premium Pils, Quest

    Lakefront Brewery - New Grist

    New Planet - 3R Raspberry Ale, Tread Lightly Ale

    Old Hat Brewery - Bees Knees

    Ramapo Valley Brewery▲ - Passover Honey Lager

    Sprecher - Mbege

Beets

    ... *All Fresh Beets Are Gluten/Casein/Soy Free

    Albertsons

    Del Monte - All Canned Beets

    Earthbound Farm - Organic Whole

    Hannaford Brand - Cut, Sliced, Whole

    Hy-Vee - Fancy (Diced, Sliced)

    Lowes Foods Brand - Canned Cut, Whole

    Meijer Brand - Harvard Sweet Sour, Sliced (No Salt, Pickled, Regular),
        Whole (Medium, Pickled)

    Publix - Canned

    Pure Market Express▲ - Mariachi Beet Wrap●

    S&W - All Canned Beets, Pickled

    Safeway Brand - Canned (Sliced, Whole)

    Spartan Brand - Diced, Sliced, Whole

    Wegmans Brand - Harvard, Sliced (No Salt, Pickled, Regular), Whole
        (Pickled, Regular)

Berries

    ... *All Fresh Berries Are Gluten/Casein/Soy Free

    Del Monte - Canned & Jarred Fruit (All Varieties), Fruit Snack Cups
        (Metal, Plastic)

    Gluty Free - Dried (Goji Berries●, Mulberries●, Organic Goji
        Berries●)

B

Kirkland Signature - Frozen Nature's Three
Meijer Brand - Frozen Berry Medley, Frozen Triple Berry Blend
Nuts Online - Dried Fruit (Goji Berries●, Mulberries●, Simply
   Boysenberries●, Simply Elderberries●)
Publix - Frozen Mixed Berries
Spartan Brand - Frozen Berry Medley
Stop & Shop Brand - Frozen Berry Medley
Wegmans Brand - Berry Medley
Woodstock Farms - Organic (Frozen Mixed Berries, Goji)

Beverages... see Drinks/Juice

Biscotti

Orgran▲ - Amaretti, Classic Chocolate
Really Great Food Company▲ - Anise, Lemon Poppy
Sorella▲ - Biscottines (Chocolate Almond, Cinnamon Swirl,
   Hazelnut, Vanilla)

Biscuits

1-2-3 Gluten Free▲ - Southern Glory Biscuits Mix●
Better Batter - Pancake & Biscuit Mix
Bob's Red Mill▲ - Wheat Free Biscuit & Baking Mix
Cause You're Special▲ - Hearty Gluten Free Biscuit Mix
Grandma Ferdon's▲ - Baking Powder Biscuit Mix●
Kneaded Specialties▲ - Biscuits●
Mixes From The Heartland▲ - Biscuit Mix (Country●, Garlic
   Roasted Pepper●, Sun Dried Tomato●)
Namaste Foods▲ - Biscuits Piecrust & More Mix
Really Great Food Company▲ - Biscuit Loaf Mix, Old Time
   Biscuit Mix, Spinach & Cheese Biscuit Mix Sugar Free

Bittermelon

   ... *All Fresh Bittermelon Is Gluten/Casein/Soy Free*

Black Eyed Peas... see Peas

Blackberries

   ... *All Fresh Blackberries Are Gluten/Casein/Soy Free*
Albertsons - All Plain Frozen Fruit

Gluty Free - Dried●
Great Value Brand (Wal-Mart) - Frozen
Meijer Brand - Frozen
Nuts Online - Dried Blackberries (Dried●, Simply●)
Publix - Frozen
Safeway Brand - Frozen
Spartan Brand - Frozen
Stop & Shop Brand - Frozen
Wegmans Brand - Frozen
Winn Dixie - Frozen
Woodstock Farms - Organic Frozen

Blueberries
... *All Fresh Blueberries Are Gluten/Casein/Soy Free
Albertsons - Frozen
C & W - Frozen
Full Circle - Organic Blueberries
Gluty Free - Dried (Juice Infused●, Regular●, Wild Organic●),
Freeze Dried●
Great Value Brand (Wal-Mart) - Frozen
Hy-Vee - Frozen
Kroger Brand - Plain Frozen Fruit
Meijer Brand - Frozen (Organic, Regular)
Nuts Online - Dried Blueberries (Dried●, Natural Dried●, Natural
Dried Juice Infused●, Organic Wild●, Simply●)
Publix - Frozen
Safeway Brand - Frozen
Spartan Brand - Frozen
Trader Joe's - Frozen (Fresh Blueberries, Organic Wild Blueberries,
Wild Boreal)
Wegmans Brand - Frozen
Winn Dixie - Frozen
Woodstock Farms - Organic Frozen Wild Blueberries

Bok Choy
... *All Fresh Bok Choy Is Gluten/Casein/Soy Free

B Bologna
   Applegate Farms - Turkey Bologna
   Armour - Deli (Beef Bologna, Meat Bologna)
   Boar's Head - All Varieties
   Eckrich - Deli Meat (Beef, Garlic, Low Sodium, Meat), Lunch Meat
      Bologna (Beef, Lite, Regular, Ring)
   Honeysuckle White - Turkey
   Hy-Vee - Garlic, German Brand, Regular, Thick, Thin, Turkey
   Kayem - German Style, Original
   Publix - Deli Pre Pack Sliced Lunch Meat German Bologna
   Wellshire Farms - Sliced Beef Bologna ‼
Bouillon/Bouillon Cubes
   Better Than Bouillon - Chili, Kosher Passover (Chicken, Vegetable),
      Organic (Beef, Chicken), Reduced Sodium Chicken
   Celifibr▲ -
      Bouillon Cubes (Vegetable Medley, Vegetarian Beef, Vegetarian
         Chicken)
      Bouillon Soup Base (French Onion, Vegetable Medley, Vegetarian
         Beef, Vegetarian Chicken)
   Edward & Sons - Garden Veggie, Low Sodium Veggie, Not Beef,
      Not Chick'n
   Harvest Sun - Organic (Herbal, Low Sodium, Mushroom, Onion,
      Vegetable, Yeast Free)
   Herb-Ox - Low Sodium (Granulated (Beef, Chicken), Packets Beef)
   Kum Chun - Chicken Bouillon Powder
   Lee Kum Kee - Chicken Bouillon Powder
   Marigold - Organic (Swiss Vegetable Reduced Salt, Vegetable
      (Reduced Salt, Regular, Yeast Free))
   Massel - Ultracubes (Beef Style, Chicken Style, Vegetable)
Bourbon
   ... *All Distilled Alcohol Is Gluten/Casein/Soy Free* [2]
Bowls
   Amy's - Cream Of Rice Hot Cereal Bowl !

Chi-Chi's - Fiesta Plates Salsa Chicken
Lundberg▲ - Organic Brown Rice Bowls (Country Wild, Long Grain, Short Grain)

Bratwurst... see Sausage

Bread

... *(includes Baquettes, Rolls)*

Apple's Bakery▲ - Loaf Olive Oil
Aunt Gussie's▲ - Focaccia ●, Kalamata Garlic Bread ●
Barkat - Baguettes, Rolls
Canyon Bakehouse▲ - Cinnamon Raisin, Mountain White, Rosemary & Thyme Focaccia, San Juan 7 Grain
Deerfields Gluten Free Bakery▲ - Mini Baguette, Rice Bran Dinner Rolls
El Peto▲ - Potato
Ener-G▲ -
  Sliced Breads
    Brown Rice
    Corn
    Egg Free Raisin
    Four Flour
    Hi Fiber
    Light (Brown Rice, Tapioca, White Rice, White Rice Flax)
    Papas
    Rice Starch
    Seattle Brown
    Tapioca Loaf (Dinner Rolls, Regular Sliced, Thin Sliced)
    White (Regular, Rice Flax)
    Yeast Free (Brown Rice, White Rice)
  Specialty Breads
    Bread Crumbs
    Broken Melba Toast
    Communion Wafers
    Plain Croutons
Everybody Eats▲ - Dairy Free Deli Rolls, Egg Challah

B

Food For Life - Almond Rice, Bhutanese Red Rice, Brown Rice,
  Multi Seed Rice, Raisin Pecan, Rice Pecan, Wheat & Gluten Free
  Millet Bread, White Rice
French Meadow Bakery - Gluten Free Sandwich Bread●
Gluten Free Life▲ - Country Brown Pure, Multi Grain Pure,
  Pumpernickel
Gluten-Free Creations▲ -
  Almond Flax●
  Banana Tea Bread●
  Herb (Baguettes●, Loaf Bread●, Rolls●)
  Honey Oat●
  Hot Dog Buns●
  Seeded Multigrain●
  White●
  Whole Grain●
Heaven Mills▲ -
  Challa
    Gluten & Egg Free●
    Gluten & Sugar Free●
    Gluten Egg & Sugar Free●
    Gluten Free●
    Mini Dinner Rolls
      Gluten & Egg Free●
      Gluten & Sugar Free●
      Gluten Egg & Sugar Free●
      Gluten Free●
  Mezonos Bread●
  Oat Bread
    Gluten & Egg Free●
    Gluten & Sugar Free●
    Gluten Egg & Sugar Free●
    Gluten Free●
  Pita Bread●
  Vunder Bread (Herb●, Plain●)

Katz Gluten Free▲ - Bread Whole Grain●, Challah (Round Oat●, Round Oat Raisin●), Chocolate Strip●, Cinnamon Strip●, Farfel●, Honey Loaf●, Kiska Kugel●, Rolls (Oat Challah●, Sandwich●), Wholesome●

Kinnikinnick▲ -
Brown Sandwich
Candadi Yeast Free Multigrain Rice
Festive
Many Wonder Multigrain Rice
Robins Honey Brown Rice
Sunflower Flax Rice
Tapioca Rice (Italian White, Raisin, Regular)
White Sandwich
Yeast Free Tapioca

Kneaded Specialties▲ -
Cinnamon Rolls●
Deluxe Sandwich●
Dinner Rolls●
French Bread Loaf●
French Bread Rolls●
Orange Danish Rolls●
Sweet Bread (Banana●, Cinnamon Raisin●, Cranberry●, Pumpkin●)
White Sandwich●

Lakewood Matzoh - Oat Bread Machine Made, Oat Matzoh Hand Made

Laurel's Sweet Treats▲ - Banzo Bread, Dinner Rolls

Nu-World Foods▲ - Flatbread Amaranth (Buckwheat●, Garbanzo●, Sorghum●)

PaneRiso▲ - Brown Rice●, Flax Seed●, No Rye Rye●, Raisin & Cinnamon Bread●, White Rice●

Pure Market Express▲ - Butter Walnut●, Garlic●, Onion●, Tuscan●

Rose's Bakery▲ - Banana, French Bread (Loaf, Rolls), Millet, Orange Cranberry Tea, Pita, Sandwich Bread, Seeded Sandwich Bread, Teff

B

Rudi's Gluten-Free Bakery - Cinnamon Raisin●, Multigrain●, Original●

Silly Yak Bakery -
CFGF
Cinnamon Apple Swirl●
Cinnamon Raisin●
Cinnamon Swirl●
Cranberry Orange Yeast●
Garlic Chive●
Honey Brown Rice●
Honey Swirl Brown Rice●
Multi Seed●
Onion Dill●
Raisin Walnut●
Rice●
Tomato Basil●

Trader Joe's - Gluten Free (Bagels, French Rolls), Ryeless "Rye"

Udi's Gluten Free Foods▲ - Gluten Free (White Sandwich, Whole Grain)

Whole Foods Market Gluten Free Bakehouse▲ - Bread Honey Oat

Bread Mix

... (includes Baking Mix)

1-2-3 Gluten Free▲ - Aaron's Favorite Rolls●, Meredith's Marvelous Muffin/Quickbread Mix●

AgVantage Naturals▲ - Master Blend Baking Mix●, Multi Grain Bread Mix●, Sandwich Bread Mix●

Arnel's Originals - Bread Mix

Arrowhead Mills - All Purpose Baking Mix

Authentic Foods▲ - White Bread Mix, Wholesome Bread Mix

Bob's Red Mill▲ - Bread Mix Cinnamon Raisin

Breads From Anna▲ - Bread Mix (All Purpose, Banana, Classic Herb, Original, Pumpkin)

Chebe▲ - Bread Mix (All Purpose●, Cinnamon Rolls●, Focaccia Italian Flatbread●, Pizza Crust●)

bread mix

B

El Peto▲ - Breadmaker (Potato, White)
Ener-G▲ - Mix (Corn, Potato, Rice)
Gifts Of Nature▲ - Sandwich White Bread & Roll Mix
Gillian's Foods▲ - All Purpose Baking Mix
Gluten-Free Creations▲ - Bread Mix (Almond Flax●, Cinnamon
    Raisin●, Honey Oat●, Seeded Multigrain●)
Gluten-Free Essentials▲ -
    All Purpose Baking Mix●
    Holiday Gingerbread●
    Lemon Poppy Seed●
    Multi Grain (Cinnamon Spice●, Meatloaf Starter●, Original●,
        Zesty Italian●)
Grandma Ferdon's▲ - Banana●
Hodgson Mill▲ - Gluten Free Multi Purpose Baking Mix
King Arthur Flour▲ - Gluten Free Bread Mix●
Kinnikinnick▲ - All Purpose Mix, Candadi Yeast Free Rice, Kinni
    Kwik Bread & Bun Mix, Kinni Kwik Sunflower Flax, Kinni Kwik
    Sunflower Flax Bread & Bun Mix, Tapioca Rice
Lakewood Matzoh - Matzoh Meal
Mixes From The Heartland▲ - Sweet Bread Mix (Banana●,
    Banana Flax Seed●, Blueberry●, Cranberry●, Hawaiian●)
Namaste Foods▲ - Bread Mix
Nuts Online - Gluten Free (Bread Mix Cinnamon Raisin●,
    Cornbread Mix●)
Orgran▲ - Bread Mix (Alternative Grain Wholemeal, Easy Bake)
Pamela's Products▲ - Gluten Free Bread Mix & Flour Blend
Really Great Food Company▲ - Bread Mix (Brown Rice, Dark
    European, French/Country Farm, Home Style Cornbread, Old
    Fashioned Cinnamon, Original White, Rye Style), Irish Soda
    Bread Mix
Schar▲ - Classic White Bread Mix
Simply Organic▲ - Banana Bread Mix
The Cravings Place▲ - Create Your Own

B

Timtana Gluten Free - Bread Mix (Gluten Free Timtana Dark●, Gluten Free Timtana Lite Brown●, Gluten Free Timtana PrOatina Brown●, Gluten Free Timtana PrOatina Lite●)

Breadcrumbs... see Coating

Breadsticks

Chebe▲ - Garlic Onion Breadsticks Mix●

Schar▲ - Italian Breadsticks

Breakfast

Farmer John -

Breakfast Sausage Links & Patties

Hot Habanero Links

Old Fashioned Maple Skinless

Original (Roll, Skinless)

Premium (PC Links Lower Fat, Sausage Patties Lower Fat)

Garrett County Farms - Frozen Breakfast Links (Chicken Apple!, Original!, Sunrise Maple!, Turkey Maple!)

Great Value Brand (Wal-Mart) - Sausage (Beef Breakfast, Fully Cooked Pork Links, Maple Pork Patties, Original Pork Patties)

Honeysuckle White - Breakfast Sausage (Links, Patties, Roll)

Ian's - Wheat Free Gluten Free Recipe (French Toast Sticks)

Jennie-O Turkey Store -

Breakfast Lover's Turkey Sausage

Fresh Breakfast Sausage Mild Patties

Frozen Fully Cooked Sausage (Links, Patties)

Jimmy Dean -

Fully Cooked Sausage Crumbles (Hot Hearty, Original Hearty, Turkey Hearty)

Fully Cooked Sausage Links (Maple, Original, Turkey)

Fully Cooked Sausage Patties (Hot, Maple, Original, Sandwich Sized, Turkey)

Maple Fresh Sausage (Links, Patties)

Original Fresh Sausage (Links, Patties)

Pork Roll Sausage (All Natural Regular, Hot, Italian, Light, Maple, Mild Country, Regular, Sage)

Johnsonville - Brown Sugar & Honey Links, Original Sausage (Links, Patties), Sausage Roll (Hot, Mild Country, Regular), Vermont Maple Syrup Sausage (Links, Patties)

Jones Dairy Farm -

All Natural

Hearty Pork Sausage Links●

Light Pork Sausage and Rice Links●

Little Link Pork Sausage●

Maple Sausage Links●

Original Pork Roll Sausage●

Pork Sausage Patties●

Golden Brown All Natural Fully Cooked

Beef Sausage Links●

Maple Sausage (Links●, Patties●)

Mild Sausage (Links●, Patties●)

Pork & Uncured Bacon Sausage Links●

Sausage & Rice Links●

Spicy Sausage Links●

Turkey Sausage Links●

Medifast - Scrambled Eggs ●

Only Oats - Breakfast Blend (Apple & Cinnamon●, Maple & Roasted Flax●)

Broccoli

... *All Fresh Broccoli Is Gluten/Casein/Soy Free*

Albertsons - All Plain Frozen Broccoli

Birds Eye - All Plain Frozen Broccoli

C & W - All Plain Frozen Broccoli

Dr. Praeger's - Broccoli Littles**!**

Earthbound Farm - Organic Whole

Freshlike - Plain Frozen Broccoli

Green Giant -

Frozen (Chopped, Immunity Boost)

Valley Fresh Steamers (Broccoli Cuts, Chopped Broccoli, Select Broccoli Florets)

B

Hy-Vee - Frozen (Chopped, Cuts, Florets)
Kroger Brand - All Plain Broccoli (Canned, Frozen)
Kroger Value - All Plain Frozen Broccoli
Lowes Foods Brand - Frozen (Chopped, Cuts, Deluxe Baby Florets, Deluxe Florets, Spears)
Meijer Brand - Frozen (Chopped, Cuts, Spears)
Mezzetta - Broccoli Flowerettes
Midwest Country Fare - Frozen (Chopped, Cuts)
Nuts Online - Simply Broccoli Freeze Dried Vegetables●
Pictsweet - All Plain Frozen Broccoli
Private Selections - All Plain Frozen Broccoli
Publix - Frozen (Chopped, Cuts, Spears)
Safeway Brand - Frozen (Cuts, Florets, Steam In Bag)
Spartan Brand - Cuts, Florets, Spears
Stop & Shop Brand - Broccoli (Chopped, Cuts, Spears), Broccoli & Cauliflower
Trader Joe's - Frozen Broccoli Florets, Frozen Organic Broccoli Florets
Wegmans Brand - Broccoli (Chopped, Cuts), Broccoli Cuts & Cauliflower Florets, Spears
Winn Dixie - Frozen (Chopped, Cuts, Florets, Spears), Steamable Broccoli Cut
Woodstock Farms - Organic Frozen Broccoli Florets

Broth
Baxters - Chicken
Bowman & Landes - Chicken, Turkey
Caskey's - Beef, Chicken
College Inn Broth - Garden Vegetable
Full Circle - Chicken!, Vegetable!
Imagine - Low Sodium (Beef, Free Range Chicken, Vegetable), No Chicken, Regular (Beef, Free Range Chicken, Vegetable)
Kroger Brand - Canned (Beef!, Chicken!, Fat Free Beef!, Vegetable!), Culinary Stock (Beef!, Chicken!)

Lowes Foods Brand - Beef, Chicken (Low Sodium, Regular)
Member's Mark - All Natural Chicken Broth
O Organics - Chicken!!, Low Sodium Chicken!!, Vegetable!!
Pacific Natural Foods -
   Natural
     Beef
     Free Range Chicken
   Organic
     Beef
     Free Range Chicken
     Low Sodium (Chicken, Vegetable)
     Mushroom
     Vegetable
Progresso - Beef Flavored, Chicken (Reduced Sodium, Regular)
Publix - Beef, Chicken
Safeway Brand - Chicken Box
Shelton's - Chicken (Fat Free Low Sodium, Regular), Organic
   (Chicken, Chicken Fat Free Low Sodium)
Spartan Brand - Beef, Chicken
Swanson - Chicken Broth (Canned, Carton), Natural Goodness
   Chicken Broth (Canned, Carton)
Trader Joe's - Organic (Free Range Chicken!!, Hearty Vegetable!!,
   Low Sodium Chicken!!)
Winn Dixie - Canned (Clear Beef, Clear Chicken)
Brown Sugar... see Sugar
Brownies/Brownie Mix
   1-2-3 Gluten Free▲ - Divinely Decadent Brownies Mix●
   Better Batter - Fudge Brownie Mix
   Bob's Red Mill▲ - Gluten Free Brownie Mix
   Breakaway Bakery▲ - Brownie Batter●
   Cause You're Special▲ - Chocolate Fudge Mix
   Celiac Specialties▲ - Brownies Plain
   Ener-G▲ - Brownies
   Foods By George▲ - Brownies

B

French Meadow Bakery - Gluten Free (Frozen Fudge Brownies●, Fudge Brownie Bites●, Fudge Brownies●)
Gifts Of Nature▲ - Chocolate Fudge Brownie Mix
Gillian's Foods▲ - Brownie Mix
Gopal's - Brownies (Cherry, Original)
Hodgson Mill▲ - Gluten Free Brownie Mix
King Arthur Flour▲ - Gluten Free Brownie Mix●
Kneaded Specialties▲ - Ooey Gooey Fudge Brownie●
Laurel's Sweet Treats▲ - Chocolate Dream Brownie Mix
Mixes From The Heartland▲ - Brownie Mix (Microwave●, Pumpkin●, Sweet Potato●)
Namaste Foods▲ - Blondies Mix, Brownie Mix
Pure Market Express▲ - Brownie Bites w/Vanilla Frosting●
Really Great Food Company▲ - Aunt Tootsie's Brownie Mix
Rose's Bakery▲ - Brownies
Simply Organic▲ - Cocoa Brownie Mix
Trader Joe's - Gluten Free Brownie Mix

Bruschetta

Classico - All Varieties
Member's Mark
Tassos - Mediterranean, Olivara
Trader Joe's - Bruschetta Sauce (Fresh!!, Regular!!)

Brussel Sprouts

... *All Fresh Brussel Sprouts Are Gluten/Casein/Soy Free*
Birds Eye - All Plain Frozen Brussel Sprouts
C & W - All Plain Frozen Brussel Sprouts
Hy-Vee - Frozen
Meijer Brand - Frozen
Mezzetta - Dilled Brussels Sprouts
Midwest Country Fare - Frozen
Pictsweet - All Plain Frozen Brussel Sprouts
Publix - Frozen
Safeway Select - Petite
Spartan Brand - Frozen

Stop & Shop Brand - Frozen
Wegmans Brand - Frozen Regular
Winn Dixie - Frozen

Buckwheat
Arrowhead Mills
Arzu - Chai●, Original●, Southwest●
Bob's Red Mill▲ - Organic Buckwheat (Groats, Kasha)
Gluty Free - Raw Organic White●
Pocono - Buckwheat Flour (Light, Whole)

Buckwheat Bread... see Bread

Buckwheat Groats
Arrowhead Mills
Wolff's - Whole

Buffalo Wings... see Wings

Buns
Canyon Bakehouse▲ - Hamburger
El Peto▲ - Hamburger Buns (Potato), Hot Dog Buns (Potato)
Ener-G▲ -
Hamburger Buns (Brown Rice, Seattle Brown, Tapioca, White Rice)
Hot Dog Buns (Seattle Brown, Tapioca)
Gluten-Free Creations▲ - Hamburger Buns (Regular●, White●),
Hot Dog Buns●
Kinnikinnick▲ - Tapioca Rice Buns (Cinnamon, Hamburger Buns,
Hot Cross, Hot Dog)
Kneaded Specialties▲ - Hamburger●, Hamburger Buns w/Sesame
Seeds●, Hot Dog●
Schar▲ - Classic White Rolls
Silly Yak Bakery - CFGF (Garlic Chive●, Multi Seed●, Onion Dill●,
Raisin Walnut●, Rice Millet●, Tomato Basil Buns●)

Burgers
*... *All Fresh Ground Meat Is Gluten/Casein/Soy Free (Non-Marinated,
Unseasoned)*
Applegate Farms - Organic (Beef, Turkey)
Asherah's Gourmet - Vegan Burgers (Chipotle●, Original●)

B

Butcher's Cut - Beef Burgers
Butterball - Turkey Burgers Frozen (All Natural, Seasoned)
Great Value Brand (Wal-Mart) - 100% Frozen Beef Patties
Honeysuckle White -
    Fresh Ground Turkey Patties
    Frozen Turkey Burgers
Jennie-O Turkey Store -
    Fresh Lean Turkey Patties
    Frozen Turkey Burgers
Kirkland Signature - Frozen (Ground Beef Patties, Ground Sirloin Patties, Turkey Burgers)
Organic Prairie - Frozen Organic Ground Beef Patties 10.6 oz.
Perdue - Ground Burgers (Chicken, Turkey)
Shelton's - Turkey
Sunshine Burgers - Organic (Barbecue, Breakfast, Falafel, Garden Herb, Original, South West)
Trader Joe's - Chili Lime Chicken, Premium Salmon Patties **! !**
Wellshire Farms - All Natural Frozen (Beef Hamburgers **! !**, Turkey Burgers **! !**)
Winn Dixie - Frozen Angus Beef Patties (Original, w/Grill Seasoning, w/Sweet Onion)

Burritos
    Amy's - Gluten Free Dairy Free Burrito **!**

Butter... see also Spread
    Earth Balance▲ - Natural Buttery Spread Soy Free **!**
    Eden Organic - Apple, Apple Cherry, Montmorency Tart Cherry
    Gluty Free - Organic Cacao Butter●
    Nuts Online - Organic Cacao Butter●, Prune Butter●
    O'dell's - Clarified Butter, Popcorn Butter, Seafood Butter
    Phildesco - Coconut Butter
    Purity Farms - Organic Ghee Clarified Butter

C

Cabbage
  ... *All Fresh Cabbage Is Gluten/Casein/Soy Free*

Cake/Cake Mix
  1-2-3 Gluten Free▲ -
      Delightfully Gratifying Bundt Poundcake Mix●
      Devil Food Cake Mix●
      Peri's Perfect Chocolate Bundt Poundcake Mix●
      Yummy Yellow Cake Mix●
  AgVantage Naturals▲ -
      Angel Food Cake Mix●
      Dark Chocolate Cake Mix●
      Vanilla Supreme Cake Mix●
  Augason Farms▲ - Gluten Free Cake Mix (Angel Food●,
      Chocolate●, Yellow●)
  Authentic Foods - Cake Mix (Devil's Food Chocolate, Vanilla)
  Betty Crocker▲ - Gluten Free Cake Mix (Devil's Food, Yellow)
  Bob's Red Mill▲ - Cake Mix (Chocolate, Vanilla)
  Breakaway Bakery▲ - Cupcake Batter (Chocolate●, Chocolate
      Chip●, Golden Cinnamon Lemon●)
  Cause You're Special▲ - Golden Poundcake, Moist (Lemon, Yellow),
      Rich Chocolate
  Celiac Specialties▲ - Angel Food Cake
  Cherrybrook Kitchen - Gluten Free Chocolate Cake Mix *(Box Must
      Say Gluten-Free)*, Gluten Free Yellow Cake Mix *(Box Must Say
      Gluten-Free)*
  EasyGlut - Cake Mix (Devil's Food, Yellow)
  Ener-G▲ - Poundcake
  Food-Tek Fast & Fresh▲ - Cake Mix Dairy Free Minute (Chocolate,
      Cinnamon Coffee, White, Yellow)
  Full Circle - Gluten Free Spice Cake Mix

C

Gifts Of Nature▲ - Yellow Cake Mix

Gluten-Free Creations▲ - Angel Food Cake●, Carrot Picnic Cake●,
Winkies●

Gluten-Free Essentials▲ -

Mix

Extreme Chocolate Cake●

Holiday Gingerbread●

Yellow Velvet Cake●

Speedy Bake Mix

Chocolate Mud●

Spice Is Nice●

Yella Vanilla●

Grandma Ferdon's▲ - Angel Food Cake Mix●

Heaven Mills▲ - Cake (Brownie●, Carrot●, Marble●, Strip
Chocolate●), Sprinkled Cupcakes●

Hodgson Mill▲ - Gluten Free (Chocolate Cake Mix, Yellow
Cake Mix)

Jennies▲ - Pound Cake Minis (Classic●, Marble●, Raisin●)

Katz Gluten Free▲ - Cupcake (Chocolate●, Vanilla●),
Marble Cake●

King Arthur Flour▲ - Gluten Free Chocolate Cake Mix●

Kinnikinnick▲ - Cake Mix (Angel Food, Chocolate, Sponge, White)

Kneaded Specialties▲ -

Coffee Cake●

Cupcakes

Chocolate●

Vegan (Chocolate Creme●, Vanilla Creme●)

White●

Luscious Lemonade Cake●

Laurel's Sweet Treats▲ - Cake Mix (Cinnamon Spice, Mom's
Chocolate, Vanilla)

Mixes From The Heartland▲ -

Cake Mix

Cheesecake●

Chocolate Angel Food●

    Chocolate Poundcake●
    Cinnamon Orange●
    Lime Angel Food●
    Lime Poundcake●
    Orange Angel Food●
    Raspberry Poundcake●
    Strawberry Angel Food●
    Strawberry Poundcake●
    Vanilla Angel Food●
    Vanilla Poundcake●

Namaste Foods▲ - Cake Mix (Chocolate, Spice, Vanilla)

Orgran▲ - Cake Mix (Chocolate, Vanilla)

Pamela's Products▲ - Cake Mix (Chocolate, Classic Vanilla)

Pure Market Express▲ - Cheesecake (Chocolate●, Key Lime●)

Really Great Food Company▲ -

  Cake Mix
    Angel Food
    Banana Bread
    Chocolate
    Chocolate Cupcake
    Colonial Spice
    Devil's Food
    Gingerbread
    Golden
    Grandma's Poundcake
    Lemon Poppy
    Orange
    Pineapple
    Pumpkin Bread
    Pumpkin Spice
    White
    Yellow
  Coffee Crumb Cake

Ruby Range - Gluten Free Baking Mix (Chocolate Truffle Cake & Cupcakes●, Spice Cake & Cupcakes●)

C   **Simply Organic ▲** - Carrot Cake Mix, Cocoa Cayenne Cupcake Mix
Sof'ella - Gluten Free Chocolate Cake Mix & Frosting Mix●
The Cravings Place ▲ - Cake & Cookie Mix, Cinnamon Crumble
     Coffeecake Mix, Create Your Own, Dutch Chocolate Cake Mix
Whole Foods Market Gluten Free Bakehouse ▲ - Carrot Cake

Candy/Candy Bars

   Candy Tree - Licorice (Cherry (Bites, Laces, Vines), Raspberry (Bites,
     Laces, Vines), Strawberry (Bites, Laces, Vines))
   Caring Candies - Sugar Free Lollipops
   ChocAlive - Truffles (Almond, Chocolate Chip Mint, Coconut, Dark
     Chocolate, Dark Chocolate Crunch, Pistachio)
   Dots - Crows, Fruit Flavor, Tropical Flavor
   Enjoy Life - Boom Choco Boom Bars (All Varieties)
   Great Value Brand (Wal-Mart) - Cinnamon Discs, Fruit Slices,
     Gummy Bears, Orange Slices, Spearmint Starlight Mints, Spice
     Drops, Starlight Mints
   Hannaford Brand -
     Butterscotch**!**
     Canada (Mints**!**, Wintergreen**!**)
     Circus Peanuts**!**
     Gummi (Bears**!**, Sour Neon Worms**!**, Worms**!**)
     Jelly (Beans**!**, Rings**!**)
     Jumbo Gum Drops**!**
     Orange Slices**!**
     Spice Drops**!**
     Sugar Free (Cinnamon Buttons**!**, Peppermint Starlights**!**)
   Haribo -
     Alphabet Letters
     Build A Burger
     Centipedes
     Clown Fish
     Colossal Crocs
     Fizzy Cola
     Frogs

C

    Fruit (Blasts, Salad)
    Fruity Frutti
    Gold Bears
    Grapefruit
    Gummi Apples
    Happy Cola
    Mini Rainbow Frogs
    Peaches
    Pink Grapefruit
    Raspberries
    Rattle Snakes
    Root Beer Barrels
    Roulettes (Mega, Regular)
    Sour Cherries
    Stock Cars
    Strawberries
    Super Cola
    Techno Bears
    Tropi Frutti
    Twin Cherries

Hershey's - Jolly Ranchers Hard Candy

Hy-Vee -
    Assorted Gum Balls
    Butterscotch Buttons
    Cinnamon Imperials
    Circus Peanuts
    Dum Dum Suckers
    Gummi (Bears, Peach Rings, Worms)
    Lemon Drops
    Orange Slices
    Smarties
    Spice Drops
    Starlight Mints
    Wax Bottles

C

Indie Candy -
　All Natural Sugar Free Bon Bons
　Chocolate (Angel, Dancing Santa, Teddy Bears)
　Christmas (Lights Lollipops, Tree Gummies)
　Dark Chocolate (Covered Glacee' Oranges, Drizzled Fresh
　　Marshmallows, Lollipop Shapes)
　Halloween (Chocolate Lollipops, Crystal Lollipop Assortment,
　　Gummies Allergen Free)
　Lollipop (Birthday Bouquet, Flowers)
　Make Your Own Gummies Kit
　Swirly Lollipops
　Zoo Animals (Gummies, Lollipops)
Jolly Ranchers - Hard Candy
Kroger Brand -
　Gummi
　　Assorted Orange Slices
　　Bears
　　Fruit Slices
　　Sour (Bears, Slices, Worms)
　　Worms
　Hard Candy
　　Butterscotch
　　Peppermint
　　Spearmint
　Jelly Beans
　Juju Fish
　Soft Mints
Let's Do...Organic - Gummy Bears (All Varieties)
Lifesavers - All Flavors
Lucky Leaf - Cherries Jubilee
Necco - Canada Mint & Wintergreen Lozenges, Candy Stix,
　Sweethearts Conversation Hearts *(Valentines Only)*
Nestle - Spree
Nik-L-Nip - Wax Bottles
Nuts Online - Turkish Delight (Almond●, Mixed Nut●, Pistachio●)

Private Selections - Gourmet Jelly Beans

Publix -

Gummi (Sour Worms **! !**, Worms **! !**)

Smarties Candy **! !**

Spearmint Starlight Mints **! !**

Starlight Mints Candy **! !**

Pure Market Express▲ - Bliss Balls●

Razzles - Gum Regular

Safeway Brand - Gummi Bears, Gummi Worms

Seitenbacher -

Cherry Dolphins

Roses For You

Smooch Lions

Strawberry Alligators

Sunhats (Black Currant, Cherry, Passion Fruit, Strawberry)

Vampires Lunch

Sharkies▲ - Kids Sports Chews Berry Blasters, Kids Sports Chews Tropical Splash, Organic Energy Sports Chews (Berry Blast, Citrus Squeeze, Fruit Splash, Watermelon Scream)

Sipahh - Milk Flavoring Straws

Skittles - All Varieties

Smarties - All Varieties

Spangler▲ - Candy Canes, Cane Classics, Dum Dum (Canes, Chewy Pops, Pops), Marshmallow Circus Peanuts, Saf T Pops, Swirl Saf T Pops

St. Claire's Organics - All Candy, Mints, Sweets (Licorice, Organic Ginger), Tarts (Lemon, Lime, Peach, Raspberry)

Starburst - All Varieties

Surf Sweets - Gummi Bears, Gummi Swirls, Gummi Worms, Jelly Beans, Sour Berry Gummi Bears

Swedish Fish - Aqualife, Assorted, Red

The Ginger People -

Crystallized Ginger Candy **!**

Gin Gins **!**

Ginger Chews (Hot Coffee **!**, Original **!**, Peanut **!**, Spicy Apple **!**)

C Wonka -
    Bottlecaps!
    Gobstoppers (Chewy!, Original!)
    Lik M Aid Fun Dip!
    Nerds (Chewy!, Regular!)
    Pixy Stix!
    Runts (Chewy!, Original!)
    Spree!
    Sweet Tarts!
Woodstock Farms - Vegetarian (Gummy Cubs, Jelly Pebbles)
Yummy Earth - Lollipops

Canned Chicken
    Hormel - Chicken, Chunk Meats Breast Of Chicken
    Meijer Brand - Chicken Chunk White
    Member's Mark - Premium Chunk Chicken Breast In Water,
        Premium Chunk Chicken Breast In Water
    Spartan Brand - Chunk Chicken Breast
    Sweet Sue - Chunk White

Canned Ham
    Great Value Brand (Wal-Mart) - Luncheon Meat
    Hormel - Chunk Meats Ham
    Malone's - Ham Spread, Potted Meat
    SPAM - Classic, Hickory Smoke Flavored, Less Sodium, Lite
    Underwood - Deviled Ham Spread

Canned Salmon... see Fish

Canned Tuna... see Tuna

Canned Turkey
    Hormel - Chunk Meats Turkey
    Member's Mark - Premium Chunk Turkey Breast In Water
    SPAM - Oven Roasted Turkey

Canola Oil... see Oil

Cantaloupe
    *... *All Fresh Fruits & Vegetables Are Gluten/Casein/Soy Free*
    Gluty Free - Dried Chunks●, Dried●
    Nuts Online - Fruit (Chunks●, Whole●)

C

Capers
  B&G - Capote, Nonpareil
  Mezzetta - Capote Capers, Non Pareil (Capers, Capers In Balsamic Vinegar)
  Safeway Select - Nonpareil
  Trader Joe's - Nonpareil
  Wegmans Brand - Italian Classics (Capote, Nonpareil)
Cappuccino... see Coffee
Carbonated Beverage... see Soda Pop/Carbonated Beverages
Carrots
  ... *All Fresh Carrots Are Gluten/Casein/Soy Free
  Albertsons - All Plain Carrots Canned & Frozen
  Birds Eye - All Plain Frozen Carrots
  C & W - All Plain Frozen Carrots
  Del Monte - All Canned Plain Carrots
  Earthbound Farm - Bunched & Cello, Mini Peeled
  Freshlike - Frozen Plain Carrots
  Grand Selections - Frozen Whole Carrots
  Great Value Brand (Wal-Mart) - Canned Sliced Carrots, Microwavable Plastic Cup Frozen
  Hannaford Brand - All Frozen Carrots, Sliced, Whole Baby
  Hy-Vee - California, Classic Cut & Peeled Baby, Frozen Crinkle Cut, Sliced
  Kroger Brand - All Plain Carrots (Canned, Frozen)
  Lowes Foods Brand - Deluxe Whole Baby, Peas & Carrots, Sliced
  Meijer Brand - Canned Sliced (No Salt, Regular), Frozen Carrots (Crinkle Cut, Whole Baby)
  Mezzetta - Gourmet Baby
  Midwest Country Fare - Sliced Carrots
  Nuts Online - Simply Carrots Freeze Dried Vegetables●
  Pictsweet - All Plain Frozen Carrots
  Publix - Canned Carrots, Frozen (Crinkle Cut, Whole Baby)
  Publix GreenWise Market - Organic (Baby, Carrots, Chips, Juicing, Shredds, Snack)

C

S&W - All Canned Carrots

Safeway Brand - Carrots Sliced

Spartan Brand - Canned (Peas & Sliced Carrots, Sliced), Frozen (Crinkle Cut, Peas & Carrots, Whole Baby)

Wegmans Brand - Baby Cut, Carrots/Potatoes/Celery & Onions, Crinkle Cut, Organic (Baby Cut, Regular), Sliced Carrots (No Salt Added, Regular), Whole Style

Winn Dixie - Frozen (Crinkle Cut, Whole Baby)

Cashews... see Nuts

Cauliflower

... *All Fresh Cauliflower Is Gluten/Casein/Soy Free*

Albertsons - All Plain Cauliflower Frozen

Birds Eye - All Plain Frozen Cauliflower

C & W - All Plain Frozen Cauliflower

Earthbound Farm - Organic Whole

Freshlike - Frozen Plain Cauliflower

Hy-Vee - Frozen Cauliflower Florets

Kroger Brand - All Plain Cauliflower (Canned, Frozen)

Lowes Foods Brand - Frozen Cauliflower

Meijer Brand - Frozen Cauliflower Florets

Mezzetta - Dilled, Hot

Midwest Country Fare - Frozen Cauliflower

Pictsweet - All Plain Frozen Cauliflower

Publix - Frozen

Safeway Brand - Frozen

Spartan Brand - Frozen Florets

Trader Joe's - All Plain Frozen Cauliflower

Wegmans Brand - Florets

Winn Dixie - Frozen

Caviar

Romanoff - Black (Lumpfish, Whitefish), Red (Lumpfish, Salmon)

Celery

... *All Fresh Celery Is Gluten/Casein/Soy Free*

C

Celery Salt... see Seasonings
Cereal
  Amy's - Cream Of Rice Hot Cereal Bowl **!**
  Ancient Harvest Quinoa - Quinoa Flakes
  Arrowhead Mills - Hot (Rice & Shine, Yellow Corn Grits), Maple
    Buckwheat Flakes, Rice Flakes Sweetened
  Bakery On Main - Granola (Apple Raisin Walnut●, Cranberry
    Orange Cashew●, Extreme Fruit & Nut●, Nutty Cranberry Maple●,
    Rainforest●)
  Barbara's Bakery - Organic Brown Rice Crisps
  Bob's Red Mill▲ - Creamy Rice Hot Cereal (Organic, Regular),
    Flaxseed Meal, Gluten Free Mighty Tasty Hot, Organic Creamy
    Buckwheat
  Cerealvit - Coffee Flakes, Corn Flakes
  Chex▲ - Corn, Honey Nut, Rice
  Earth's Best Organic Baby Food - Whole Grain Rice Cereal
    (Apples, Plain)
  Eco-Planet▲ - 7 Whole Grains Hot Cereal (Apples & Cinnamon●,
    Maple & Brown Sugar●, Original●)
  El Peto▲ - Corn Flakes Whole Grain, Cream Of Rice (w/Apple &
    Cinnamon, White, Whole Grain Brown)
  Ener-G▲ - Rice Bran
  Enjoy Life▲ -
    Crunchy (Flax●, Rice●)
    Granola Crunch (Cinnamon●, Cranapple●, Very Berry●)
  Erewhon -
    Aztec Crunchy Corn & Amaranth
    Brown Rice Cream
    Corn Flakes
    Crispy Brown Rice (Cocoa, Gluten Free Regular, w/Mixed Berries)
    Rice Twice, Strawberry Crisp
  General Mills▲ - Chex (Corn, Honey Nut, Rice)
  Glutano▲ - Cornflakes

C

Gluten Free Sensations▲ - Cream Of Brown Rice, Granola (Cherry Vanilla Almond, Cranberry Pecan, French Vanilla Almond)

Gluty Free - Super Food (Acai Blueberry●, Cacao Crunch●, Chia Ginger●, Hemp & Greens●)

Hodgson Mill▲ - Gluten Free Creamy Buckwheat w/Milled Flax

Kinnikinnick▲ - KinniKrisp Rice Cereal

Lundberg▲ - Hot 'N Creamy Purely Organic Rice

Meijer Brand - Grits (Buttered Flavored Instant, Quick)

Montana Monster Munchies - Whole Grain Oat Bran●

Nabisco - Cream Of Rice Hot Cereal

Nature's Path -
  Corn Puffs**!**
  Country (Maple Sunrise**!**, Vanilla Sunrise**!**)
  Envirokidz Organic Amazon Frosted Flakes
  Millet Puffs**!**
  Nature's Path Organic
    Corn Flakes
    Crispy Rice
    Honey'd Corn Flakes
    Mesa Sunrise
    Whole O's
  Rice Puffs**!**

New Morning - Cocoa Crispy Rice

Nuts Online -
  Organic Hot Cereal
    Amaranth●
    Buckwheat Toasted●
    Raw White Buckwheat●
  Superfood Cereal
    Acai Blueberry●
    Cacao Crunch●
    Chia Ginger●
    Hemp & Greens●
  Teff Whole Grain Hot Cereal●

Nu-World Foods▲ -
  Amaranth (Berry Delicious●, Cinnamon Delight●)
  Amaranth O's (Original●, Peach●)
  Cereal Snaps (Cinnamon●, Cocoa●, Original●)
  Puffed Amaranth Cereal●
Only Oats - Oat Bran●
Orgran▲ - Itsy Bitsy Cocoa O's, Multigrain O's w/Quinoa, Puffed
  Amaranth Breakfast Cereal, Rice O's Wild Berry
Pocono - Cream Of Buckwheat
Pure Market Express▲ - Count Rawcula●, Honey Wheaties●,
  Strawberry Crunch●
Ruth's Hemp Power - Chia Goodness (Apple Almond Cinnamon,
  Cranberry Ginger, Original)
Seitenbacher - Musli #7, Whole Grain Cornflakes
Wegmans Brand - Fruity Rice Crisps
Chamomile Tea... see Tea
Champagne
  ... *All Champagne Made In The USA is Gluten/Casein/Soy Free* [2]
Cheese
  Daiya - Shreds (Cheddar Style, Mozzarella Style)
  Eat In The Raw - Parma Vegan Parmesan (Chipotle Cayenne,
    Original)
  Galaxy Nutritional Foods - Rice Vegan (All Varieties)
  Gopal's - Rawmesan, Rawmesan Herbs N Spice
  Pure Market Express▲ -
    Cheddar Spread●
    Cilantro Jalapeno Cheese●
    Creamy Herb Cheese●
    Good As Gouda●
    Mexi Cheese●
    Pepper Jack Cheese●
    Simply Basil●
    Spicy Peppercorn●
    Sundried Tomato Basil Cheese●
    Wasabi Chive●

C

Rice Shreds **(Galaxy Nutritional Foods)** - Rice Vegan (All Varieties)

Road's End Organics - Organic (GF Alfredo Chreese Mix, GF Cheddar Chreese Mix)

Wayfare - We Can't Say It's Cheese (Cheddar Sauce●, Cheddar Spread●, Hickory Cheddar●, Mexi Cheddar●)

Cherries

... *All Fresh Cherries Are Gluten/Casein/Soy Free*

Fruit Advantage - Premium Dried Cherries

Gluty Free - Dried (Bing●, Rainier●, Sour●)

Great Value Brand **(Wal-Mart)** - Maraschino

Hy-Vee - Frozen Cherry Berry Blend, Red Maraschino Cherries (Regular, w/Stems)

Kroger Brand - Maraschino

Lucky Leaf - Red Tart Pitted Cherries

Meijer Brand - Frozen (Dark Sweet, Tart), Maraschino Cherry (Red, Red w/Stems)

Mezzetta - Maraschino Cherries (w/Stems, w/o Stems)

Midwest Country Fare - Maraschino Cherries

Musselman's - Red Tart Pitted Cherries

Nuts Online - Dried Fruit (Bing●, Organic Bing●, Rainier●, Simply●, Sour Tart●)

Publix - Frozen (Cherries, Dark Sweet), Maraschino

S&W - All Canned/Jarred Fruits

Safeway Brand - Frozen Dark Sweet, Maraschino Cherries

Santa Barbara Olive Co. - Maraschino (Green, Red)

Spartan Brand - Frozen Dark Sweet Cherries, Maraschino Cherries Red (Regular, Salad, w/Stems)

Stop & Shop Brand - Frozen Dark Sweet Cherries

Trader Joe's - Frozen Very Cherry Berry Blend

Wegmans Brand - Dark Sweet, Maraschino (Jumbo w/o Stems, w/o Stems, w/Stems), Triple Cherry Fruit Mix In Light Syrup

Winn Dixie - Dark Sweet Cherries, Maraschino Cherries

Woodstock Farms - Dried Cherries Unsulphured, Organic Frozen Dark Sweet Cherries

Chewing Gum

C

    B Fresh

    Bazooka

    Between - Dental Gum

    Glee Gum - All Varieties

    Indie Candy - Make Your Own Chewing Gum Kit

    Meijer Brand - Nicotine Gum (Mint, Regular)

    Nicorette

Chick Peas... see Beans

Chicken

    ... *All Fresh Chicken Is Gluten/Casein/Soy Free (Non-Marinated, Unseasoned)

    Al Fresco -

        Breakfast Sausages (Apple Maple, Country Style, Wild Blueberry)

        Dinner Sausage Fully Cooked (Buffalo Style, Roasted Garlic, Spicy Jalapeno, Sundried Tomato, Sweet Apple, Sweet Italian Style)

        Fresh Dinner Sausages (Buffalo Style, Sweet (Apple, Italian Style))

    Applegate Farms - Organic (Roasted Chicken Breast, Smoked Chicken Breast)

    Boar's Head - All Varieties

    Butcher's Cut - Boneless Skinless Chicken Breast, Young Chicken Thighs

    Butterball - Deli Meat Thin Sliced Oven Roasted Chicken Breast

    Carl Buddig - Deli Cut Rotisserie Chicken, Fix Quix Regular

    Castle Wood Reserve - Deli Meat Oven Roasted Chicken

    Chi-Chi's - Fiesta Plates Salsa

    Coleman's Natural Foods -

      Bone In Skin On Thigh●

      Boneless Skinless

        Breast●

        Fresh For The Freezer Breasts●

        Thigh●

      Chicken Sausage

        Mild Italian●

        Spicy (Andouille●, Chipotle●, Chorizo●, Italian●)

C

    Sun Dried Tomato & Basil●
    Sweet Apple w/Maple Syrup●
  Drummettes●
  Drumsticks●
  Organic
    Bone In Skin On Thigh●
    Chicken Sausage
      (Mild Italian●, Sun Dried Tomato & Basil●, Sweet Apple●)
    Drummettes●
    Drumsticks●
    Fresh For The Freezer Breasts●
    Split Breast●
    Whole Chicken●
    Wings●
  Split Breast●
  Uncured Hickory Smoked●
  Whole Chicken●
  Wings●

Dinty Moore - Microwave Meal Rice w/Chicken

Empire Kosher - Chicken Bologna Slices, Chicken Franks, Fresh Chill Pack, Fresh Rotisserie, Frozen, Fully Cooked Barbecue Chicken (Fresh, Frozen), Individually Quick Frozen Chicken Parts, Rendered Chicken Fat

Farmer John - California Natural Chicken Sausage (Chicken Brat Smoked, Lemon Cracked Pepper Chicken Smoked, Mango & Habanero Smoked)

Garrett County Farms - Chicken Franks!, Frozen Chicken Apple Breakfast Links!

Great Value Brand (Wal-Mart) - Frozen (Boneless Skinless Breast, Drumsticks, Thighs), Frozen Wing Sections

Hannaford Brand - Chicken Breast Chunk In Water

Hans All Natural - Breakfast Links (Organic●, Skinless●)

Hillshire Farms - Deli Select Oven Roasted Chicken Breast

Honeysuckle White - Chicken Breast Deli Meat Oil Browned

C

Hormel - Carved Chicken Breast (Grilled, Oven Roasted), Chunk Meats (Breast Of Chicken, Chicken), Natural Choice Strips (Grilled, Oven Roasted)

Hy-Vee -
- 100% Natural Fresh
  - Boneless (Skinless, Skinless Breasts)
  - Breast Tenderloins
  - Drumsticks
  - For Roasting w/Neck & Giblets
  - Gizzards
  - Leg Quarters
  - Split (Breasts, Breasts w/Ribs)
  - Thighs
  - Whole Cut Up w/Neck & Giblets
  - Wing Drummettes
  - Wings
  - Young w/Neck & Giblets
- Canned 98% Fat Free Breast Of Chicken

Ian's - Wheat Free Gluten Free Recipe (Chicken Finger Kids Meal, Chicken Nuggets, Chicken Patties)

Kirkland Signature - Chunk Chicken Breast, Fresh Breasts, Frozen (Breasts, Tenderloin, Thighs, Wings), Grilled Breast Strips

Kroger Brand - Canned (Premium, Regular), Fresh & Frozen Plain (Breast, Thighs, Wings), Pouch

Manor House - All Varieties In 4 lb. Resealable Bags

Meijer Brand - Canned Chicken Chunk White

Member's Mark - Canned Premium Chunk Chicken Breast In Water, Chicken Sausage Gourmet Chicken & Apple

O Organics - Fresh Chicken Breast (Regular, Tenders)

Organic Prairie - Fresh Organic Sliced Roast Chicken Breast ! !, Frozen Organic (Chicken Italian Sausage ! !, Ground Chicken 12 oz., Whole Young Chicken), Roast Chicken Breast Slices ! !

C

Oscar Mayer - Deli Fresh (Oven Roasted Chicken Breast 98% Fat Free, Thin Sliced Oven Roasted Chicken Breast), Shaved Deli Fresh (Cajun Seasoned Chicken Breast, Rotisserie Style Chicken Breast)

Perdue -
Ground Chicken (Breast Of Chicken, Burgers)
Individually Frozen Chicken (Breasts, Tenderloins, Wings)
Perfect Portions Boneless Skinless Chicken Breast (Regular)
Rotisserie Chicken (Barbeque, Italian, Lemon Pepper, Oven Roasted, Toasted Garlic, Tuscany Herb Roasted)
Rotisserie Oven Stuffer Roaster (Breast, Regular)

Publix - All Natural Fresh, Frozen (Boneless Skinless Chicken (Breasts, Cutlets), Chicken Breast Tenderloins, Chicken Wingettes)

Publix GreenWise Market - Boneless Breast, Boneless Thighs, Cutlet, Drummettes, Drumsticks, Fillet, Ground Chicken, Skinless Drumstick, Skinless Thighs, Split Breast, Tenderloin, Thighs, Whole, Wings

Rocky Jr. -
Bone In Skin On Thigh●
Boneless Skinless (Breast●, Thigh●)
Breast Tenders●
Drummettes●
Drumsticks●
Rocky Dogs Uncured Hot Dog●
Split Breast●
The Range Chicken●
Whole Chicken●
Wings●

Rosie -
Organic
Bone In Skin On Thigh●
Boneless Skinless (Breast●, Thigh●)
Breast Tenders●
Drummettes●

Drumsticks●
Split Breast●
Whole Chicken●
Wings●

Safeway Brand - Canned Chunk White Breast

Sara Lee - Deli Meat Slices Oven Roasted Chicken Breast

Saz's - Barbecue Chicken Meat Tub

S'Better Farms▲ - Chicken (Ballontine, Fingers, Party Wings, Siciliano, Szechwan)

Shaner's - Frozen (Breast Tenders, Breasts w/Rib Meat, Drumsticks, Split Breasts w/Ribs)

Shelton's - Capon, Free Range (Breasts, Thighs, Whole), Organic (Boneless/Skinless Breast, Breast, Cut Up, Whole Chicken, Whole Legs)

Smart Chicken - All Varieties

SPAM - Hickory Smoke Flavored

Spartan Brand - Canned Chicken Breast Chunk, Frozen Boneless Skinless (Breasts, Tenders)

Sweet Bay - All Fresh Chicken

Trader Joe's -
BBQ Pulled Chicken Breast In Smoky BBQ Sauce
Fully Cooked & Seasoned Roasted Chicken**!!**
Grilled Breast Strips
Balsamic & Rosemary**!!**
Chili Lime**!!**
Lemon Pepper**!!**
Plain**!!**
Grilled Chicken Breast Strips
Balsamic & Rosemary**!!**
Chili Lime**!!**
Lemon Pepper**!!**
Plain**!!**

Tropical Traditions - Whole Chicken, Whole Chicken Cut Into Parts

Tyson - All Natural Fresh (All Varieties)

C

 Valley Fresh - All Fresh Chicken
 Wellshire Farms - Chicken Franks!!, Oven Roasted Chicken
   Breast!!
 Winn Dixie - Canned Breast, Frozen (Breasts, Tenderloins)
Chicken Nuggets... see Chicken
Chicken Wings... see Wings
Chiles
 Chi-Chi's - Green Chiles
 La Victoria - Green Fire Roasted (Diced, Whole)
 Meijer Brand - Diced Mild Mexican Style
 Old El Paso - Green (Chopped, Whole)
 Ortega - Diced Hot, Green (Diced, Whole)
 Safeway Brand - Diced Green
 Spartan Brand - Green Chiles
Chili
 Albertsons - Hot w/Beans, w/Beans
 Amy's - Medium Black Bean!, Organic Chili (Medium
   w/Vegetables!, Southwestern Black Bean!)
 Frontera - Chipotle & Black Bean
 Hormel - Chili Master (Chipotle Chicken No Bean, Chipotle
   Chicken w/Beans), Chili w/Beans (Hot, Regular)
 Hy-Vee - Hot Chili w/Beans, Mild w/Beans
 Kettle Cuisine - Angus Beef Steak Chili w/Beans●, Three Bean●
 Meijer Brand - Chili (No Beans Regular, w/Beans Regular),
   Hot Dog Chili Sauce
 Shelton's - Mild Chicken, Mild Turkey, Spicy Chicken, Spicy Turkey
 Spartan Brand - w/Beans
 Stagg - Classic, Ranch House Chicken, Steak House
 Trader Joe's - Chicken Chili w/Beans
 Winn Dixie - w/Beans
Chili Powder
 Chugwater Chili
 Durkee - Dark
 Hy-Vee

Marcum Spices
McCormick - Hot Mexican Style, Regular
Meijer Brand
Midwest Country Fare
Spartan Brand
Spice Islands
Tones
Chili Sauce
   A Taste Of Thai - Garlic Chili Pepper Sauce, Sweet Red Chili Sauce
   Frank's RedHot - Chile 'N Lime
   Hannaford Brand
   Heinz
   Hy-Vee
   Kroger Brand
   Las Palmas - Red Chile
   Lee Kum Kee - Sriracha Chili
   Meijer Brand - Hot Dog Chili
   Safeway Brand
   Spartan Brand
   Thai Kitchen - Roasted Red Chili Paste, Spicy Thai, Sweet Red
   Trader Joe's - Chili Pepper!!, Sweet!!
   Wegmans Brand
Chips
   Boulder Canyon Natural Foods -
      Canyon Cut Potato Chips
         Honey Barbeque
         Salt & Cracked Pepper
         Totally Natural
      Kettle Cooked Potato Chips
         50% Reduced Salt
         60% Reduced Sodium
         Balsamic Vinegar & Rosemary
         Hickory Barbeque
         Limon

C

    No Salt Added
    Olive Oil
    Red Wine Vinegar
    Sea Salt & Cracked Pepper
    Sweet Lemon & Cracked Pepper
    Tomato & Basil
    Totally Natural
Rice & Adzuki Bean Snack Chips
    Lemon & Cracked Black Pepper
    Natural Salt
    Sundried Tomato w/Basil
Tortilla Strips w/Hummus
    Lightly Salted
    Sesame

Brothers All Natural▲ - Potato Crisps (Black Pepper & Sea Salt, Fresh Onion & Garlic, Original w/Sea Salt, Szechuan Pepper & Fresh Chives)

Cape Cod -
Potato
    40% Reduced Fat
    Classic
    Robust Russet
    Sea Salt & (Vinegar, Vinegar 40% Less Fat)
    Sweet & Spicy Jalapeno
    Sweet Mesquite Barbeque (40% Less Fat, Regular)

Chi-Chi's - All Varieties

Covered Bridge Potato Chips▲ - Old Fashioned Kettle Style (Sea Salt●, Sea Salt & Cracked Pepper●, Sea Salt & Vinegar●, Smokin' Sweet BBQ●, Sweet Potato w/Cinnamon & Brown Sugar●)

Deep River Snacks - Cracked Pepper & Sea Salt, Lightly Salted, Mesquite BBQ, Original Salted, Salt & Vinegar, Sweet Maui Onion, Zesty Jalapeno

Eat Smart - Naturals (Garden Veggie (Crisps●, Stix), MultiGrain Tortilla●)

Eden Organic - Brown Rice

Flamous Brands - Falafel Chips (Original●, Spicy●)

Food Should Taste Good - Tortilla Chips (Jalapeno●, Lime●, Olive●, Sweet Potato●, The Works●, Yellow Corn●)

Fritos - Corn Chips (Lightly Salted**!!**, Original**!!**, Scoops**!!**)

Full Circle -
All Natural (BBQ, Natural Potato, Ripple)
Kettle Cooked Lightly Salted
Organic Tortilla Chips (Blue Corn, White Corn, Yellow Corn)
Popcorn Salted

Garden Of Eatin' -
Mini Tortilla
Rounds (White, Yellow)
White Strips
Tortilla
Black Bean
Blue Chips (No Salt Added, Regular)
Key Lime Jalapeno
Popped Blues
Red Chips
Sesame Blues
Sunny Blues
Three Pepper
White Chips
Yellow Chips
Veggie Chips
Beet & Garlic
Vegetable Medley

Glenny's - Spud Delites Natural Potato Crisps (Sea Salt ●, Texas BBQ ●)

Gluty Free - Banana●, Fruit●, Green Bean●, Organic Banana●, Veggie Regular●, Veggie (No Added Salt)●

Good Health Natural Foods▲ -
Potato Chips
Avocado Oil (Barcelona Barbeque**!!**, Regular**!!**)

C

    Glories Sweet‼

    Olive Oil (Cracked Pepper & Sea Salt‼, Rosemary‼, Sea Salt‼)

Goraw▲ - Super Chips (Pumpkin●, Spirulina●)

Grandma Ferdon's▲ -

    Taco Seasoned Tortilla Chips●

    Tortilla Chips●

Green Mountain Gringo▲ - Tortilla Strips (Blue Corn ●, Original ●, White Corn ●)

Herr's -

    Corn Chips Regular

    Potato Chips (No Salt, Old Fashioned)

    Tortilla Chips Restaurant Style

Kettle Brand -

    Baked Potato Chips (Hickory Honey Barbeque, Salt & Fresh Ground Pepper, Sea Salt, Sea Salt & Vinegar)

    Krinkle Cut Potato Chips (Classic Barbeque, Salt & Fresh Ground Pepper, Sea Salt)

    Organic Potato Chips (Chipotle Chili Barbeque, Lightly Salted, Sea & Fresh Ground Pepper, Sea Salt)

    Potato Chips (Backyard Barbeque, Death Valley Chipotle, Honey Dijon, Jalapeno, Sea Salt & Vinegar, Spicy Thai, Unsalted)

Kroger Brand - Cornito, Pork Rinds Original, Potato (Classic, Wavy), Tortilla (Bite Size, Regular, Sea Salt)

Late July - Sea Salt By The Seashore●

Lay's -

    Potato Chips

        Balsamic Sweet Onion‼

        Classic‼

        Kettle Cooked (Crinkle Cut Original‼, Original‼, Reduced Fat Original‼, Sea Salt & Cracked Pepper‼)

        Light Original‼

        Lightly Salted‼

Limon!!
Pepper Relish!!
Wavy Regular!!
Lundberg▲ - Rice Chips (Honey Dijon, Pico De Gallo, Santa Fe Barbecue, Sea Salt, Wasabi)
Maui Style - Potato Chips Regular!!
Michael Season's - Thin & Crispy (Honey Barbecue, Lightly Salted, Ripple Lightly Salted, Salt & Pepper, Unsalted)
Miguel's - Tortilla Chips (Blue Corn●, White Corn●)
Miss Vickie's - Kettle Cooked Potato Chips (Sea Salt & Cracked Pepper!!, Simply Sea Salt!!, Smokehouse BBQ!!)
Nuts Online - Carrot Chips●, Fruit Chips●, Green Bean Chips●, Sweet Potato Chips●, Taro Chips●, Veggie Chips (No Salt Added●, Regular●)
Old Dutch - Potato Chips (Original, RipL), Ripples Original
Pinnacle Gold - Natural Baked Potato Chips Original, Natural Baked Veggie Chips
Popchips - Potato (Original!!, Salt & Pepper!!, Sea Salt & Vinegar!!)
Potato Flyers - Homestyle Barbeque, Original
Pringles - Fat Free Original
Publix GreenWise Market - Tortilla Chips Blue, Yellow
Pure Market Express▲ - BBQ Thins●, Chili Lime Chips●, Corn Chips●, Mexi Chips●, Pizza Chips●
Que Pasa▲ - Hand Cut Organic Corn, Organic Corn Tortilla Chips (Blue, Red, White, Yellow)
RiceWorks - Rice Crisps (Salsa Fresca, Sea Salt, Tangy BBQ)
Ruffles - Potato Chips (Natural Reduced Fat Sea Salted!!, Original (Light!!, Reduced Fat!!, Regular!!))
Skeete & Ike's - Organic Sea Salt Corn!!
Snyder's Of Hanover -
Corn Tortilla Chips (Restaurant Style, White, Yellow)
Potato Chips (Barbeque, Hot Buffalo Wing, Original, Ripple Potato)

C

Solea -
  Olive Oil Chips (Cracked Pepper & Salt, Rosemary, Sea Salt)
  Polenta Chips Sea Salt!!
Spartan Brand - Kettle Cooked (Mesquite BBQ, Original, Reduced Fat), Potato (Regular, Ripple)
Terra Chips -
  Classic Potato Chips
    Au Naturel Unsalted
    Krinkle Cut Kettles (Sea Salt, Sea Salt & Vinegar)
  Exotic Potato Chips
    Blues
    Red Bliss (Fine Herbs, w/Olive Oil)
    Yukon Gold Original
  Exotic Vegetable Chips
    Exotic Harvest Sea Salt
    Original Chips
  Sweet Potato Chips
    Crinkles Sea Salt
    Plain
    Sweets & Beets
    Sweets & Carrots
The Mediterranean Snack Food Co -
  Baked Lentil (Sea Salt, Sea Salt & Cracked Pepper)
  Veggie Medley
Tostitos - Tortilla Chips Restaurant Style Natural Yellow Corn!!
Trader Joe's -
  Organic Chips
    Corn (Dippers!!, Tortilla Blue!!)
  Regular Chips
    Hickory BBQ Potato!!
    Salt N Vinegar Potato!!
    Salted Potato!!
    Sea Salt & Pepper Rice Crisps
    Sweet Potato!!
    Vegetable Root!!

C

Veggie (& Flaxseed Tortilla**!**, Regular**!!**)
Yellow Corn Tortilla Chips**!!**
Ridge Cut Potato Chips (Lightly Salted**!!**, Salt N Pepper**!!**)
Roasted Plantain
Tortilla Chips Reduced Guilt Tortilla Strips**!!**

UTZ -
All Natural Kettle Cooked
Dark Russet
Gourmet Medley
Lightly Salted
Home Style Kettle Cooked Plain
Kettle Classics
Dark Russet
Plain
Sweet Potato
Kettle Cooked
Barbeque
Grandma
Plain
Mystic Kettle Cooked Chips
Dark Russet
Plain
Reduced Fat
Regular Chips
Barbeque
Crab
Honey BBQ
No Salt Regular
Plain (Ripple, Wavy Cut)
Red Hot
Reduced Fat
Tortilla Chips Baked

Wegmans Brand - Chips Corn Original, Kettle Original, Potato
Original, Tortilla 100% White Corn Blue Corn, Wavy, Yellow Corn
Tortilla

C

Winn Dixie - Classic, Natural Reduced Fat, Pork Rinds

Chocolate

Baker's - Unsweetened!!

Dagoba - Chocodrops, Organic Cacao Nibs

Earth Source Organics▲ - Organic Raw Chocolate Bar (Acai●, Caramel●, Goji●, Maca●)

Enjoy Life - Boom Choco Boom Bars (All Varieties)

Ghirardelli - Baking Bars 100% Cocoa Unsweetened

Gluty Free - Organic Raw Cacao Nibs●

Indie Candy - Chocolate (Angel, Dancing Santa, Teddy Bears), Dark Chocolate Lollipop Shapes, Halloween Chocolate Lollipops

Nuts Online -

Organic Cacao Paste●

Organic Chocolate Covered Cacao Nibs●

Organic Sugar Cacao Nibs●

Raw Cacao Almonds & Raisins●

Raw Cacao Brazil Nuts & Mulberries●

Raw Organic Cacao Nib●

White Chocolate Chip Almonds Cashews & Cacao Nibs●

Organic Nectars - Raw Cacao 54%

Oskri Organics - Honey Mint Patties

Chocolate Bars... see Chocolate and/or Candy/Candy Bars

Chocolate Chips... see Baking Chips

Chocolate Dip

Walden Farms - Chocolate Fruit Dip

Chocolate Sauce

Emmy's Organics▲ - Peppermint, Regular

Chocolate Syrup... see Syrup

Chutney

Baxters - Albert's Victorian, Cranberry & Caramelized Red Onion, Spiced Fruit, Tomato

Garner's - Organic Apple & Onion Sweet

Native Forest - Chutney (All Varieties)

Sharwood's - Green Label (Mango, Mango Chili, Mango Smooth)

Trader Joe's - Mango Ginger!!

Wild Thymes - Apricot Cranberry Walnut, Caribbean Peach Lime, Mango Papaya, Plum Currant Ginger

Cider/Cider Mix

Crispin - Artisanla Reserves (Honey Crisp, Lansdowne, The Saint), Natural Hard Apple Cider (Brut, Light, Original) *(Alcoholic)*

Doc's Draft - Apple, Pear, Raspberry *(Alcoholic)*

Kroger Brand - Instant Spiced Regular, Instant Spiced Sugar Free

Lucky Leaf - Apple Cider, Sparkling Apple Cider

Magners - Cider *(Alcoholic)*

Musselman's - Cider, Fresh Pressed, Sparkling Cider

Pure Market Express▲ - Mulled Apple Cider●

Safeway Brand - Apple Cider

Sonoma Sparkler - Natural (Peach, Pear, Raspberry), Organic (Apple, Lemonade)

Strongbow - *(Alcoholic)*

Woodchuck▲ - Hard Cider (All Varieties) - *(Alcoholic)*

Woodpecker▲ - Premium Cider *(Alcoholic)*

Wyder's▲ - Hard Cider (All Varieties) - *(Alcoholic)*

Cinnamon

Albertsons

Durkee - Ground

McCormick - Ground, Sticks

Spice Islands

Tones

Watkins - Purest Ground

Cinnamon Rolls

Chebe▲ - Cinnamon Roll Mix●

Heaven Mills▲ - Chocolate Buns●, Cinnamon Buns●

Pure Market Express▲ - Cinnamon Rolls●

Silly Yak Bakery - CFGF Cinnamon Roll●

Udi's Gluten Free Foods▲ - Gluten Free Cinnamon Rolls

Clams

*... *All Fresh Seafood Is Gluten/Casein/Soy Free (Non-Marinated, Unseasoned)*

Bumble Bee - Chopped, Fancy Smoked, Fancy Whole Baby, Minced

C

    Chicken Of The Sea - Minced, Premium Whole Baby Clams, Whole Baby Clams

    Crown Prince - Baby Boiled, Natural (Baby Clams Boiled In Water, Clam Juice, Smoked Baby Clams In Olive Oil)

    Ocean Prince - Chopped

Club Soda... see Soda Pop/Carbonated Beverages

Coating

    Choice Batter - Original Recipe w/Spices●, Unspiced●

    Ener-G▲ - Breadcrumbs

    Gillian's Foods▲ - Breadcrumbs (Cajun Style, Italian Style, Plain)

    Gluten-Free Essentials▲ - Breading & Batter Mix (Seasoned●, Unseasoned●)

    Glutino▲ - Bread Crumbs

    Grandma Ferdon's▲ - Fish Batter Mix●

    Hol Grain▲ - Batter Mix (Onion Ring●, Tempura●), Brown Rice Bread Crumbs●, Crispy Chicken Coating Mix●

    Kinnikinnick▲ - Bread Cubes, Panko Style Bread Crumbs

    Laurel's Sweet Treats▲ - All Purpose Batter Mix

    Nu-World Foods▲ - Amaranth Bread Crumbs●

    Orgran▲ - All Purpose Rice Crumbs, Corn Crispy Crumbs

    Southern Homestyle▲ - Corn Flake Crumbs, Tortilla Crumbs

Cocktail Mix

    Big Bucket - Margarita, Strawberry Margarita/Daiquiri

    Margaritaville - Margarita Mix (Mango, Regular)

    Mr. & Mrs. T's -

        Bloody Mary

            Bold & Spicy *(Except Premium Blend)*

            Original *(Except Premium Blend)*

        Mai Tai

        Manhattan

        Margarita

        Old Fashioned

        Pina Colada

        Strawberry Daiquiri/Margarita

Sweet & Sour

Tom Collins

Whiskey Sour

On The Border -

Buckets (Cran Appletini, Frozen Margarita, Mango Passion, Mojito, Strawberry Frozen Daiquiri)

Straight Ups (Cosmopolitan, Margarita, Margarita Lite, Pina Colada)

Rose's -

Grenadine

Infusions

Blue Raspberry

Cosmopolitan

Pomegranate Twist

Sour Apple

Infusions Light Mix

Cosmopolitan

Tropical Fruit Twist

Mango

Passion Fruit

Sweetened Lime Juice

Traditional

Cocktail Sauce... see also Seafood Sauce

Frontera - Cocktail & Ceviche Sauce (Cilantro Lime, Tomato Chipotle)

Kroger Brand

Lee Kum Kee - Shrimp Sauce

McCormick - Extra Hot, Golden Dipt, Original Cocktail Sauce, Seafood Sauce (Cajun Style, Mediterranean, Santa Fe Style)

Royal Food Products - Garden Fresh, Royal Deluxe

Safeway Brand

Steels Gourmet - Agave

Trader Joe's - Seafood Cocktail Sauce!!

C Cocoa Mix/Powder
    Dagoba - Professional Cocoa Powder
    Ghirardelli - Baking Cocoa Premium Unsweetened Cocoa**!!**
    Ginger Evans - Baking Cocoa, Cocoa
    Hershey's -
        Chocolate Syrup (Lite, Regular, Special Dark)
        Cocoa (Special Dark, Unsweetened Regular)
    Nuts Online - Organic Cacao Powder●, Raw Organic Cacao Powder●
    Shiloh Farms - Organic Cocoa Powder
    St. Claire's Organics - Hot Cocoa (Cherry, Mandarin)
    Watkins - Baking Cocoa

Coconut
    Albertsons - Fancy Flake Sweetened
    Baker's - Angel Flake Sweetened In (Bag**!!**, Cans**!!**)
    Ginger Evans - Sweetened
    Gluty Free - Diced Dried●, Shredded Organic●, Unsweetened
        (Chips●, Organic Chips●)
    Great Value Brand (Wal-Mart) - Sweetened Flaked
    Hannaford Brand - Fancy Sweetened
    Hy-Vee - Regular, Sweetened Flake
    Kroger Brand - Regular, Sweetened
    Let's Do...Organic - Creamed, Organic (Flakes, Shredded (Reduced
        Fat, Regular, Unsweetened))
    Nuts Online - Diced●, Organic Unsweetened Chips●, Shredded
        Organic●, Unsweetened Chips●
    Peter Paul - Toasted Coconut Chips
    Phildesco - Dessicated, Sweetened, Toasted
    Publix - Flakes
    Safeway Brand - Coconut Sweetened
    Spartan Brand - Flakes
    Tropical Traditions - Chips, Flakes, Shredded
    Wegmans Brand - Sweetened Flakes
    Winn Dixie
    Woodstock Farms - Organic Medium Shred

Coconut Milk
- **A Taste Of Thai** - Lite, Regular
- **Ka-Me** - Lite!, Regular!
- **Native Forest** - Organic (Classic, Light)
- **Peter Paul** - Coconut Cream, Regular
- **Phildesco** - Regular
- **So Delicious** - Original●, Unsweetened●, Vanilla●
- **Thai Kitchen** - Lite, Organic (Lite, Regular), Regular

Cod
> ... *All Fresh Fish Is Gluten/Casein/Soy Free (Non-Marinated, Unseasoned)*

Coffee
- **Albertsons** - All Varieties
- **Brown Gold** - All Varieties
- **Caribou** - All Coffee Beans, All Ground Coffee
- **Folger's** - All Instant & Roasts
- **Full Circle** -
  - Organic
    - Ground
      - Decaffeinated
      - Ecothentic Espresso
      - Ethiopia
      - Guatemala
      - Morning Blend
      - Sumatra
    - Whole Bean
      - Blue Coast Blend
      - Bolivia
- **Great Value Brand (Wal-Mart)** -
  - 100% Colombian Classic Ground Coffee (Naturally Decaf, Regular)
  - Dark Roast 100% Arabica Premium Ground Coffee
  - Instant Coffee Naturally Decaf Premium
  - Instant Coffee Regular

C

Hannaford Brand - All Varieties
Higgins & Burke - All Varieties
Hy-Vee -
  100% Colombian
  Breakfast Blend
  Classic (Blend, Decaf)
  Coffee (Instant, Regular)
  Decaf (Classic, Instant, Regular)
  French Roast
Kirkland Signature - 100% Columbian, Dark Roast Decaf, Decaf,
  Pouches, Regular
Kroger Brand - All Varieties
Kroger Value - All Varieties
Lowes Foods Brand - Brick Decaf
Maxwell House -
  Coffee Bags (Decaf, Master Blend, Regular)
  Filter Packs & Singles (Decaf, Original)
  Ground (All Varieties)
  Instant (Decaf, Original, Reduced Caffeine/Lite)
McDaniel's - Ground, Instant (Decaffeinated, Regular)
Meijer Brand - Decaf, French Roast, Ground (Colombian, French
  Roast, Lite 50% Decaf), Regular
Midwest Country Fare - Classic Blend
Mother Parkers - All Varieties
Mountain Blend - Instant
Nescafe - Classic Instant, Taster's Choice Instant (Flavored, Non
  Flavored, Singles (All Varieties))
O Organics - All Coffee Beans
Publix - All Varieties
Pura Vida - All Varieties *(Except French Vanilla)*
Safeway Brand - Decaf Classic Roast, Espresso Coffee Beans
Safeway Select - Whole Bean Flavored
Sanka - Decaf Coffee

C

Spartan Brand -
  French Roast
  Ground (Colombian, Decaf Roast, Half Caff, Regular Roast)
  Instant (Decaf, Regular)
  Regular
Taster's Choice - All Varieties
Wegmans Brand -
  Ground
    100% Colombian (Medium Roast, Regular)
    Breakfast Blend Light Roast (Decaf, Regular)
    Decaf
    Espresso Dark Roast
    French Roast
    Lite Caffeine (Medium Roast, Regular)
    Traditional
  Instant
  Pure Origin Coffee
    Day Break Roast
    Ground Jamaican Mid Day
    Kona Evening
    Smooth Morning
    Sumatra Night
  The Ultimate Coffee Adventure (All Varieties)
  Traditional Coffee Singles
  Whole Bean Coffee
    100% Colombian Medium Roast
    Breakfast Blend Light Roast
    Espresso Dark Roast (Decaf, Regular)
Winn Dixie - All Varieties
Yuban - Ground (100% Arabica, 100% Columbian, Breakfast Blend,
  Dark Roast, Decaf, Hazelnut, Original), Instant Regular, Organic
  (Latin American, Medium Roast)
Coffee Beans... see Coffee
Coffee Creamer... see Creamer

C Cold Cuts... see Deli Meat

Cole Slaw Dressing... see Salad Dressing

Collards... see Greens

Communion Wafers
  Ener-G▲ - Communion Wafers

Concentrate... see Drinks/Juice

Cones
  Goldbaum's▲ - Gluten Free Ice Cream Cones (Cocoa, Cups, Jumbo, Sugar)

Cookie Mix... see also Cookies/Cookie Dough
  1-2-3 Gluten Free▲ - Chewy Chipless Scrumdelicious Cookies●, Lindsay's Lipsmackin' Roll Out & Cut Sugar Cookies●, Sweet Goodness Pan Bars●
  AgVantage Naturals▲ - Basic Cookie Mix●
  Augason Farms▲ - Gluten Free Basic●
  Cause You're Special▲ - Classic Sugar
  Cherrybrook Kitchen - Gluten Free Sugar Cookie Mix (*Box Must Say Gluten-Free*)
  Doodles Cookies - Double Chocolate Chip Habanero, Organic Gluten Free Nut Butter, Organic Gluten Free Sugar
  Earthly Treats▲ - Sugar Cookie Mix●
  Food-Tek Fast & Fresh▲ - Cookie Mix Sugar
  Full Circle - Gluten Free Cookie Mix
  Gifts Of Nature▲ - Fancy Cookie Mix, Triple Treat Cookie Mix
  Gluten Free Life▲ - The Ultimate Gluten Free Cookie Mix
  Gluten Free Sensations▲ - Chocolate Chip Cookie Mix, Sugar Cookie Cutout Mix
  Hodgson Mill▲ - Gluten Free Cookie Mix
  Jules Gluten Free▲ - Cookie Mix●, Graham Cracker/ Gingersnap Mix●
  King Arthur Flour▲ - Gluten Free Cookie Mix●
  Laurel's Sweet Treats▲ - Roll 'Em Out Sugar
  Marion's Smart Delights▲ - Cookie & Muffin Mix●, Lemon Bar Baking Mix●
  Namaste Foods▲ - Cookie Mix

Only Oats - Grandma's Oatmeal Cookie Mix●
Pure Living -
  Cookie Mix
    European Chocolate Truffle w/Tart Cherry Slivers●
    Julienne Cranberries Zante Currants & Essence Of Raspberry
      Orange Blossom●
    Saigon Cinnamon Oat Zante Currants & Essence Of Chia Tea●
Really Great Food Company▲ - Butter, Chocolate Crinkle, Versatile
Ruby Range - Old Fashioned Cookies Gluten Free Baking Mix●
Silly Yak Bakery - GF Snickerdoodle Cookie Mix
The Cravings Place▲ - Create Your Own, Peanut Butter, Raisin Spice
Cookies/Cookie Dough
Aleia's▲ - Almond Horn●, Chocolate Coconut Macaroon●,
  Coconut Macaroon●, Pignoli Nut●
Andean Dream - Cookies (Chocolate Chip, Cocoa Orange,
  Coconut, Orange Essence, Raisins & Spice)
Andrea's Fine Foods▲ - Oatmeal
Apple's Bakery▲ - Gluten Free Cookies Dusty Miller Molasses
Aunt Gussie's▲ - Big Sugar Cookie ●
Breakaway Bakery▲ - Chocolate Chip Cookie Dough●
Cookie Momsters▲ - Soy Free (Chocolate Chip, Double
  Chocolate)
El Peto▲ - Chocolate Coconut Macaroons, Cinnamon/Hazelnut,
  Coconut Macaroons, Old Fashion Sugar
Emmy's Organics▲ - Macaroons (Chai Spice, Chocolate Orange,
  Coconut Vanilla, Dark Cacao, Lemon Ginger, Mint Chip)
Ener-G▲ - Chocolate (Chip Biscotti, Chip Potato, Regular),
  Cinnamon, Ginger, Sunflower Cookies, Vanilla
Enjoy Life▲ -
  Chewy Chocolate Chip●
  Double Chocolate Brownie●
  Gingerbread Spice●
  Happy Apple●

C

    Lively Lemon●
    No Oats "Oatmeal"●
    Snickerdoodle●

Fabe's Bakery - Organic Mini Macaroons●

French Meadow Bakery - Gluten Free (Chocolate Chip Cookie Dough●, Chocolate Chip Cookies●)

Glow Gluten Free▲ - Double Chocolate Chip●, Snickerdoodle●

Glutano▲ - Cookies Hoops

Gluten-Free Creations▲ - Oatmeal Raisin●, Pecan Wedding●, Snickerdoodle●

Gluten-Free Essentials▲ - Vanilla Sugar Cookies●

Gopal's - Nature's Gift Cookies (Almond Raisin, Goldenberry Brazil, Hazelnut Cherry, Macadamia Goji, Pineapple Flax)

Goraw▲ - Super Cookies (Chocolate●, Original●)

Grandma Ferdon's▲ - Pumpkin Bar Mix●

Heaven Mills▲ - Cookies Honey●, Hamantaschen (Apricot●, Raspberry●), Rugelach (Chocolate●, Cinnamon●, Vanilla●)

Jennies▲ - Zero Carb Macaroons (Carob, Chocolate, Coconut)

Katz Gluten Free▲ - Apricot Tart●, Raspberry Tart●, Rugelech (Chocolate●, Cinnamon●), Vanilla●

Kinnikinnick▲ - Cookies Ginger Snap

Kneaded Specialties▲ -
    Chocolate (Cherries Jubilie●, Chip●)
    Double Chocolate Chip●
    Holiday Sugar●
    Lemon Sugar●
    Snickerdoodle●
    Vegan Chocolate Cookie Dreams●

Kookie Karma - All Varieties●

Mary's Gone Crackers▲ - Cookies (Ginger Snaps●, N'Oatmeal Raisin●)

Mrs. Crimble's - Macaroons Coconut

Nana's -
    Cookie Bars (Berry Vanilla●, Chocolate Munch●, Nana Banana●)
    Cookie Bites (Fudge●, Ginger Spice●, Lemon Dreams●)

No Gluten Cookie (Chocolate●, Chocolate Crunch●, Ginger●, Lemon●)

Orgran▲ - Classic Chocolate Cookie, Itsy Bitsy Bears, Mini Outback Animals (Chocolate, Vanilla), Outback Animals (Chocolate, Vanilla), Wild Raspberry Fruit Flavored Biscuits

Pamela's Products▲ - Extreme Chocolate Mini Cookies, Ginger (Mini Snapz, w/Sliced Almonds), Organic Spicy Ginger w/ Crystallized Ginger, Peanut Butter

Pure Market Express▲ - Caramel Macaroons●, Chocolate Chip Cookies●, Chocolate Chocolate Chip Cookies●, Chocolate Macaroons●, Macaroon Trio●, No Bake Cookies●, Vanilla Macaroons●

Rose's Bakery▲ - Cookies (Gingersnap, Macaroons)

Schar▲ - Ladyfingers

Sunstart - Crunch Golden (Ginger, Raspberry, Supreme)

Trader Joe's - Meringues (All Varieties)**!!**

Cooking Spray
Publix - Grill
Safeway Brand - Grill
Winn Dixie - Grill

Cooking Wine
Eden Organic - Mirin Rice
Holland House - All Varieties
Publix
Regina - All Varieties

Corn
... *All Fresh Corn Is Gluten/Casein/Soy Free
Albertsons - Canned (Creamed Style, Regular), Frozen
Birds Eye - All Plain Frozen Corn
C & W - All Plain Frozen Corn
Del Monte - All Plain Canned Corn
Freshlike - Frozen Plain Corn
Full Circle - Organic Frozen Whole Kernel Corn, Organic Gold Corn

C

Gluty Free - Organic Purple Corn Kernels●, Sweet Corn
　Freeze Dried●

Grand Selections - Crisp & Sweet Whole Kernel, Frozen (Super
　Sweet Cut, White Shoepeg)

Great Value Brand (Wal-Mart) -
　Canned
　　Cream Style Corn
　　Golden Sweet Whole Kernel Corn
　　No Salt Added Golden Sweet Whole Kernel Corn
　Microwaveable Plastic Cups Golden Kernel Corn

Green Giant -
　Canned
　　Cream Style Sweet Corn
　　Mexicorn
　　Niblets (Extra Sweet, No Salt Added, Whole Kernel Extra Sweet
　　　Corn, Whole Kernel Sweet Corn)
　　Southwestern Style
　　Super Sweet Yellow & White Corn
　　White Shoepeg Corn
　Frozen
　　Cream Style Corn
　　Nibblers (12 Count, 24 Count)
　　Steamers Niblets Corn
　Valley Fresh Steamers
　　Extra Sweet Niblets
　　Niblets Corn
　　Select White Shoepeg Corn

Hannaford Brand - Cream Style, Crisp & Sweet, Whole Kernel

HealthMarket - Organic Whole Kernel

Hy-Vee -
　Corn On The Cob
　Cream Style Golden Corn
　Frozen Cut Golden Corn
　Steam In A Bag Frozen Corn

C

Whole Kernel (Corn, Gold Corn, White Sweet Corn)
Kirkland Signature - Sweet
Kroger Brand - All Plain Corn (Canned, Frozen)
Kroger Value - All Plain Corn (Canned, Frozen)
Lowes Foods Brand - Frozen (Corn Cob Full Ear, Corn Cob
Mini Ear, Cut)
Meijer Brand -
Canned
Cream Style
Golden Sweet Organic
Whole Kernel (Crisp & Sweet, Golden, Golden No Salt, White)
Frozen (Corn Cob Mini Ear, Corn On The Cob, Whole Kernel,
Whole Kernel Golden)
Mezzetta - Gourmet Baby
Midwest Country Fare - Cream Style, Frozen Cut, Whole Kernel
Native Forest - Organic Cut Baby Corn
Nuts Online - Simply Sweet Corn Freeze Dried Vegetables●
O Organics - Canned Whole Kernel, Frozen Golden Cut
Pictsweet - All Plain Frozen Corn, Seasoned Corn &
Black Beans
Private Selections - Frozen White Corn
Publix -
Canned (Cream Style Golden, Golden Sweet, Whole Kernel)
Frozen (Corn On The Cob, Cut)
Publix GreenWise Market - Organic Canned Whole Kernel
S&W - All Canned Corn
Safeway Brand - Cream Style, Frozen Corn On The Cob, No Salt
Whole Kernel, Steam In Bag (Petite, White)
Spartan Brand -
Canned Golden (Crisp & Sweet, Sweet Corn Cream Style, Whole
Kernel)
Frozen (Baby Corn Blend, Corn On The Cob, Mini Ear Corn On
The Cob, Plain, White Super Sweet)

C

Stop & Shop Brand - Corn (& Peas, Cut, On The Cob, Super Sweet Corn On The Cob), Whole Kernel Corn

Trader Joe's - Frozen (Cut White Corn, Organic Super Sweet Cut Corn, Roasted Corn), Frozen Pacific Northwest Cut White Corn

Wegmans Brand -
>Canned (Bread & Butter, Cream Style Golden Sweet, Crisp 'n Sweet Whole Kernel, Whole Kernel, Whole Kernel No Salt)
>Frozen (Baby Corn Cleaned & Cut, Bread & Butter Sweet Whole Kernel, Super Sweet Steamable)

Westbrae - Whole Kernel (Golden, White)

Winn Dixie -
>Canned (Creamed Style, White Whole Kernel, Yellow Whole Kernel, Yellow Whole Kernel No Salt)
>Frozen (On The Cob (Mini, Regular), Organic Yellow Cut, Steamable Yellow Cut, White Cut, Yellow Cut)

Woodstock Farms - Organic Frozen Cut Corn (Regular, Supersweet (Regular, White)), Toasted Corn

Corn Dogs
Ian's - Wheat Free Gluten Free Recipe Popcorn Turkey Corn
S'Better Farms▲ - Beef Corn Dogs**!!**

Corn Oil... see Oil

Corn Starch... see Starch

Corn Syrup... see Syrup

Cornbread/Cornbread Mix
1-2-3 Gluten Free▲ - Micah's Mouthwatering Cornbread Mix●
Bob's Red Mill▲ - Gluten Free Cornbread Mix
Chi-Chi's - Fiesta Sweet Corn Cake Mix
Food-Tek Fast & Fresh▲ - Dairy Free Minute Cornbread Mix
Grandma Ferdon's▲ - Cornbread Mix●
Laurel's Sweet Treats▲ - Good Ol' Cornbread
Really Great Food Company▲ - Home Style Cornbread Mix
The Cravings Place▲ - Grandma's Unsweetened Cornbread Mix

Corned Beef... see also Beef
Albertsons - Hash

Armour - Corned Beef Hash
Castle Wood Reserve - Deli Meat Angus Corned Beef
Dietz & Watson▲ - Brisket●, Flat●
Great Value Brand (Wal-Mart) - Corned Beef Hash
Hargis House - Hash
Hormel - Deli (Bread Ready, Counter Regular), Hash, Natural Choice
Kayem - Extra Lean
Meijer Brand - Hash
Spartan Brand - Hash
Wellshire Farms - Corned Beef Brisket (Half**! !**, Whole**! !**), Round
　　Corned Beef**! !**, Sliced Round Corned Beef**! !**
Cornflake Crumbs... see Coating
Cornish Hens
　　... *All Fresh Poultry Is Gluten/Casein/Soy Free (Non-Marinated,
　　Unseasoned)*
　　Shelton's - Game Hens
Cornmeal
　　Arrowhead Mills - Organic Blue, Organic Yellow
　　Bob's Red Mill▲ - Cornmeal
　　Cause You're Special▲ - Cornmeal
　　Gifts Of Nature▲ - Yellow Cornmeal
　　Hodgson Mill - Organic Yellow, Plain White, Plain Yellow
　　Kinnikinnick▲
　　Really Great Food Company▲ - Cornmeal
　　Safeway Brand - Yellow Corn Meal
　　Shiloh Farms - Polenta (Coarse Corn Meal)
Couscous
　　Lundberg▲ - Brown Rice (Mediterranean Curry, Plain Original,
　　Savory Herb)
Crabmeat
　　... *All Fresh Seafood Is Gluten/Casein/Soy Free (Non-Marinated,
　　Unseasoned)*
　　Bumble Bee - Lump, Pink Crabmeat, White
　　Chicken Of The Sea - All Crab Products

C

 Crown Prince - Fancy Pink, Fancy White, Lump White, Natural
  Fancy White Lump
 Great Value Brand (Wal-Mart) - Smoked Crab Meat
 Ocean Prince - Pink
 Private Selections - Canned

Crackers
 Back To Nature - Rice Thins Sesame Ginger
 Bi-Aglut - Original
 Crunchmaster - Rice Crackers Toasted Sesame●
 Edward & Sons - Brown Rice Snaps (Onion Garlic, Toasted Onion,
  Unsalted Plain, Unsalted Sesame, Vegetable)
 Ener-G▲ - Cinnamon, Seattle
 Foods Alive - Flax Crackers (BBQ, Hemp, Italian Zest, Maple &
  Cinnamon, Mexican Harvest, Mustard, Onion Garlic)
 Hol Grain▲ - Brown Rice (Lightly Salted●, No Salt●, Onion &
  Garlic●, Organic●, w/Sesame Seeds Lightly Salted●)
 Kookie Karma - All Varieties●
 Mrs. Crimble's - Sun Dried Tomato & Pesto
 Pure Market Express▲ - Carrotini Crackers●, Italian Flax Crackers●,
  Thai Flax Crackers●
 Real Foods▲ - Corn Thins (Cracked Pepper & Lemon!!,
  Multigrain!!, Original!!, Sesame!!), Rice Thins Regular!!
 Riega - Crispbreads Rice Corn
 Schar▲ - Table Crackers
 Simply Rice - Organic Brown Rice Crisps (Sea Salt, Spicy Chili)

Cranberries
 ... *All Fresh Cranberries Are Gluten/Casein/Soy Free
 Gluty Free - Dried●, Organic Dried●
 Nuts Online - Dried Fruit (Natural Juice Infused●, Organic●,
  Simply●, Sliced●, Whole●)
 Ocean Spray - Craisins (Blueberry, Cherry, Original, Pomegranate)
 Trader Joe's - Frozen Sliced Sweetened Cranberries
 Woodstock Farms - Organic Sweetened, Sweetened

Cranberry Sauce
 Albertsons

Baxters
Great Value Brand (Wal-Mart) - Jellied, Whole Berry
Hannaford Brand
Hy-Vee - Jellied, Whole Berry
Marzetti - Homestyle
Ocean Spray - Jellied, Whole Berry
Publix - Whole
S&W - All Canned/Jarred Fruits
Safeway Brand - Jellied, Whole
Spartan Brand - Jellied, Whole
Wegmans Brand - Jellied, Whole Berry
Wild Thymes - Cranberry Apple Walnut, Cranberry Fig, Cranberry
    Raspberry, Original
Winn Dixie - Jellied

Creamer... see also Milk Alternative
MimicCreme - Almond & Cashew Cream (Sugar Free Sweetened,
    Sweetened, Unsweetened), For Coffee (French Vanilla, Hazelnut
    Biscotti, Unsweetened Original), Healthy Top Whipping Cream
So Delicious - Coconut Milk (French Vanilla●, Hazelnut●, Original●)

Crepes
Pure Market Express▲ - Banana Crepes●, Maple Apple Crepes●

Crispbreads
Bi-Aglut - Fette Tostate (Mediterranean, Original)
Orgran▲ -
    Crackers Premium Deli
    Crispibites (Balsamic Herb, Corn, Onion & Chive)
    Crispibread (Corn, Essential Fibre, Rice, Rice & Cracked Pepper,
        Rice & Garden Herb, Salsa Corn, Toasted Buckwheat, Toasted
        Multigrain)

Crisps
Brothers All Natural▲ -
    Fruit Crisps (Asian Pear, Banana, Fuji Apple, Pineapple, Strawberry,
        Strawberry Banana, White & Yellow Peach)
    Potato Crisps (Black Pepper & Sea Salt, Fresh Onion & Garlic,
        Original w/Sea Salt, Szechuan Pepper & Fresh Chives)

C Cucumbers
... *All Fresh Cucumbers Are Gluten/Casein/Soy Free Cupcakes*
D Cupcakes... see also Cake/Cake Mix
    Crave Bakery▲ - Chocolate, Confetti, Vanilla
    Heaven Mills▲ - Sprinkled●
Curry Paste
    A Taste Of Thai - Curry Paste (Green, Red, Yellow)
    Sharwood's - Green, Red
    Thai Kitchen - Curry Paste (Green, Red, Roasted Red Chili)
Curry Powder... see also Seasonings
    Durkee
    McCormick
    Tones
Curry Sauce
    Sharwood's - Thai (Green, Red)
Custard
    Orgran▲ - Custard Mix

D

Dates
    Gluty Free - Coconut●, Dried Medjool●, Organic (Dried Medjool●, Dried Pitted●), Pitted●
    Nuts Online - Dried Fruit (Jumbo Medjool●, Organic Medjool●, Organic Pitted●, Pitted●)
Deli Meat
    Applegate Farms -
        Natural
            Black Forest Ham
            Coppa
            Genoa Salami
            Herb Turkey
            Honey & Maple Turkey Breast

    Honey Ham
    Hot (Genoa Salami, Soppressata)
    Pancetta
    Pepperoni
    Roast Beef
    Roasted Turkey
    Slow Cooked Ham
    Smoked Turkey Breast
    Soppressata
    Turkey (Bologna, Salami)
  Organic
    Genoa Salami
    Herb Turkey Breast
    Roast Beef
    Roasted Chicken
    Smoked (Chicken, Turkey Breast)
    Uncured Ham
Armour -
  Bologna
    Beef
    Original
  Ham
    Cooked
    Cooked Ham & Water Product
    Honey Cured
    Lite
    Spiced Luncheon Meat
    Virginia Brand
  Sandwich Style Pepperoni
  Turkey
    Oven Roasted (w/Broth, Regular)
    Smoked

D

Boar's Head - All Varieties *(Except Italian Roast Beef, Pesto Parmesan Ham, Pesto Parmesan Italian Roast Beef)*

Busseto -
Bresaola
Coppa (Dry, Hot)
Dry Salami (Black Pepper, Italian, Rosette De Lyon)
Herbs De Providence
Pancetta
Prosciutto
Salami (Pepper Coated, Premium Genoa)

Butterball -
Extra Thin Turkey Breast
   Honey Roasted
   Oven Roasted
   Smoked
Lean Family Size
   Honey Roasted Turkey Breast
   Oven Roasted Turkey Breast
   Smoked Turkey Breast
   Turkey (Bologna, Ham)
Thin Sliced Oven Roasted Chicken Breast
Thin Sliced Turkey Breast
   Honey Roasted
   Oven Roasted
   Smoked

Carl Buddig -
Deli Cuts (Baked Honey Ham, Brown Sugar Baked Ham, Honey Roasted Turkey, Oven Roasted Turkey, Pastrami, Roast Beef, Rotisserie Chicken, Smoked Ham)
Extra Thin Original (Beef, Ham, Honey Ham, Honey Roasted Turkey, Mesquite Turkey, Oven Roasted Turkey, Pastrami, Turkey)
Original (Beef, Brown Sugar Ham, Ham, Honey Ham, Honey Roasted Turkey, Mesquite Turkey, Oven Roasted Turkey, Pastrami, Turkey)

Castle Wood Reserve -
    Angus (Corned Beef, Roast Beef)
    Black Forest Ham
    Genoa Salami
    Hard Salami
    Herb Roasted Turkey
    Hickory Smoked Turkey
    Honey Ham
    Oven Roasted (Chicken, Turkey)
    Smoked Ham
    Turkey Pastrami
    Virginia Brand Smoked Ham

Dietz & Watson▲ -
    Beef (Premium Homestyle Roast Beef●, Spiced Pastrami●)
    Black Forest Smoked Turkey●
    Capocollo (Hot●, Sweet●)
    Ham
        Black Forest Smoked●
        Capocolla●
        Cooked●
        Gourmet Lite Cooked●
        Smoked Maple●
        Tavern●
        Virginia Brand●
    Pancetta●
    Prosciutto●
    Salami Genoa●
    Sopressata●

Eckrich -
    Deli Counter
        Bologna
            Beef
            Garlic
            Low Sodium
            Meat

D

Corned Beef Cooked
Ham
  Black Forest Brand Nugget
  Brown Sugar Nugget
  Canadian Maple
  Chopped
  Ham Steak
  Honey (Cured, Maple)
  Imported
  Lite
  Off The Bone
  Smoked Pitt
  Spiced Luncheon Meat
  Spiral Sliced Holiday
  Virginia Baked
Loaf (Head Cheese, Honey, Souse)
Lunch Meat
  Bologna (Beef, Lite, Meat, Ring Bologna)
  Ham (Chopped, Cooked, Virginia Brand Thin Sliced)
  Loaf Honey
  Salami (Cotto Salami, Hard Salami)
Pastrami (Regular)
Pepperoni (Regular)
Regular Summer Sausage
Roast Beef (Black Angus, Lite)
Salami (Genoa, Hard)
Turkey
  Mesquite Smoked
  Oven Roasted
  Smoked Pitt
Fairgrounds - Honey Ham, Premium Ham (Chopped, Cooked)
Farmer John - Lunch Meats (Brown Sugar & Honey Ham, Lower Sodium Sliced Ham, Premium Oven Roasted Turkey Breast, Sliced Ham, Sliced Turkey)

Great Value Brand (Wal-Mart) -
> 97% Fat Free (Baked Ham Water Added, Cooked Ham, Honey
> Ham Water Added)
> Fat Free (Smoked Turkey Breast, Turkey Breast)
> Thinly Sliced (Honey Turkey, Mesquite Smoked Turkey Breast,
> Oven Roasted Turkey, Smoked Ham, Smoked Honey Ham)

Hannaford Brand -
> Sliced (Cooked Ham, Danish Brand Ham, Honey Ham, Oven
> Roasted Turkey)
> Thin Sliced (Black Forest Turkey Breast, Honey Cured Turkey
> Breast, Honey Ham, Oven Roasted Turkey)

Hillshire Farms -
> Deli Select
>> Baked Ham
>> Brown Sugar Baked Ham
>> Corned Beef
>> Honey (Ham, Roasted Turkey Breast)
>> Mesquite Smoked Turkey Breast
>> Oven Roasted (Chicken Breast, Turkey Breast)
>> Premium Hearty Slices Virginia Brand Baked Ham
>> Roast Beef
>> Smoked (Chicken Breast, Ham, Turkey Breast)
> Deli Select Premium Hearty Slices
>> Honey (Ham, Roasted Turkey)
>> Oven Roasted Turkey Breast
> Deli Select Ultra Thin
>> Brown Sugar Baked Ham
>> Hard Salami
>> Honey (Ham, Roasted Turkey Breast)
>> Mesquite Smoked Turkey
>> Oven Roasted Turkey Breast
>> Pastrami
>> Roast Beef
>> Smoked Ham

D

Honeysuckle White -
   Lunch Meats Deli Sliced
      Hickory Smoked Turkey Breast (Honey, Regular)
      Oven Roasted Turkey Breast
      Turkey Pastrami
   Turkey Bologna
   Turkey Breast Deli Meats
      Cajun Style Hickory Smoked
      Hickory Smoked (Original, Pastrami, Peppered)
      Honey Mesquite Smoked
      Oven Prepared
   Turkey Breast Estate Recipe
      Canadian Brand Maple
      Dry Roasted
      Hickory Smoked (Honey Pepper, Original)
      Honey Smoked
      Mesquite Smoked
   Turkey Ham
Hormel -
   Bread Ready (Cooked Pastrami, Corned Beef, Ham, Hard Salami,
      Honey Ham, Oven Roasted Turkey Breast, Prosciutto Ham,
      Roast Beef, Smoked Ham, Smoked Turkey Breast)
   Natural Choice
      Cooked Deli Ham
      Deli Counter (Cherrywood Ham, Cooked Ham, Corned Beef,
         Honey Mesquite Turkey Breast, Medium Roast Beef, Oven
         Roasted Turkey Breast, Pastrami, Rare Roast Beef, Smoked
         Ham)
      Hard Salami
      Honey Deli (Ham, Turkey)
      Oven Roasted Deli Turkey
      Pepperoni
      Roast Beef
      Smoked Deli (Ham, Turkey)
Hy-Vee - Loaf Spiced Luncheon, Luncheon Meat

deli meat

D

Jennie-O Turkey Store - Hickory Smoked Turkey Breast Cracked Pepper

Kayem -
- Bologna (German Style, Large, Original)
- Extra Lean Corned Beef
- Ham (Amber Honey Cured, Black Forest, Carving, Honeycrust, Olde English Tavern, Peppercrust)
- Old World Liverwurst
- Olive Loaf
- Pastrami (Extra Lean Black, New England Red, New York Style Black)
- Peppercrust Loaf
- Pickle & Pepper Loaf
- Roast Beef (Classic, Seasoned Garlic Oven Roasted, Seasoned Original Oven Roasted)
- Turkey (Homestyle Breast, Homestyle Breast w/Skin On)

Kirkland Signature - Ham (Extra Lean, Smoked Honey)

Kroger Brand -
- Deli Style (Chicken, Honey Smoked Turkey, Smoked Ham, Smoked Turkey)
- Fat Free (Honey Ham, Oven Roasted White Turkey, Smoked Ham)
- Honey Turkey Breast Fat Free
- Lean Sliced (Pastrami, Turkey)
- Luncheon Canned
- Thin Sliced (Honey Ham, Honey Turkey, Mesquite Smoked Turkey, Oven Roasted Turkey, Smoked Ham)

Kroger Value - Deli Shaved Ham, Ham (Chopped, Cooked, Honey, Turkey), Turkey (Ham, White)

Oscar Mayer -
- Bologna (All Varieties)
- Chopped Ham
- Deli Fresh Meats
    - Cooked Ham
    - Honey Ham

D

Oven Roasted
  98% Fat Free Turkey
  Chicken Breast
  Turkey Breast
Smoked (Turkey Breast, Ham)
Lean White Honey Smoked Turkey
Oven Roasted White Turkey
Shaved Deli Fresh Meats
  Black Forest Ham
  Brown Sugar Ham
  Cajun Seasoned Chicken Breast
  Cracked Black Peppered Turkey Breast
  French Dip Roast Beef
  Honey (Ham, Smoked Turkey Breast)
  Oven Roasted Turkey Breast
  Rotisserie Style Chicken Breast
  Slow Roasted Roast Beef
  Smoked (Ham, Turkey Breast)
  Virginia Brand Ham
Smoked White Turkey
Thin Sliced Deli Fresh
  Brown Sugar Ham
  Honey Smoked Turkey Breast
  Oven Roasted (Chicken Breast, Turkey Breast)
  Smoked (Ham, Turkey Breast)
Primo Naturale - Sliced (Dried Pepperoni, Original Salami, Premium
  Genoa Salami, Salami w/Black Pepper, Salami w/Herbs,
  Sopressata)
Primo Taglio - Black Forest Ham w/Natural Juices Coated w/
  Caramel Color, Maple Ham Old Fashioned w/Natural Juices,
  Mortadella Black Pepper Added, Prosciutto Dry Cured Ham,
  Turkey Breast w/Natural Smoke Flavoring
Publix -
  Deli Pre Pack Sliced Lunch Meat
    Beef Bottom Round Roast

Cooked Ham
Extra Thin Sliced
Honey Ham
Oven Roasted Turkey Breast
Smoked Turkey Breast
German Bologna
Hickory Smoked Maple Ham
Low Salt Ham
Smoked Turkey
Sweet Ham
Tavern Ham
Turkey Breast

Sara Lee - Slices (Brown Sugar Ham, Cooked Ham, Cracked Pepper Turkey Breast, Hardwood Smoked Turkey Breast, Hickory Smoked Ham, Honey Ham, Honey Roasted Turkey Breast, Oven Roasted Chicken Breast, Oven Roasted Turkey Breast, Roast Beef, Virginia Brand Baked Ham)

Smithfield -
Ham (Black Forest, Brown Sugar, Chopped, Cooked, Turkey, Virginia Brand)
Turkey Breast (Mesquite, Oven Roasted, Smoked)

Trader Joe's - Oven Roasted Turkey Breast, Sliced Prosciutto, Smoked Turkey Breast

Wegmans Brand - Turkey Breast No Salt, Turkey Oven Browned

Winn Dixie - Thin Sliced (All Varieties) *(Except Chicken & Corned Beef)*

Dill Pickles... see Pickles

Dinner Meals... see Meals

Dip/Dip Mix
Eat Smart - Naturals Tres Bean Dip
Fantastic World Foods - Original Hummus
Frontera - Guacamole Mix
Hannaford Brand - Italian Dressing Mix

D

Mixes From The Heartland▲ -
   Dessert Dip Mix (Black Raspberry●, Cantaloupe●, Key Lime●,
      Lemon●, Orange●, Pumpkin Pie●, Raspberry●, Strawberry●)
   Snack Dip Mix (Dilly●, Fiesta●, Garlic Roasted Pepper●, Garlic Sun
      Dried Tomato●, Green Chili Veggie●, Italian Veggie●, Spinach &
      Chives●, Veggie●)
Road's End Organics - Non Dairy Nacho Chreese Dip (Mild, Spicy)
Salpica - Dip (Chipotle Black Bean, Cowboy White Bean)
Scarpetta - Spreads (Artichoke & Olive, Asparagus, Olive & Almond,
   Red Pepper & Eggplant, Spicy Red Pepper)
Sharwood's - Green Label Mango Chutney Chili
Trader Joe's - Fat Free Spicy Black Bean, Guacamole (Avocado's
   Number, w/Spicy Pico De Gallo!!)
UTZ - Mt. Misery Mike's Salsa Dip, Sweet Salsa Dip
Walden Farms - Fruit Dip (Caramel, Chocolate, Marshmallow),
   Veggie & Chip Dip (Bacon, Blue Cheese, French Onion, Ranch)
Donuts/Doughnuts
   Ener-G▲ - Chocolate Iced Doughnuts, Plain Doughnut
      (Holes, Regular)
   Gluten-Free Creations▲ - Cinnamon & Sugar●, Plain Jane●,
      Superb Sprinkles●
   Kinnikinnick▲ - Chocolate Dipped, Cinnamon Sugar, Maple
      Dipped, Pumpkin Spice, Vanilla Glazed
   Pure Market Express▲ - Donut Holes●
Dressing... see Salad Dressing and/or Stuffing
Dried Fruit
   Bare Fruit - Bananas, Bananas & Cherries, Cherries, Cinnamon
      Apple, Fuji Apple, Granny Smith Apple, Mangos, Pears, Pineapple &
      Mangos, Pineapples
   Brothers All Natural▲ - Fruit Crisps (Asian Pear, Banana, Fuji Apple,
      Pineapple, Strawberry, Strawberry Banana, White & Yellow Peach)
   Dole - All Dried Fruit *(Except Real Fruit Bites)*
   Earthbound Farm - Cranberries, Dates, Mangos, Plums, Premium
      Jumbo Raisins, Thompson Seedless Raisin Mini Packs, Thompson
      Seedless Raisins

Eden Organic - Cranberries, Montmorency Dried Tart Cherries, Wild Blueberries

Fairfield Farms - Prunes, Raisins

Fruit Advantage - Blueberries, Organic Blueberries, Premium Dried Cherries, Red Raspberries, Strawberries

Gluty Free -

Apples●

Bing Cherries●

Blackberries●

Blueberries●

California Apricots●

California Figs●

Cantaloupe Chunks●

Cantaloupe●

Cinnamon Apples●

Cranberries●

Currants●

Diced (Apricots●, Mango●, Papaya●, Pineapple●)

Dried Nectarines●

Freeze Dried (Bananas●, Blueberries●, Fruit Cocktail●, Strawberries●)

Goji Berries●

Guava●

Juice Infused Blueberries●

Kiwi●

Mango●

Medjool Dates●

Mission Figs●

Mulberries●

Natural (Papaya●, Pineapple●)

Organic (Apples●, California Figs●, Cranberries●, Goji Berries●, Mango●, Medjool Dates●, Mission Figs●, Persimmons●, Pineapple●, Pitted Dates●, Pitted Prunes●, Strawberries●, Turkish Apricots●, Turkish Figs●, Wild Blueberries●)

Papaya●

D

Papaya Chunks●
Peaches●
Pears●
Persimmons●
Pineapple●
Pluots●
Rainier Cherries●
Red Raspberries●
Sour Cherries●
Star Fruit●
Strawberries●
Sun Dried Tomatoes●
Turkish (Apricots●, Figs●)
Unsulphured Mango●
White Peaches●

Great Value Brand (Wal-Mart) - 100% Natural California Sun Dried Raisins, Pitted Prunes

Hy-Vee - Apples, Apricots, Banana Chips, Blueberries, Cherries, Cranberries, Mixed (Berries, Fruit), Pineapple

Member's Mark - Mediterranean Dried Apricots

Mrs. May's Naturals - All Varieties●

Nuts Online -

Apples

Cinnamon Wedges●
Diced Fuji●
Dried●
Infused Dried Wedges●
Organic (Chips●, Dried●)
Simply Organic●

Apricots

California●
Diced●
Dried●
Organic (California●, Turkish●)

D

Bananas
  Chips●
  Organic (Chips●, Simply●)
  Simply●
Blackberries●
Blueberries
  Dried●
  Natural (Dried●, Dried Juice Infused●)
  Organic Wild●
  Simply●
Cantaloupe
  Dried●
  Dried Chunks●
Cherries
  Bing●
  Organic Bing●
  Rainier●
  Simply●
  Sour Tart●
Cranberries
  Natural Juice Infused●
  Organic●
  Simply●
  Sliced●
  Whole Dried●
Currants●
Dates
  Jumbo Medjool●
  Organic (Medjool●, Pitted●)
  Pitted●
Diced Fruit Medley●
Figs
  California●
  Diced●
  Mission●

D

    Organic (California●, Calimyrna●, Mission●, Turkish●)
    Turkish●
Fruit Chips●
Ginger
  Crystallized●
  Organic Crystallized●
Goji Berries●
Guava●
Kiwi●
Lemons●
Mango
  Dried
    Diced●
    Less Sugar Added●
    Organic●
    Regular●
  Simply●
Mulberries●
Nectarines
  Dried●
  Natural●
  Organic●
  White●
Organic Dried Oranges●
Organic Goji Berries●
Organic Lucuma Slices●
Papaya
  Dried (Diced●, Chunks●)
  Natural●
  Organic●
  Regular●
Peaches (Diced●, Dried●, Natural●, Organic●, Simply●, White●)
Pears (Diced●, Dried●, Natural●, Organic●, Simply●)

Cecelia's Marketplace Gluten/Casein/Soy Free Grocery Shopping Guide

D

Persimmons
  Dried●
  Organic●
Pineapple
  Dried (Chunks●, Diced●, Regular●)
  Natural●
  Organic Chunks●
  Organic●
  Simply●
Plums
  Angelino●
  Jumbo Prunes●
  No Pit●
  October Sun●
  Organic (Angelino●, No Pit●)
Pluots●
Raisins
  Crimson●
  Dark●
  Jumbo
    Flame●
    Golden●
    Golden Flame●
    Thompson Seedless●
  Midget●
  Organic●
Raspberries
  Dried Red●
  Organic Red●
  Simply●
Simply
  Black Currants●
  Blackberries●
  Boysenberries●
  Elderberries●

D

    Fruit Cocktail●
    Grapes●
    Pomegranates●
  Strawberries
    Dried●
    Natural Dried Juice Infused●
    Organic●
    Organic Simply●
    Simply●
    Simply Whole●
  Strawberry Rhubarb●
  Tomatoes
    Julienne●
    Sun Dried
      Organic●
      Regular●
      w/Olive Oil●

Ocean Spray - Craisins (Blueberry, Cherry, Original, Pomegranate)

Oskri Organics - 3.5oz Bag (Apricots, Blueberries, Cherries, Cranberries, Dates, Figs, Golden Raisins, Prunes, Strawberries)

Publix - Dried Plums

Safeway Brand - Raisins

Sensible Foods - Apple Harvest, Cherry Berry, Orchard Blend, Tropical Blend

Shiloh Farms - Cranberries , Pitted Prunes , Turkish Apricots , Wild Blueberries

Spartan Brand - Cranberries, Pitted Prunes, Raisins

Sun-Maid - Raisins (Baking, Golden, Natural California, Regular), Zante Currants

thinkFruit - Dried Fruit Snacks (Blueberries, Cherry, Cinnamon Apple, Cranberries, Peaches, Pineapple Tidbits)

Trader Joe's - Roasted Plantain Chips

Wegmans Brand - Dried Pitted Prunes, Seedless Raisins

Wild Garden - Apricots, Mango, Pineapple

Woodstock Farms -
    Apple Rings (Organic, Unsulphured)
    Apricots Turkish
    Banana Chips (Organic, Sweetened)
    Blueberries
    Calmyrna Figs
    Cherries Unsulphured
    Cranberries Sweetened
    Dates Deglet w/Pits
    Ginger (Organic Crystalized w/Raw Sugar, Slices Unsulphured)
    Goji Berries
    Mango (Diced, Slices (Regular, Unsulphured))
    Organic
      Black Mission Figs
      California Medjool Dates w/Pit
      Kiwi Slices
      Pitted Prunes
      Raisins (Flame, Jumbo Thompson, Select Thompson,
        Thompson)
    Papaya Spears Lo Sugar Unsulphered
    Pineapple Slices Unsulphered
    Thompson Raisins
Drink Mix
  Crystal Light -
    Enhanced (Immunity Natural Cherry Pomegranate, Metabolism
      Green Tea Peach Mango)
    Iced Tea (Green Tea Peach Mango, Green Tea Raspberry, Peach,
      Raspberry, Regular)
    Pure Fitness (Grape, Lemon Lime, Strawberry Kiwi)
    Refreshment (Cranberry Apple, Fruit Punch, Raspberry Ice,
      Strawberry Kiwi, White Grape)
    Skin Essentials White Peach Tea
    Sunrise Classic Orange
  Flavor Aid - Powdered Soft Drinks

D

Hannaford Brand -
Regular (Cherry, Fruit Punch, Lemonade, Orange, Strawberry)
Sugar Free (Fruit Punch, Iced Tea, Lemon Lime, Lemonade, Raspberry Lemonade)

Hy-Vee -
Splash Drink Mix (Cherry, Grape, Lemonade, Orange, Raspberry, Strawberry, Tropical, Tropical Fruit Punch)
Sugar Free Splash Drink Mix (Fruit Punch, Iced Tea, Lemonade, Pink Lemonade, Raspberry)

Kool-Aid -
Soft Drink Mix
Sugar Free (All Varieties)
Sugar Sweetened (All Varieties)
Unsweetened (All Varieties)

Meijer Brand - Breakfast Orange, Cherry, Chocolate Flavor, Grape, Ice Tea, Lemon Sugar Free, Lemonade, Lemonade Stix, Orange (Free & Lite, Regular), Pink Lemonade (Regular, Sugar Free), Punch, Raspberry Stix, Raspberry Sugar Free, Strawberry (Flavor, Regular), Strawberry/Orange/Banana

Nestea - Instant Iced Tea Mix (Sweetened Lemonade Flavored, Sweetened w/Lemon, Unsweetened Decaf, Unsweetened Regular)

Safeway Brand - Cherry (Light, Regular), Peach (Light, Regular), Pink (Light, Regular), Spiced Apple Cider, Strawberry (Light, Regular), Sugar Free Raspberry & Lemonade

Spartan Brand - Cherry, Fruit Punch, Lemonade, Pink Lemonade, Raspberry

Wegmans Brand - Powdered Drink Mix (Lemonade Flavor, Pink Lemonade)

Winn Dixie - Regular (Cherry, Fruit Punch, Grape, Lemonade, Orange, Pink Lemonade, Raspberry, Strawberry Kiwi), Sugar Free (Fruit Punch, Lemon Iced Tea, Lemonade, Peach Iced Tea, Pink Lemonade)

Wyler's - Powdered Soft Drinks (Light, Regular, Sugar Free)

Drinks/Juice (Non-Carbonated)

... (Carbonated Drinks... see Soda Pop/Carbonated Beverages)

Adina - Holistics (Blackberry Hibiscus w/Rooibos●, Coconut Guava w/Lychee●, Cranberry Grapefruit w/Goji●, Jade Green Tea w/Tulsi●, Mango Orange w/Chamomile●, Passion Peach w/Amalaki●, Pomegranate Acai w/Yumberry●)

Albertsons - All 100% Juices

Apple & Eve - All Drinks

Bragg - Organic Apple Cider Vinegar Drink (Apple Cinnamon, Concord Grape Acai, Ginger Spice, Vinegar & Honey)

Campbell's -
Tomato Juice
Healthy Request
Low Sodium
Organic
Original

Capri Sun - All Flavors

Ceres - All Varieties

Crystal Geyser - All Juice Squeeze Flavors, All Tejava Flavors

Dei Fratelli - Juice (Tomato (Regular, Tasty Tom Spicy), Vegetable)

Diane's Garden - Tomato Juice

Dole - All Fruit Juice

Earthbound Farm - Carrot

Eden Organic - Apple Juice, Cherry Concentrate, Concord Grape, Montmorency Tart Cherry Juice

Fruit Advantage - Juice Concentrates (All Varieties)

Fruit2O - All Varieties

Full Circle - Organic (Apple, Blueberry Juice, Cranberry Cocktail, Cranberry Red Raspberry, Grape, Tomato Juice, Vegetable Juice)

Fuze -
Empower (Goji Wild Berry, Pomegranate Acai Berry)
Slenderize (Blueberry Raspberry, Cranberry Raspberry,

D

Dragonfruit Lime, Strawberry Melon, Tangerine Grapefruit, Tropical Punch)

Tea (Black & Green Tea, Diet Green Tea w/Orange Ginger, Diet White Tea w/Pomegranate, Green Tea w/Honey, White Tea Agave Gogi Berry)

Vitalize (Blackberry Grape, Fruit Punch, Orange Mango)

Garelick Farms - Chug (Apple Juice, Fruit Punch, Lemonade, Orange Juice From Concentrate, Orange Juice Not From Concentrate), Orange Juice Calcium Rich

Gold Peak - Iced Tea Lemon

Great Value Brand (Wal-Mart) -

From Concentrate

100% Juice Unsweetened Apple Juice

Cranberry (Apple, Black Cherry, Grape, Regular)

Cranberry Juice Blend

Grape

Grape Cranberry

Natural Strength Lemon Juice

Pineapple

Ruby Red Grapefruit

Unsweetened White Grapefruit Juice

Vegetable Juice

White Grape

White Grape Peach

Frozen Juice Concentrate

100% Grape

Apple

Country Style Orange Juice Pure Unsweetened

Florida Grapefruit Juice Pure Unsweetened

Fruit Punch

Grape Juice Drink

Lemonade

Limeade

Orange Juice w/Calcium

Pink Lemonade

Prune Juice

Refrigerated Drinks Orange Juice
  High Pulp
  Pulp Free (Regular, w/Calcium)

Refrigerated Orange Juice
  Country Style
  Regular
  w/Calcium

Vegetable Juice Blends
  Acai Mixed Berry
  Light (Pomegranate Blueberry, Strawberry Banana)

Hannaford Brand - All (Frozen, Refrigerated, Shelf Stable)

Hansen's - All Varieties

Hollywood - Organic Carrot Juice

Honest -
  Ade (Cranberry Lemonade, Limeade, Orange Mango w/
    Mangosteen, Pomegranate Blue, Super Fruit Punch)
  Kids (Apply Ever After, Berry Berry Good Lemonade, Goodness
    Greatness, Super Fruit Punch, Tropical Tango Punch)
  Mate (Agave, Maqui Berry, Sublime, Tropical Tango Punch)

Hood - All Juices

Hy-Vee -
  100% Juice Blend (Blueberry Pomegranate, Cherry Pomegranate,
    Cranberry, Cranberry Apple, Cranberry Raspberry)
  Apple
  Apple Cranberry Splash
  Concord Grape Juice
  Frozen Concentrate (Apple Light Regular, Fruit Punch, Grape Juice
    Cocktail, Grapefruit Juice, Lemonade, Limeade, Orange
    (Regular, w/Calcium), Pineapple, Pink Lemonade)
  Juice Cocktail From Concentrate (Cranberry, Cranberry Apple,
    Cranberry Grape, Cranberry Raspberry, Grapefruit, Lemon,
    Light (Apple, Apple Cherry, Apple Kiwi Strawberry, Apple
    Raspberry, Grape), Light Cranberry Raspberry, Ruby Red
    Grapefruit)

D

Juice From Concentrate (100% Apple, 100% Grapefruit w/ Calcium, 100% Unsweetened Prune, 100% Unsweetened Prune w/Pulp, 100% White Grape, Apple, Apple Calcium Fortified, Apple Kiwi, Country Style Orange, Cranberry Strawberry, Lemon, Lemonade, Light (Apple Raspberry, Grape Cranberry) Orange Juice, Orange Juice w/Calcium, Pineapple, Pomegranate, Prune Juice, Tomato, Unsweetened Apple Cider, Vegetable)

Just (Apple, Berry, Cherry, Fruit Punch, Grape, Orange Tangerine)

Lite (Cranberry, Cranberry Grape, Cranberry Raspberry)

No Concentrate (Country Style Orange, Orange, Orange w/ Calcium, Ruby Red Grapefruit)

Splash (Fruit Punch, Light (Blue Fruit Punch, Fruit Punch, Grape Punch, Orange Punch), Orange Pineapple, Strawberry Kiwi Punch)

Izze - All Varieties

Juicy Juice - All Flavors, Sparkling Fruit Juice (All Flavors)

Kirkland Signature - Frozen Orange Juice Concentrate, Juice (Apple, Apple Peach & Passionfruit, Cranberry, Cranberry Raspberry), Organic Carrot Juice

Kool-Aid - Bursts (Cherry, Grape, Lime, Tropical Punch), Juice Jammers (All Varieties)

Kroger Brand - Active Lifestyle Drink Sticks, Frozen (All Varieties), Fruit Juices, In An Instant Drink Powders, Shelf Stable Juices, Vegetable Juice

Lakewood - All 100% Pure Fruit & Vegetable

Langers Juices - All Flavors

Lincoln - Apple Juice

Litehouse - Apple Cider (All Varieties)

Lowes Foods Brand - Juice (Apple (Natural●, Regular●), Cranberry Apple, Cranberry Cocktail Regular, Cranberry Grape, Cranberry Raspberry, Grape, Grove Select Orange, Lemon Regular, Orange (Original, Premium), Orange Plus Calcium, Premium Cranberry Blend 100% Juice, Prune, Vegetable Juice, White Grape)

D

Lucky Leaf - Apple (Cider, Juice, Premium Juice, Sparkling Cider)
Meijer Brand -
>   100% Juice (Berry, Cherry, Cranberry/Raspberry, Grape, Punch)
>   Cranberry Juice Drink (Grape, Raspberry, Strawberry, White)
>   Drink Thirst Quencher (Fruit Punch, Lemon Lime, Orange)
>   Frozen Concentrate Juice (Apple, Fruit Punch, Grape, Grapefruit,
>   Lemonade, Limeade, Orange, Pink Lemonade, White Grape)
>   Frozen Concentrate Orange Juice (High Pulp, Pulp Free,
>   w/Calcium)
>   Fruit Punch (Genuine, Light, Regular)
>   Juice (Apple, Apple Natural, Cherry, Fruit Mix, Grape, Grapefruit,
>   Lemon, Lime, Pineapple, Pink Grapefruit, Prune, Ruby Red
>   Grapefruit, Tangerine & Ruby Red, White Grape, White
>   Grapefruit)
>   Juice Blend (Acai & Blueberry, Acai & Grape, Pomegranate &
>   Blueberry, Pomegranate & Cranberry, White Cranberry, White
>   Grape & Peach, White Grape & Raspberry)
>   Juice Cocktail (Cranapple, Cranberry (Light, Regular), Cranberry
>   Grape (Light, Regular), Cranberry Raspberry (Light, Regular),
>   Cranberry Strawberry, Cranberry White Peach, Light Grape
>   Splenda, Ruby Red Grapefruit (Light, Light 22%, Regular),
>   White Cranberry, White Cranberry Peach, White Cranberry
>   Strawberry, White Grape, White Grapefruit)
>   Juice Refrigerated Orange (Original, Reconstituted)
>   Juice Refrigerated Orange Premium (Calcium Carafe, Carafe, Hi
>   Pulp Carafe, Original, Pulp, w/Calcium)
>   Lemon Juice Squeeze Bottle
>   Orange Reconstituted (Original, Pulp, w/Calcium)
>   Organic Juice (Apple, Concord Grape, Cranberry, Lemonade)
>   Splash (Berry Blend, Strawberry/Kiwi, Tropical Blend)
Midwest Country Fare - 100% Concentrated Orange Juice, 100%
>   Unsweetened From Concentrate (Apple Cider, Apple Juice), Juice
>   Cocktail (Cranberry, Cranberry Apple, Cranberry Raspberry),
>   Juice From Concentrate Grape

D

Minute Maid - Lemonade (Light, Original), Multi Vitamin Orange Juice, Pomegranate Flavored Tea, Pomegranate Lemonade

Mondo - Fruit Squeezers (Chillin' Cherry, Global Grape, Kiwi Strawberry Splash, Legendary Berry, Outstanding Orange, Primo Punch)

Mott's - All Varieties

Mountain Sun - Bottled (Blueberry Green Tea, Grape & Acai, Pomegranate & Black Cherry, Pomegranate Rooibos Tea, Pure Cranberry)

Musselman's - Apple (Cider, Fresh Pressed Cider, Juice, Premium Juice, Sparkling Cider)

Nantucket Nectars - All Varieties

Nature Factor - Organic Young Coconut Water

Nestea - Green Tea Citrus Diet, Lemon (Diet, Sweetened), Red Tea

Newman's Own -

Gorilla Grape

Green Tea w/Honey

Lemonade (Lightly Sweetened, Old Fashioned Roadside Virgin, Organic, Pink Virgin, Pomegranate, Reduced Sugar Pink)

Orange Mango Tango

Raspberry Kiwi Juice Cocktail

Virgin Lemon Aided Iced Tea

Virgin Limeade

O Organics - Bottle Juices (Apple, Berry Blend, Blueberry Blend, Cranberry Cocktail, Grape, Lemonade, Unfiltered Apple), Refrigerated Orange

Ocean Spray - All Varieties

Organic Valley - Orange Juice (Calcium Added, w/o Pulp, w/Pulp)

Phildesco - Coconut Water

Powerade - Ion 4 (Grape, Lemon Lime, Mountain Berry Blast, Sour Lemon, White Cherry, Zero)

Prairie Farms - Flavored Drinks Lemonade, Orange Juice (Light Pulp Premium, Plus Calcium, Regular)

Publix -
From Concentrate (Orange Juice (Regular, w/Calcium), Ruby Red Grapefruit Juice)
Frozen Concentrated Orange
Refrigerated (Premium Orange Juice (Calcium Plus, Grove Pure, Old Fashioned, Original), Premium Ruby Red Grapefruit Juice)
Shelf Stable (Apple, Cranberry (Apple Juice Cocktail, Juice Cocktail, Reduced Calorie Cocktail), Grape, Grape Cranberry Juice Cocktail, Lemonade Deli Old Fashion, Pineapple, Raspberry Cranberry Juice Cocktail, Ruby Red Grapefruit Regular, Tomato, White Grape)

Publix GreenWise Market - Organic (100% Apple, Cranberry, Grape, Lemonade, Tomato)

Pure Market Express▲ - Cacao Bean●, Classic Q●, Drop Of Sunshine Juice●, Green Sweet Tart Juice●

ReaLemon - 100% Lemon Juice

ReaLime - 100% Lime Juice

Safeway Brand -
Frozen
Apple
Berry Punch
Cranberry
Grape
Lemonade
Limeade
Orange (Country Style, Regular, w/Calcium)
Pink Lemonade
Raspberry Lemonade
Juice
Apple (Cider, Regular)
Cranberry
Apple
Cocktail
Light (Cocktail, Raspberry)
Raspberry

D

Grape (Light, Regular)
Grapefruit (Cocktail, Pink, Regular, Ruby Red Cocktail, White)
Lemon
Orange
Prune
Tomato
Vegetable
White Grape

Santa Cruz - 100% Citrus (All Varieties), Bottled Juice (All Varieties), Juice Boxes (All Varieties), Super Fruits (All Varieties)

Simply - Apple, Grapefruit, Lemonade (Original, w/Raspberry), Limeade, Orange (Grove Made High Pulp, Original Pulp Free, w/ Calcium & Vitamin D Pulp Free, w/Mango Pulp Free, w/Pineapple Pulp Free)

Snapple - 100% Juice (All Varieties), Cranberry Raspberry, Diet Cranberry Raspberry, Fruit Punch, Grape Berry Punch, Grapeade, Kiwi Strawberry, Mango Madness, Noni Berry, Orangeade, Peach Mangosteen, Raspberry Peach, Very Cherry Punch

SoBe -
Adrenaline Rush (Original, Sugar Free)
Energize (Green Tea, Mango Melon, Power Fruit Punch)
Energy
Green Tea
Lean Diet (Cranberry Grapefruit, Fuji Apple Cranberry, Honey Green Tea, Raspberry Lemonade)
Vita Boom (Cranberry Grapefruit, Orange Carrot)

Sonoma Sparkler - Natural (Peach, Pear, Raspberry), Organic (Apple, Lemonade)

Spartan Brand -
Apple Cider
Apple Juice (Apple Cherry, Regular)
Apricot
Cranberry Juice Cocktail (Lite, Low Calorie, Regular)

D

Cranberry Juice Drink (Apple, Pomegranate, Raspberry)
Frozen Concentrate (Fruit Punch, Grape Juice Cocktail, Lemonade,
   Orange Juice (Country Style, Pulp Free, Regular, w/Calcium), Pink
   Lemonade)
Grape Juice (Regular, White)
Grapefruit Juice
Lemon Juice
Pineapple
Pomegranate
Premium Orange Juice (Country Style Pulp, Regular, w/Calcium)
Reconstituted Orange Juice (Country Style Pulp, Regular,
   w/Calcium)
Tomato Juice
Vegetable Juice Cocktail
Sweet Leaf - Bottled Original Lemonade
The Ginger People - Ginger Beer!, Ginger EnerGizer!, Ginger
   Juice!, Ginger Soother!, Lemon Ginger Beer!
Tipton Grove - Apple Juice 100% Juice
Trader Joe's - Concentrate (Lemon, Orange), French Market
   Sparkling Beverages (All Flavors), Juices (All Varieties), Organic
   Mango Lemonade, Sparkling Juice Beverages (All Flavors)
Tropicana - All 100% Juices
V8 -
   Diet Splash (Berry Blend, Tropical Blend)
   Splash (Berry Blend, Fruit Medley, Mango Peach, Strawberry Kiwi
      Blend, Tropical Blend)
   V Fusion (Acai Mixed Berry, Cranberry Blackberry, Goji Raspberry,
      Passionfruit Tangerine, Peach Mango, Pomegranate Blueberry,
      Strawberry Banana, Tropical Orange)
   V Fusion Light (Acai Mixed Berry, Cranberry Blackberry, Peach
      Mango, Pomegranate Blueberry, Strawberry Banana)
   Vegetable Juice (100% Vegetable Juice, Calcium Enriched,
      Essential Antioxidants, High Fiber, Low Sodium, Low Sodium Spicy
      Hot, Organic, Spicy Hot)

D

Vitaminwater (Glaceau) - Defense Connect, Dwnld, Energy, Essential, Fruit Punch, Multi-V, Power-C, Revive, Spark, Stur-D, XXX

Vruit - Apple Carrot, Berry Veggie, Orange Veggie, Tropical

Walnut Acres - Apple Juice

Wegmans Brand -

100% Juice

Cranberry (Blend, Raspberry)

Ruby Red Grapefruit Blend

Frozen Juice Concentrate

Apple

Fruit Punch

Lemonade

Limeade

Orange

Pink Lemonade

Juice

Apple (Natural Style, Regular)

Cranberry (Peach, Raspberry, Regular)

Grape (Juice Cocktail, Regular, White)

Grapefruit

Juice Blends

Berry

Cherry

Cranberry (Apple, Concord Grape)

Ruby Red Grapefruit

Sparkling Cranberry

White Grape (Cranberry, Peach)

Lemon Juice

Orange (Regular, Unsweetened)

Prune

White Grape (Peach Blend, Raspberry Blend, Regular)

Juice From Concentrate

100% Juice (Orange, Tomato Vegetable (No Salt Added, Regular)

Blueberry Flavor Juice Blend

Lemon
Lemonade
Limeade
Orange Juice (Regular, w/Calcium)
Pineapple Orange
Pomegranate Flavor Juice Blend
Organic Juice From Concentrate
    Apple
    Apricot Nectar
    Cranberry
    Mango Nectar
    Orange
Premium 100% Juice
    Orange
        Extra Pulp
        No Pulp
        Some Pulp
        w/Calcium
        w/Calcium & Vitamins
    Ruby Red Grapefruit
Premium Orange Juice (No Pulp, Some Pulp)
Punch (Berry, Fruit)
Sparkling Beverage
    Calorie Free
        Lemon
        Mandarin Orange
        Mixed Berry
        Raspberry
        Tangerine Lime
    Diet
        Black Cherry
        Cranberry Raspberry
        Key Lime
        Kiwi Strawberry

D

   Mixed Berry
   Peach
   Peach Grapefruit
   Tangerine Lime
   White Grape
  Lemonade
  Lime
 Welch's - All Varieties
 Winn & Lovett - Juice (Black Cherry, Cranberry, Pomegranate)
 Winn Dixie -
  All Frozen Juice Varieties
  Juice
   Cranberry (Apple, Raspberry, Regular)
   Light (Cranberry, Cranberry Grape, Grape)
   Pomegranate (Blend, Blueberry Blend, Cranberry Blend)
   Premium Apple
   Reconstituted Lemon
   Ruby Red (Grapefruit, Grapefruit Cocktail)
   Vegetable
  Juice From Concentrate
   Apple (Cider, Regular)
   Grape
   Grapefruit
   Prune (Regular, w/Pulp)
   White Grape
  Nectar Drinks
   Guava
   Mango
   Mango Pineapple Guava
   Peach
   Pear
  Orange Juice
   From Concentrate (Regular, w/Calcium)
   Premium Not From Concentrate

Organic Juice
  Apple
  Cranberry
  Grape
  Lemonade
  Mango Acai Berry Blend
  Orange Mango Blend
  Tomato
Woodstock Farms -
  Non Organic Juices (All Varieties)
  Organic Juices (All Varieties)
Duck
  *... *All Fresh Poultry Is Gluten/Casein/Soy Free (Non-Marinated, Unseasoned)*
  Shelton's - Duckling
Duck Sauce
  Ah So - Duck Sauce
Dumplings
  Mixes From The Heartland▲ - Country Dumpling Mix●
  Mrs. Crimble's - Dumpling Mix

E

Egg Replacer/Substitute
  All Whites - All Varieties
  Better'n Eggs - All Varieties
  Coburn Farms - Eggzactly (100% Egg Whites, Regular)
  Ener-G▲ - Egg Replacer
  Great Value Brand (Wal-Mart) - Liquid Egg Whites
  Hannaford Brand - Egg Mates, Egg Whites
  Lucerne - Liquid Eggs All Whites
  Meijer Brand - Refrigerated Egg Substitute
  NuLaid - Egg Substitute
  Orgran▲ - No Egg Egg Replacer

E

Publix - Egg Stirs
Spartan Brand - Eggmates
Wegmans Brand - Egg Busters, Liquid Egg Whites

Eggplant
... *All Fresh Eggplant Is Gluten/Casein/Soy Free*
Tasty Bite - Punjab Eggplant !
Trader Joe's - Caponata Appetizer, Frozen Misto Alla Grigio ! !,
   Garlic Spread

Eggs
... *All Fresh Eggs Are Gluten/Casein/Soy Free*

Enchilada Sauce
Kroger Brand - Verde
Las Palmas - Red
Spartan Brand

Energy Bars... see Bars

Energy Drinks
AMP - Lightning, Sugar Free
Blue Sky - Blue (Natural, Shot, Zero Calorie), Juiced Energy
Emerge - All Varieties
Full Throttle - Blue Agave, Citrus, Red Berry
Hansen's - All Varieties
Inko's - White Tea Energy
Monster - Absolutely Zero, Assault, DUB Edition, Energy + Juice
   Khaos, Lo Carb, M 80, MIXXD), Heavy Metal, Import, Import Light,
   Regular
NOS - All Varieties
Red Bull - Cola, Energy Shots, Regular, Sugar Free
Red Rain - Diet, Regular
SoBe - Adrenaline Rush (Original, Sugar Free)

English Muffins
Aunt Gussie's▲ - Cinnamon Raisin ●, Plain ●
Ener-G▲ - Brown Rice Flax, Regular
Food For Life - Wheat & Gluten Free Brown Rice
Foods By George▲ - English Muffins (Cinnamon Currant, No Rye
   Rye, Plain)

Espresso... see Coffee

Extract

    Albertsons - Imitation Vanilla, Pure Vanilla

    Baker's - Imitation Vanilla **! !**

    Durkee - Vanilla (Imitation, Pure)

    Flavorganics - Almond, Anise, Chocolate, Coconut, Hazelnut, Lemon, Orange, Peppermint, Rum, Vanilla

    Great Value Brand (Wal-Mart) - Imitation Vanilla

    Hannaford Brand - Imitation (Almond, Vanilla), Pure (Lemon, Vanilla)

    Hy-Vee - Vanilla (Imitation, Pure)

    Kroger Brand - All Extracts

    Marcum -

        Imitation Vanilla

        Pure Vanilla Extract

    McCormick - Cinnamon, French Vanilla Blend, Gourmet Collection 100% Organic Pure Madagascar Vanilla, Imitation (Almond, Banana, Cherry, Clear Vanilla, Coconut, Maple, Rum, Strawberry, Vanilla Butter & Nut), Premium Vanilla, Pure (Almond, Anise, Lemon, Mint, Peppermint, Vanilla), Raspberry, Root Beer

    Meijer Brand - Imitation Vanilla, Vanilla

    Midwest Country Fare - Imitation Vanilla Flavor

    Nielsen-Massey - Orange Blossom Water●, Pure (Almond●, Chocolate●, Coffee●, Lemon●, Madagascar Bourbon Vanilla●, Mexican Vanilla●, Orange●, Organic Vanilla●, Peppermint●, Tahitian Vanilla●, Vanilla Extract Blend●), Rose Water●

    Publix - Almond, Lemon, Vanilla

    Safeway Brand - All Varieties

    Spartan Brand - Imitation Vanilla, Pure Vanilla

    Spice Islands - Vanilla (Imitation, Pure)

    Tones - Vanilla (Imitation, Pure)

    Watkins - Pure Almond, Pure Lemon, Pure Orange, Pure Peppermint, Pure Vanilla

    Wegmans Brand - Vanilla Extract

F F

Fajita Seasoning Mix... see also Seasonings
   McCormick - Fajita Seasoning Packet
   Safeway Brand
Falafel Mix
   Authentic Foods▲
   Gluty Free - ●
   Heaven Mills▲ - ●
   Orgran▲
Fettuccini... see Pasta
Figs
   Gluty Free - Dried (California●, Mission●, Organic (California●,
      Mission●, Turkish●), Turkish●)
   Nuts Online - Dried Fruit (California●, Diced●, Mission●, Organic
      (California●, Calimyrna●, Mission●, Turkish●), Turkish●)
Fish
   ... *All Fresh Fish Is Gluten/Casein/Soy Free (Non-Marinated, Unseasoned)*
   Captain's Choice - Cod Fillets
   Crown Prince - Kipper Snacks, Natural Kipper Snacks
   Dr. Praeger's - All Natural Potato Crusted (Fish Fillets!, Fish Sticks!,
      Fishies!)
   Great Value Brand (Wal-Mart) - Canned Alaskan Pink Salmon
   Henry & Lisa's - Fish Nuggets Wild Alaskan
   Hy-Vee - Canned Alaskan Pink Salmon, Frozen (Salmon, Tilapia)
   Ian's - Wheat Free Gluten Free Recipe (Fish Sticks, Lightly Battered
      Fish)
   Kirkland Signature - Fresh (Catfish, Steelhead, Tilapia), Frozen
      (Pacific Cod Fillets, Steelhead Trout, Tilapia Fillets)
   Kroger Brand - Canned Jack Mackerel
   Meijer Brand - Canned Salmon (Pink, Sock Eye Red)
   Member's Mark - Canned Atlantic Salmon In Water
   Ocean Prince - Imitation Abalone

Port Side -
  Canned (Jack Mackerel, Pink Salmon)
  Frozen (Ocean Perch, Pollock, Salmon Filets, Tilapia, Whiting)
Publix - Fillets (Bass, Cod, Flounder, Haddock, Halibut, Mahi Mahi,
  Orange Roughy, Snapper, Swordfish Fillets, Whiting)
Pure Market Express▲ - Julie's Sushi●
Starfish - Crispy Battered Wild Caught Fish (Cod●, Haddock●,
  Halibut●)
Sweet Bay - All Frozen Fillets
Trader Joe's - Marinated Ahi Tuna Steaks, Premium Salmon Patties**!!**,
  Seasoned Mahi Mahi Fillets
Wegmans Brand -
  Alaskan Halibut
  Atlantic Salmon Fillets Farm Raised
  Chilean Sea Bass
  Lobster Tail
  Pacific Cod
  Smoked Salmon (Nova, Scottish Style)
  Sockeye Salmon
  Tilapia Fillets
  Yellowfin Tuna Sashimi Grade
Winn Dixie - Frozen (Cod, Grouper, Tilapia, Whiting)
Fish Sauce
  A Taste Of Thai - Regular
  Thai Kitchen - Premium Fish Sauce
Fish Sticks
  Dr. Praeger's - All Natural Potato Crusted (Fish Sticks**!**, Fishies**!**)
  Henry & Lisa's - Fish Nuggets Wild Alaskan
  Ian's - Wheat Free Gluten Free Recipe Fish Sticks
Flan
  Royal - All Varieties
Flax Seed
  Arrowhead Mills - Flax Seed Meal, Flax Seeds (Golden, Regular)
  Bob's Red Mill▲ - Flaxseed Meal (Golden, Original), Organic
  Flaxseed (Golden, Original)

F

Gluty Free - Organic Flax Seed Meal●, Organic Golden●

Hodgson Mill▲ - Brown Milled, Organic Golden Milled, Travel Flax All Natural Milled, Travel Flax Organic Golden Milled, Whole Grain Brown

Nature's Path - Organic FlaxPlus Flax Seeds, Organic FlaxPlus Meal !

Shiloh Farms - Brown Flax Meal, Golden Flax Seeds

Spectrum - Organic (Ground, Ground w/Mixed Berries, Roasted Tomato, Whole)

Flax Seed Oil... see Oil

Flour

AgVantage Naturals▲ - Master Blend●, Millet Flour●, Premium Fine Milled Sorghum Flour●, Quinoa Flour●, Rice Flour●, Sorghum Flour●

Amazing Grains - Montina (All Purpose Flour Blend, Brown Rice Flour Blend, Pure Baking Flour Supplement)

Andrea's Fine Foods▲ - Gluten Free Flour Blend, Super Fine Grind Rice (Brown, Sweet)

Arrowhead Mills - All Purpose Baking Mix, Brown Rice, Organic (Buckwheat, Millet, White Rice)

Augason Farms▲ - Gluten Free (Bette's Original●, Brown Rice●, Featherlite●, Tapioca Flour/Starch●)

Authentic Foods▲ -

Almond Meal

Arrowroot

Bette's Flour Blend (Featherlight Rice, Four)

Brown Rice Flour Superfine

Garbanzo

Gluten Free Classical Blend

Multi Blend Gluten Free

Potato (Flour, Starch)

Sorghum

Sweet Rice Flour Superfine

Tapioca

White (Corn, Rice Flour Superfine)

Better Batter - Gluten Free All Purpose Flour

Bob's Red Mill▲ -
  Almond Meal/Flour
  Black Bean
  Brown Rice
  Fava Bean
  Garbanzo (& Fava, Bean)
  Gluten Free (All Purpose Baking, Sorghum)
  Green Pea
  Hazelnut Meal/Flour
  Millet
  Organic (Amaranth, Brown Rice, Coconut, Quinoa, White Rice)
  Potato
  Sweet White Rice
  Tapioca
  Teff
  White (Bean, Rice)
Cause You're Special▲ - All Purpose, White Rice
Chateau Cream Hill Estates - Lara's Whole Grain Oat Flour●
ConAgra Mills - All Purpose Blend●, Amaranth●, Millet●,
  Multigrain●, Quinoa●, Sorghum●, Teff●
Deerfields Gluten Free Bakery▲ - Quick Mix For Sugar Buttons
Domata - Gluten Free All Purpose Flour●
Dowd & Rogers▲ - California Almond, Italian Chestnut
Eagle Mills - All Purpose Multigrain Flour Blend
EasyGlut - Rice
El Peto▲ - All Purpose Flour Mix, Arrowroot, Bean, Brown Rice, Corn,
  Flax Seed, Millet, Organic Amaranth, Potato, Quinoa, Sorghum,
  Sweet Rice, Tapioca Starch, White Rice
Ener-G▲ - Brown Rice, Gluten Free Gourmet Blend, Potato (Flour,
  Starch), Sweet Rice, Tapioca, White Rice
Expandex▲ - Modified Tapioca Starch●
Flour Nut - Almond Flour
Gifts Of Nature▲ - All Purpose Blend, Baby Lima Bean, Brown Rice,
  Chick Pea, Montina All Purpose Flour Blend, Sweet Rice, Tapioca,
  White Rice

F

Gillian's Foods▲ - Brown Rice, Chick Pea, Imported Tapioca, Potato Starch, Rice

Glutano▲ - Flour Mix It

Gluten Free Mama▲ - Gluten Free Coconut Nut Blend Flour●, Mama's Almond Blend●

Gluten-Free Creations▲ - Baking Flours (Basic●, Enriched●, Sweet●)

Gluty Free - All Purpose Baking●, Almond●, Arrowroot Powder●, Chestnut●, Chia Seed●, Chickpea●, Hazelnut●, Natural Almond●, Organic Brown Rice●, Organic Coconut●, Pistachio●, Potato●, Tapioca●, White Chia Seed●

Grandma Ferdon's▲ - Grandma Ferdon's Flour Mix●, Potato●, Rice (Sweet●, White●)

Heaven Mills - Oat Flour

Hodgson Mill▲ - Gluten Free All Purpose Baking Flour

Jules Gluten Free▲ - All Purpose Flour●

King Arthur Flour▲ - Gluten Free Multi Purpose Flour●

Kinnikinnick▲ -
All Purpose Celiac
Brown Rice
Corn
Sweet Rice
White Rice

Laurel's Sweet Treats▲ - Baking Flour Mix

Let's Do...Organic - Coconut Flour

Lundberg▲ - Brown Rice Flour (California Nutra Farmed, Organic California)

Mixes From The Heartland▲ - All Purpose●, Mix (Brown Rice●, Tapioca Flour Starch●, White Rice●), Potato●

Montana Monster Munchies - Whole Grain Oat Flour●

Montina▲ - All Purpose Baking Flour Blend●, Brown Rice Flour●, Pure Baking Supplement●

Namaste Foods▲ - Perfect Flour Blend

Nuchia - 100% Chia Seed●

food coloring

F

Nuts Online - Arrowroot Powder•, Flour (Almond•, Cashew•, Chestnut•, Chia•, Chickpea•, Gluten Free (All Purpose Baking•, Black Bean•, Corn•, Fava Bean•, Garbanzo Fava•, Green Pea•, Masa Harina Corn•, Organic Coconut•, Sweet White Rice•, Sweet White Sorghum•, White Bean•), Hazelnut•, Millet•, Natural Almond•, Organic (Almond•, Amaranth•, Brown Rice•, Quinoa•, White Rice•), Peanut•, Pistachio•, Potato•, Sprouted Super•, Tapioca•, Teff•, White Chia•)

Nu-World Foods▲ - Amaranth (Flour•, Pre Gel Powder•, Toasted Bran Flour•)

Only Oats - Oat Flour•

Orgran▲ - All Purpose Pastry Mix, Gluten Substitute, Plain All Purpose, Self Raising

Peter Paul - Coconut Flour

Phildesco - Coconut Flour

Pocono - Buckwheat Flour

PrOatina Gluten Free - Gluten Free Oat Flour•

Really Great Food Company▲ - All Purpose Rice, Brown Rice, Sweet Rice, Tapioca, White Rice

Ruby Range - Mesquite•, Ruby Range Mix (Basic•, Flour•, Spice•), Teff•

Shiloh Farms - Almond , Brown Rice!!, Corn!!, Mesquite!!, Potato!!, Quinoa!!, Tapioca!!, Teff!!

Tom Sawyer▲ - All Purpose Gluten Free

Tropical Traditions - Organic Coconut Flour

Twin Valley Mills▲ - Sorghum Flour

Food Coloring

Durkee - All Varieties

Hy-Vee - Assorted

Kroger Brand - Food Colors

McCormick - All Varieties

Safeway Brand - Assorted

Spice Islands

Tones

F

Frankfurters... see Sausage
French Fries
  Alexia Foods -
    Crispy Potatoes w/Seasoned Salt Waffle Fries!
    Julienne Fries (Spicy Sweet Potato!, Sweet Potato!, w/Sea Salt
      Yukon Gold!)
    Olive Oil & Sea Salt Oven Fries!
    Olive Oil Rosemary & Garlic Oven Fries!
    Organic (Classic Oven Crinkles!, Oven Crinkles Onion & Garlic!,
      Oven Crinkles Salt & Pepper!, Yukon Gold Julienne Fries
      w/Sea Salt!)
    Yukon Gold Potatoes w/Seasoned Salt Potato Nuggets!
  Ian's - Alphatots
  Publix - Frozen Southern Style Hash Browns
  Woodstock Farms - Organic Frozen (Crinkle Cut Oven Fries,
    Shredded Hash Browns, Tastee Taters)
French Toast
  Ian's - Wheat Free Gluten Free Recipe French Toast Sticks
Frosting... see Baking Decorations & Frostings
Frozen Desserts... see Ice Cream
Frozen Dinners... see Meals
Frozen Vegetables... see Mixed Vegetables
Frozen Yogurt... see Ice Cream
Fruit Bars... see Bars and/or Ice Cream
Fruit Cocktail
  Albertsons - Heavy Syrup, Light
  Del Monte - Canned/Jarred Fruit (All Varieties), Fruit Snack Cups
    (Metal, Plastic)
  Gluty Free - Freeze Dried●
  Great Value Brand (Wal-Mart) - In Heavy Syrup
  Hannaford Brand - All Fruit Cups
  Hy-Vee - Lite, Regular
  Lowes Foods Brand - In Heavy Syrup, In Juice

Meijer Brand - Heavy Syrup, In Juice, In Pear Juice Lite
Midwest Country Fare
Publix - Canned (In Heavy Syrup, Lite In Pear Syrup)
Safeway Brand - Canned (Lite, Regular)
Spartan Brand - Heavy Syrup, Light Juice
Stop & Shop Brand - Heavy Syrup, Pear Juice
Wegmans Brand - In Heavy Syrup, In Pear Juice, Regular
Winn Dixie - Fruit Cocktail (Heavy Syrup, Light Syrup)
Fruit Drinks... see Drinks/Juice
Fruit Leather...see also Fruit Snacks
  Kaia Foods▲ -
    Goji Orange●
    Lime Ginger●
    Spiced Apple●
    Vanilla Pear●
  Matt's Munchies - Apple Licious●, Apple Pie●, Banana●, Chili Chocolate●, Choco Nana●, Ginger Spice●, Island Mango●, Mango●, Raspberry Delight●
  Stretch Island Fruit Co. - All Varieties
  Trader Joe's - All Varieties
Fruit Salad
  Meijer Brand - Tropical
  Native Forest - Organic Tropical
  Safeway Brand - Tropical Fruit
Fruit Snacks
  Annie's - Organic Bunny Fruit Snacks (Berry Patch!!, Summer Strawberry!!, Sunny Citrus!!, Tropical Treat!!)
  Brothers All Natural▲ - Fruit Crisps (Asian Pear, Banana, Fuji Apple, Organic Strawberry, Pineapple, Strawberry, Strawberry Banana, White & Yellow Peach)
  Fruit By The Foot -
    Berry Blast
    Berry Tie Dye
    Boo Berry

F

   Color By The Foot
   Minis (Berry Wave, Trick Or Treat Berry, Wicked Webs Halloween)
   Razzle Blue Blitz
   Strawberry
   Tropical Twist
   Variety Pack (Berry Tie Dye, Color By The Foot, Strawberry)
   Watermelon
Fruit Gushers - Blue Raspberry, Flavor Shock, Halloween Tropical
   Mix, Mouth Mixers Punch Berry, Strawberry, Strawberry/Tropical,
   Triple Berry Shock, Tropical, Tropical Spooky Fruit, Variety Pack
   Strawberry/Watermelon, Watermelon Blast
Fruit Roll-Ups -
   Around The World
   Blastin' Berry Hot Colors
   Boo Berry Razzle Boo Blitz
   Flavor Wave
   Franken Berry Strawberry Scream
   Minis (Screamin' Strawberry, Strawberry Craze, Wildberry Punch)
   Scoops Fruity Ice Cream Flavors
   Stickerz (Berry Cool Punch, Mixed Berry, Tropical Berry)
   Strawberry
   Strawberry Sensation
   Tropical Tie Dye
   Variety Pack (Simply Fruit Wildberry/Strawberry, Stickerz, Stickerz
      Mixed Berry/Tropical Berry, Strawberry/Berry Cool Punch)
Fruit Shapes - Care Bears, Comics, Create A Bug, Dora The Explorer,
   Easter, Halloween, My Little Pony, Nickelodeon, Scooby Doo, Shark
   Bites, Spiderman, Sponge Bob, Sunkist Mixed Fruit, Transformers,
   Valentine Hearts, Value Pack (Nickelodeon Tropical, Sunkist),
   Variety Pack (Scooby Doo/Looney Tunes)
Great Value Brand (Wal-Mart) - Fruit Smiles
thinkFruit - Dried (Blueberries, Cherry, Cinnamon Apple,
   Cranberries, Peaches, Pineapple Tidbits)
Welch's - All Varieties
Fruit Spread... see Jam/Jelly... see also Spread

G

Gai Lan
... **All Fresh Gai Lan Is Gluten/Casein/Soy Free*

Garbanzo Beans... see Beans

Garlic
... **All Fresh Garlic Is Gluten/Casein/Soy Free*

  Earthbound Farm - Organic Garlic

  Mezzetta - Crushed Garlic, Spicy Pickled Garlic

  Trader Joe's - Crushed Regular

Garlic Powder... see Seasonings

Garlic Salt... see Seasonings

Gelatin

  Gifts Of Nature▲ - Unflavored Beef Gelatin

  Ginger Evans - Cherry, Orange, Strawberry, Sugar Free (Cherry, Orange, Strawberry)

  Hannaford Brand - Sugar Free (Cherry, Lime, Orange, Raspberry)

  Hy-Vee - Gelatin (Berry Blue, Cherry, Cranberry, Lemon, Lime, Orange, Raspberry, Strawberry, Strawberry Banana), Sugar Free (Cherry, Cranberry, Lime, Orange, Raspberry, Strawberry)

  Jell-O -

    Regular Instant (Apricot, Berry Blue, Black Cherry, Cherry, Cranberry, Grape, Island Pineapple, Lemon, Lime, Margarita, Melon Fusion, Orange, Peach, Pina Colada, Raspberry, Strawberry (Banana, Daquiri, Kiwi, Regular), Tropical Fusion, Watermelon, Wild Strawberry)

    Snack Cups (Strawberry, Strawberry/Orange, Strawberry/Raspberry)

    Sugar Free Low Calorie (Black Cherry, Cherry, Cranberry, Lemon, Lime, Mixed Fruit, Orange, Peach, Raspberry, Strawberry (Banana, Kiwi, Regular))

    Sugar Free Snack Cups (Cherry/Black Cherry, Lime/Orange, Peach/Watermelon, Raspberry/Orange, Strawberry, Strawberry Kiwi/Tropical Berry)

G

Jelly Belly - All Varieties
Kool-Aid - Gels (All Varieties)
Kroger Brand - Flavored, Plain, Snack Cups
Meijer Brand -
    Gelatin Dessert (Berry Blue, Cherry, Cranberry, Grape, Lime,
      Orange, Raspberry, Strawberry, Unflavored, Wild Strawberry)
    Sugar Free Gelatin Dessert (Cherry, Cranberry, Lime, Orange,
      Raspberry, Strawberry)
Royal - All Varieties
Spartan Brand - Berry Blue, Cherry (Regular, Sugar Free), Lemon,
    Lime (Regular, Sugar Free), Orange (Regular, Sugar Free),
    Raspberry (Regular, Sugar Free), Strawberry (Regular, Sugar Free)
Wegmans Brand - Sugar Free (Cherry & Black Cherry, Grape & Fruit
    Punch, Lemon Lime & Orange, Orange & Raspberry, Strawberry)

Gin
    ... *All Distilled Alcohol Is Gluten/Casein/Soy Free* [2]

Ginger
Gluty Free - Crystallized●, Organic Crystallized●
Lee Kum Kee - Minced
Nuts Online - Dried Fruit (Crystallized●, Organic Crystallized●)
The Ginger People - Grated!, Organic Minced!, Organic Natural
    Pickled Sushi!, Syrup!
Wel-Pac - Pickled Ginger (Benzi, Kizami), Sushi Ginger

Ginger Ale... see Soda Pop/Carbonated Beverages

Glaze
Ah So - Ham Glaze
Daddy Sam's - Salmon Glaze
Marzetti - Glaze For (Blueberries, Peaches, Strawberries, Sugar Free
    Strawberries)

Graham Crackers
Jules Gluten Free▲ - Graham Cracker/Gingersnap Mix●
Laurel's Sweet Treats▲ - Honey Grahamless Crackers

Grains
Arrowhead Mills - Amaranth, Hulled Millet, Quinoa

Bob's Red Mill▲ - Organic Amaranth, Quinoa Organic, Teff Whole

Eden Organic - Brown Rice Flakes, Buckwheat, Millet, Quinoa, Red Quinoa, Wild Rice

Nuts Online -

Gluten Free (Brown Rice Farina●, Corn Grits Polenta●, Corn Meal●, Millet Grits●, Organic Brown Rice Farina●, Rice Bran●, Sweet White Sorghum Grain●)

Millet●

Organic (Amaranth●, Buckwheat Toasted●, Millet●, Purple Corn Kernels●, Quinoa●, Raw White Buckwheat●)

Simply Sweet Corn●

Teff Whole Grain●

Yellow Corn Meal●

Shiloh Farms - Hulled Millet , Whole Sorghum

Granola

Bakery On Main - Apple Raisin Walnut●, Cranberry Orange Cashew●, Extreme Fruit & Nut●, Fiber Power (Cinnamon Raisin●, Triple Berry), Nutty Cranberry Maple●, Rainforest●

Deb's Farmhouse Kitchen - Cherry Almond●, Oatmeal Cookieola●

Deerfields Gluten Free Bakery▲ - Almond Cherry, Vanilla Maple

Emmy's Organics▲ - Raw Almond

Enjoy Life▲ - Granola (Cinnamon Crunch●, Cranapple Crunch●, Very Berry Crunch●)

Flax4Life▲ - Apple Cinnamon●, Banana Coconut●, Cranberry Orange●, Hawaiian Pineapple Coconut & Mango●

Gluten Free Sensations▲ -

Cherry Vanilla Almond

Cranberry Pecan

French Vanilla Almond

GlutenFreeda▲ -

Apple Almond Honey

Cranberry Cashew Honey

Raisin Almond Honey

Goraw▲ - Granola (Apple Cinnamon●, Live●, Live Chocolate●, Simple●)

G **Kaia Foods▲** - Buckwheat Granola (Cocoa Bliss●, Dates & Spices●, Raisin Cinnamon●)

Kookie Karma - All Varieties●

Love Grown Foods▲ - Apple Walnut Delight ●, Raisin Almond Crunch ●, Simply Oats ●, Sweet Cranberry Pecan ●

Pure Market Express▲ - Tennessee Grawnola●

Rose's Bakery▲

Udi's Gluten Free Foods▲ - Gluten Free (Au Naturel, Cranberry, Original, Vanilla)

Whole Foods Market Gluten Free Bakehouse▲ - Fruit & Nut Granola

Grape Leaves

 Krinos - Imported

 Mezzetta - California Grape Leaves

 Peloponnese - Dolmas, Grape Leaves

Grapefruit

 *... *All Fresh Grapefruit Is Gluten/Casein/Soy Free*

 Del Monte - Canned/Jarred Fruit (All Varieties), Fruit Snack Cups (Metal Regular)

 Kirkland Signature - Red Grapefruit Cups

 Meijer Brand - Sections (In Juice, In Syrup)

 Winn Dixie - Canned Regular

Grapes

 *... *All Fresh Grapes Are Gluten/Casein/Soy Free*

Gravy/Gravy Mix

 Barkat - Vegetable Gravy

 Cuisine Sante▲ - Au Jus Clear Gravy●

 Full Flavor Foods▲ - Gravy (Chicken●, Pork●, Turkey●)

 Imagine - Organic Gravy Savory Beef Flavored

 Maxwell's Kitchen - Gravy Mix (Chicken, Turkey)

 Orgran▲ - Gravy Mix

Green Beans... see Beans

Green Peppers

 *... *All Fresh Green Peppers Are Gluten/Casein/Soy Free*

Green Tea... see Tea

Greens

... *All Fresh Greens Are Gluten/Casein/Soy Free*

Albertsons - Canned & Frozen Mustard Greens, Canned & Frozen Turnip Greens

Birds Eye - All Plain Frozen Greens

Bush's Best - Chopped (Collard, Kale, Mixed, Mustard, Turnip, Turnip w/Diced Turnips)

C & W - All Plain Frozen Greens

Lowes Foods Brand - Frozen (Chopped Collard, Turnip Greens)

Meijer Brand - Canned Chopped (Kale, Mustard, Turnip), Chopped (Collards, Kale, Mustard, Turnip)

Pictsweet - All Plain Frozen Greens

Publix - Frozen (Collard Chopped, Turnip Chopped, Turnip w/ Diced Turnips)

Publix GreenWise Market - Mixed Baby Blend

Spartan Brand - Chopped (Collard, Mustard, Turnip)

Stop & Shop Brand - Collard Greens, Mustard Greens

Winn Dixie -

Canned (Collard No Salt, Mustard, Turnip)

Frozen (Collard Greens Chopped, Mustard Greens, Steamable Mixed Vegetables)

Grits

Bob's Red Mill▲ - Gluten Free Corn Grits/Polenta

Meijer Brand - Butter Flavored Instant, Quick

San Gennaro Foods - Southern Style

Groats

Arrowhead Mills - Buckwheat

Chateau Cream Hill Estates - Lara's Oat Groats●

Montana Monster Munchies - Raw & Sproutable Oat Groats●

Pocono - Kasha Whole Buckwheat

Ground Beef... see Beef

Ground Turkey... see Turkey

G Guacamole... see also Dip/Dip Mix
H   Calavo - Mild Spice, Pico De Gallo Recipe (Medium Spice)
       Fischer & Wieser - Guacamole Starter
       Trader Joe's - Avocado's Number, w/Spicy Pico De Gallo **! !**

Guar Gum
   AgVantage Naturals▲ - ●
   Authentic Foods▲
   Bob's Red Mill▲
   Gillian's Foods▲
   Gluten-Free Essentials▲ - ●
   Grandma Ferdon's▲ - ●
   Kinnikinnick▲
   Nuts Online - ●

Gum... see Chewing Gum

H

Halibut... see Fish

Ham
   Applegate Farms -
      Natural (Black Forest, Honey, Slow Cooked)
      Organic Uncured
   Armour -
      1877 (Canadian Maple, Honey Cured, Virginia Baked)
      Deli (Cooked, Cooked Ham & Water Product, Honey Cured, Lite,
         Spiced Luncheon Meat, Virginia Brand)
   Bar S - Classic Chopped, Deli Shaved (Black Forest, Honey, Smoked),
      Deli Style (Honey, Smoked), Deli Thin Cut (Honey, Smoked), Extra
      Lean Cooked, Premium (Honey, Smoked), Steaks (Honey, Smoked)
   Boar's Head - All Varieties *(Except Pesto Parmesan Ham)*
   Butcher's Cut -
      Shank Cut Ham
      Spiral Sliced *(Glazing Packet Is Not Gluten Free)*
      Whole Smoked Ham

Carl Buddig -
  Deli Cuts (Baked Honey Ham, Brown Sugar Baked Ham,
    Smoked Ham)
  Extra Thin Original (Brown Sugar Ham, Honey Ham, Regular)
  Fix Quix Smoked Ham
  Original (Brown Sugar Ham, Honey Ham, Regular)
Castle Wood Reserve - Deli Meat (Black Forest Ham, Honey Ham,
  Smoked Ham, Virginia Brand Smoked Ham)
Celebrity - Boneless Cooked
Cure 81 - Regular
Dietz & Watson▲ -
  Black Forest (Cooked●, Cured Honey●, Deep Smoked●,
    Smoked●)
  Breakfast Ham Fillets w/Water Added●
  Cajun●
  Chef Carved (Hickory Smoked●, Regular●)
  Chopped●
  Classic Trimmed & Tied w/Natural Juices●
  Cooked Round●
  Cubes●
  Gourmet Lite (Cooked●, Virginia Decorated●, Virginia Low Salt●)
  Honey (Cured Dinner●, Cured Tavern●)
  Imported Cooked●
  Maple Glazed●
  Pepper●
  Prosciutto (Classico Trimmed●, Regular●)
  Rosemary●
  Semi Boneless Smoked●
  Square Red Pepper●
  Steak (Honey●, Maple Cured●, Traditional●)
  Tavern●
  Tiffany●
  Tomato & Basil●
  Virginia Baked●

H

Eckrich -
Deli Meat (Black Forest Brand Nugget, Brown Sugar Nugget,
Canadian Maple, Chopped, Ham Steak, Honey Cured, Honey
Maple, Imported, Lite, Off The Bone, Smoked Pitt, Spiced
Luncheon Meat, Spiral Sliced Holiday, Virginia Baked)
Lunch Meat (Chopped, Cooked, Virginia Brand Thin Sliced)

Fairgrounds - Lunch Meat (Honey Ham, Premium Ham (Chopped,
Cooked))

Farmer John - Bone In Ham Premium Sliced Ham Steaks, Ham Steaks
(Clove, Maple, Original, Pineapple & Mango), Lunch Meats Ham
(Brown Sugar & Honey, Sliced Cooked)

Garrett County Farms -
Black Forest Boneless Nugget!
Deli (Black Forest!, Virginia!)
Sliced (Black Forest!, Breakfast Virginia Brand Boneless Ham Steak!,
Turkey Ham (Ham Steak!, Original!), Virginia Brand Deli Ham!)

Great Value Brand (Wal-Mart) -
97% Fat Free (Baked Ham Water Added, Cooked Ham,
Honey Ham Water Added)
Thinly Sliced Smoked (Ham, Honey Ham)

Habbersett - Dainty Ham, Ham Slices, Ham Steak

Hillshire Farms -
Deli Select (Brown Sugar Baked Ham, Smoked Ham)
Deli Select Ultra Thin (Brown Sugar Baked Ham, Honey Ham)
Whole/Half (All Flavors)

Hormel -
Black Label (Canned, Chopped)
Bread Ready Deli Counter Prosciutto
Chunk Meats Ham
Natural Choice Deli Counter (Cherrywood Smoked, Cooked,
Smoked)
Natural Choice Ham (Cooked Deli, Honey, Smoked Deli)

Hy-Vee -
96% Fat Free (Cubed Cooked, Diced Cooked)
Cooked Ham

Deli Thin Slices (Brown Sugar, Honey, Smoked)

Thin Sliced (Ham w/Natural Juices, Honey Ham w/Natural Juices)

Isaly's - All Deli Meat

Jones Dairy Farm -

Boneless Fully Cooked (Dainty Hickory Smoked●, Half Family●, Whole Family●)

Deli Style Ham Slices (Honey & Brown Sugar●, Old Fashioned Cured●)

Slices Naturally Hickory Smoked●

Steak Hickory Smoked●

Whole Boneless Country Club●

Whole Hickory Smoked (Fully Cooked, Short Shanked●, Old Fashioned Cure●)

Kayem - Deli Ham (Amber Honey Cured, Black Forest, Carving, Honeycrust, Olde English Tavern, Peppercrust)

Kirkland Signature - Deli Meat (Extra Lean, Smoked Honey), Smoked (Applewood Half, Spiral Sliced Hickory)

Kroger Brand - Cooked, Cubed, Diced, Steaks

Oscar Mayer -

Deli Fresh Meats (Cooked Ham, Honey Ham, Smoked Ham)

Deli Meat Chopped

Shaved Deli Fresh Meats (Black Forest, Brown Sugar Ham, Honey Ham, Smoked Ham, Virginia Brand Ham)

Thin Sliced Deli Fresh (Brown Sugar Ham, Smoked Ham)

Primo Taglio - Black Forest Ham w/Natural Juices, Prosciutto Dry Cured Ham

Publix -

Deli Pre Pack Lunch Meat (Cooked Ham, Extra Thin Sliced Honey Ham, Low Salt Ham, Sweet Ham, Tavern Ham)

Hickory Smoked Ham Semi Boneless, Fully Cooked

Russer - Reduced Sodium Cooked, Smoked Virginia

Safeway Brand - Boneless Honey

Safeway Select - 2 Lbs Half Boneless

H

Sara Lee - Deli Meat Slices (Brown Sugar Ham, Cooked Ham, Hickory Smoked Ham, Honey Ham, Virginia Brand Baked Ham)

Smithfield - All Spiral & Glazed Hams *(Except HEB Private Label)*, Boneless Ham, Ham Steak, Quarter Ham

SPAM - Classic, Hickory Smoke Flavored, Less Sodium, Lite

Spartan Brand - Frozen Ham Loaf, Whole Boneless

Underwood - Deviled Ham Spread

Wegmans Brand -
> 97% Fat Free
> Boneless Brown Sugar Cured
> Ham Slices Boneless
> Maple Cured
> Old Fashioned Off The Bone (Brown Sugar Cured Ham, Double Smoked Ham)
> Organic Uncured Ham
> Thin Shaved (Ham, Honey Maple Flavored Ham, Smoked Ham, Smoked Honey Ham)
> Virginia Baked

Wellshire Farms -
> Black Forest (Boneless Half**! !**, Boneless Nugget**! !**, Deli**! !**, Quarter**! !**, Sliced**! !**)
> Glazed Boneless Half**! !**
> Old Fashioned Boneless (Half**! !**, Whole**! !**)
> Semi Boneless (Half**! !**, Whole**! !**)
> Sliced (Breakfast**! !**, Tavern**! !**)
> Smoked Ham (Hocks**! !**, Shanks**! !**)
> Turkey Half Ham**! !**
> Virginia Buffet Half**! !**
> Virginia Brand (Boneless Steak**! !**, Buffet**! !**, Deli**! !**, Nugget Honey**! !**, Quarter**! !**, Sliced**! !**)

Hamburger Buns... see Buns

Hamburgers... see Burgers

*... *All Fresh Meat Is Gluten/Casein/Soy Free (Non-Marinated, Unseasoned)*

Hash Browns... see Potatoes
Hearts Of Palm
   ... *All Fresh Hearts Of Palm Are Gluten/Casein/Soy Free
   Del Monte - Canned Hearts Of Palm
   Native Forest - Organic Hearts Of Palm
Herbal Tea... see Tea
Hominy
   Bush's Best - Golden, White
   Great Value Brand (Wal-Mart) - Canned (White, Yellow)
   Hy-Vee - Golden, White
   Meijer Brand - White
   Safeway Brand - Golden, White
   Spartan Brand - Golden, White
   Winn Dixie - Golden, White
Honey
   Albertsons - Honey
   Bakers & Chefs - Pure Honey
   Bramley's - Golden
   Full Circle - Organic 100% Pure Honey
   Great Value Brand (Wal-Mart) - Clover Honey
   Hannaford Brand - All Varieties
   Hy-Vee - Honey, Honey Squeeze Bear
   Kroger Brand
   Kroger Value
   Meijer Brand - Honey, Honey Squeeze Bear
   Publix - Clover, Orange Blossom, Wildflower
   Publix GreenWise Market - Organic Honey
   Safeway Brand - Pure
   Safeway Select - Regular
   Spartan Brand - Regular
   Trader Joe's - All Varieties
   Tropical Traditions - Canadian Raw Honey
   Virginia Brand - 100% All Natural

H

Wegmans Brand - Clover, Orange Blossom, Squeezeable Bear
Winn Dixie

Honey Mustard Sauce... see Mustard

Horseradish Sauce
Baxters - Regular
Dietz & Watson▲ - Red●
Hy-Vee - Prepared Horseradish
Wegmans Brand - Prepared Horseradish

Hot Chocolate Mix... see Cocoa Mix/Powder

Hot Dog Buns... see Buns

Hot Dogs... see Sausage

Hot Sauce
Albertsons
Bone Suckin' Sauce - Habanero Sauce
Dave's Gourmet -
    Adjustable Heat
    Cool Cayenne
    Crazy Caribbean
    Ginger Peach
    Hot Sauce & Garden Spray
    Hurtin' (Habanero, Jalapeño)
    Insanity Sauce
    Jump Up & Kiss Me (Chipotle, Original, Passionfruit)
    Roasted (Garlic, Red Pepper & Chipotle)
    Scotch Bonnet
    Total Insanity
    Ultimate Insanity
Frank's RedHot - Chile 'N Lime, Original, Xtra Hot
Frontera - Hot Sauce (Chipotle, Habanero, Jalapeno, Red Pepper)
Gifts Of Nature▲ - Sriracha Hot Sauce
Hannaford Brand
La Victoria - Chunky Jalapeno, Salsa Brava
Mezzetta - California Habanero Hot Sauce Twist & Shout,
    California Hot Sauce
Texas Pete - Garlic, Hotter Hot, Original

Trader Joe's - Jalapeno
Trappey's - Bull Brand Louisiana Hot Sauce, Indi Pep Pepper Sauce, Louisiana Hot Sauce, Mexi Pep Hot Sauce, Red Devil Cayenne Pepper Sauce
Winn Dixie - Louisiana Hot

Hummus

Athenos -
Hummus
Artichoke & Garlic
Black Olive
Cucumber Dill
Greek Style
Original
Pesto
Roasted (Eggplant, Garlic, Red Pepper)
Scallion
Spicy Three Pepper
NeoClassic Hummus
Original
Original w/Sesame Seeds & Parsley
Roasted (Garlic w/Garlic & Parsley, Red Pepper w/Red Peppers & Parsley)
Casbah Natural Foods - Hummus
Fantastic World Foods - Original Hummus
Melissa's - Roasted Red Pepper, Traditional
Pure Market Express▲ -
Hummus & Onion●
Hummus w/Carrotini
Crackers●
Tuscan Hummus●
Salpica - Chipotle Hummus Dip
Trader Joe's -
Chipotle Pepper**!!**
Garlic**!!**

H

I

Kalamata Olive **!!**
Mediterranean **!!**
Original **!!**
Roasted Garlic **!!**
Smooth & Creamy (Cilantro & Jalapeno, Classic Rice Bread Mix,
Roasted Red Pepper, Spicy), w/Freshly Ground Horseradish **!!**
Tribe - All Varieties (Classic, Organic, Origins)
Wegmans Brand - Regular, Traditional Flavor w/A Hint Of Lemon
Wild Garden - Black Olive, Fire Roasted Red Pepper, Jalapeno, Red
Hot Chili Pepper, Roasted Garlic, Sundried Tomato, Sweet Pepper,
Traditional
Wild Wood - Classic, Indian Spice, Low Fat Classic, Raspberry
Chipotle, Roasted Red Pepper, Spicy Cayenne

I

Ice Cream
... (includes *Frozen Desserts, Frozen Yogurt, Sherbet, Sorbet*)
Albertsons - Junior Pops
Breyer's - Pure Fruit Bars (Berry Swirls, Pomegranate Blends,
Strawberry Orange Raspberry)
Chapman's - Sorbet (Orange, Rainbow, Raspberry)
Cool Fruits - Fruit Juice Freezers (Grape & Cherry, Sour Apple)
Double Rainbow Sorbet - Sorbet (Chocolate **!!**, Coconut **!!**,
Lemon **!!**, Mango Tangerine **!!**, Raspberry **!!**)
Dreyer's -
Fruit Bars
Grape
Lemonade
Lime
Pineapple
Pomegranate
Strawberry
Tangerine

I

Variety Pack Lime/Strawberry/Wildberry
Variety Pack No Sugar Added (Black Cherry, Mixed Berry,
   Strawberry, Strawberry Kiwi, Tangerine & Raspberry)
Edy's -
   Fruit Bars (Grape, Lemonade, Lime, Pineapple, Pomegranate,
      Strawberry, Tangerine, Variety Pack Lime/Strawberry/Wildberry,
      Variety Pack No Sugar Added (Black Cherry, Mixed Berry,
      Strawberry, Strawberry Kiwi))
   Fruit Bars Variety Pack No Sugar Added (Tangerine & Raspberry)
Fla-Vor-Ice - Freezer Bars (Light, Regular, Sport, Tropical)
Frootee Ice - Assorted Freezer Bars
Haagen-Dazs - Sorbet (Mango, Strawberry, Zesty Lemon)
Hannaford Brand - Assorted Pops (Citrus, Regular, Sugar Free),
   Bars Real Fruit
Hood - Frozen Novelty Items Hoodsie Pops (6 Flavor Assortment
   Twin Pops)
Hy-Vee - Bars (Assorted Twin Pops, Pop (Cherry, Grape, Orange, Root
   Beer))
Jamba - Novelty Bars (Peach Blackberry Smash, Strawberry
   Lemonade Swirl)
Jelly Belly - Freezer Bars/Pops
Kemps - All American Pops, Pop Jr.'s, Sugar Free Pop Jr.'s, Tropical Pops
Kool Pops - Freezer Bars
Larry & Luna's Coconut Bliss -
   Bars (Dark Chocolate Bars!, Naked Coconut Bars!)
   Ice Cream (Cappuccino!, Cherry Amaretto!, Chocolate Hazelnut
      Fudge!, Chocolate Peanut Butter!, Dark Chocolate!, Mint
      Galactica!, Naked Almond Fudge!, Naked Coconut!,
      Pineapple Coconut!, Vanilla Island!)
Living Harvest - Tempt Frozen Desserts (All Varieties)
Minute Maid - Orange/Cherry/Grape Juice Bars
Mr. Freeze - Freezer Bars Assorted
NadaMoo▲ - Creamy Coconut●, Gotta Do Chocolate●, Java
   Crunch●, Mmm...Maple Pecan●, Vanilla...ahhh●

Natural Choice - Full Of Fruit Bars
North Star -
Lotta Pops (Fruita, Regular Pops, Sugar Free)
Pops (Assorted Twin, Banana Twin, Blue Raspberry Twin, Cherry
Twin, Health Wise Fat Free No Sugar Added, Melon, Patriot)
Otter Pops - Freezer Bars (Regular)
Philly Swirl - Original Swirl Stix, Philly Swirl Sorbet/Italian Ice,
Poppers, Sugar Free Swirl Stix
Pop Ice - Freezer Pops
Publix - Novelties (Banana Pops, Ice Pops, Junior Ice Pops (All Flavors),
No Sugar Added Ice Pops, Red, White & Blue Junior, Twin Pops)
Pure Market Express▲ -
Ice Cream
Cherry Chocolate Chip●
Chocolate●
Chocolate Fudge Brownie●
Coffee●
Cookie Dough●
Maple●
Maple Nut●
Mocha●
Peanut Butter Cup●
Strawberry●
Sorbet (Cherry●, Lemon●, Mango●, Peach●, Strawberry●)
Purely Decadent - Coconut Milk (Chocolate●, Coconut●,
Passionate Mango●, Vanilla Bean●)
Safeway Select - Regular Fruit Bars (Lemonade, Lime, Strawberry)
Slush Puppie - Freezer Bars Assorted
So Delicious - Coconut Water Sorbet (Hibiscus●, Lemonade●,
Mango●, Raspberry●)
So Delicious Dairy Free - Kidz Assorted Fruit Pops●
Soda Pops - Freezer Bars (A & W, Dr. Pepper)
Sweet Nothings - Non Dairy Bars (Fudge●, Mango Raspberry●)

Trader Joe's - Sorbet (All Varieties)
WarHeads - Freezer Bars Extreme Sour
Wegmans Brand - Sorbet (Green Apple, Lemon, Pink Grapefruit, Raspberry, Vanilla Raspberry)
Winn & Lovett - Frozen Fruit Bars (Caribbean, Pina Colada, Raspberry, Strawberry)
Winn Dixie - Banana Pops, Junior Pops
Wyler's - Italian Ices (Freezer Bars)
Ice Cream Cones... see Cones
Ice Cream Toppings... see also Syrup
  Hershey's - Chocolate Syrup (Lite, Regular, Special Dark)
  Smucker's▲ -
    Black Cherry
    Plate Scrapers Dessert Topping (Raspberry)
    Special Recipe (Triple Berry)
    Sugar Free (Strawberry)
    Sundae Syrups (Strawberry)
    Toppings (Apple Cinnamon, Marshmallow, Pecans In Syrup, Pineapple, Strawberry, Walnuts In Syrup)
Iced Tea/Iced Tea Mix... see Tea
Icing... see Baking Decorations & Frostings
Instant Coffee... see Coffee
Italian Dressing... see Salad Dressing

J

Jalapenos
  *... *All Fresh Jalapenos Are Gluten/Casein/Soy Free*
  Chi-Chi's - Red
  Dietz & Watson▲ - Sliced●, Spread●
  Great Value Brand (Wal-Mart) - Sliced Jalapenos En Rajas, Whole Jalapenos
  Mezzetta -
    Deli Sliced (Hot Jalapeno Peppers, Tamed Jalapeno Peppers)

J

    Gourmet Deli (Sweet & Hot Jalapeno Pepper Rings, Tamed Diced Jalapeno Peppers, Tamed Fire Roasted w/Chipotle Peppers)

Mt. Olive - Diced Jalapeno Peppers, Jalapeno Slices

Old El Paso - Slices Pickled

Ortega - Diced, Pickled Slices

Safeway Brand - Sliced Regular

Senora Verde - Jalapeno Slices

Winn Dixie - Regular

Jalfrazi

    Seeds Of Change - Jalfrazi Sauce **! !**

Jam/Jelly

    Albertsons - All (Jam, Jellies, Preserves)

    Baxters -

        Conserve (Country Berry, Raspberry, Rhubarb & Ginger, Strawberry)

        Jelly (Cranberry, Mint, Red Currant)

        Marmalade (Lemon, Orange Lemon & Grapefruit, Seville Orange)

    Bionaturae - Organic Fruit Spread (Apricot, Bilberry, Peach, Plum, Red Raspberry, Sicilian Orange, Sour Cherry, Strawberry, Wild Berry, Wild Blackberry)

    Bramley's - Jellies & Preserves

    Eden Organic - Butter (Apple, Cherry)

    Fischer & Wieser -

        Apple Pecan Butter

        Jelly Texas (Mild Green Jalapeno, Red Hot Jalapeno)

        Marmalade (Apricot Orange, Whole Lemon Fig)

        Peach Pecan Butter

        Preserves (Old Fashioned Peach, Strawberry Rhubarb, Texas (Amaretto Peach Pecan, Jalapeach))

        Southern Style

    Full Circle - Apricot, Blueberry, Concord Grape, Raspberry, Strawberry

    Hannaford Brand -

        Jelly (Apple, Currant, Grape, Strawberry)

Orange Marmalade

Preserve (Apricots, Blueberry, Grape, Red Raspberry)

Hy-Vee -

Jelly (Apple, Blackberry, Cherry, Concord Grape, Grape, Plum, Red Raspberry, Strawberry)

Orange Marmalade

Preserves (Apricot, Cherry, Concord Grape, Peach, Red Raspberry, Strawberry)

Kirkland Signature - Organic Strawberry Spread

Kroger Brand - All (Jams, Jellies, Preserves)

Kroger Value - Grape, Strawberry Spread

Lowes Foods Brand - Jam Grape, Jelly (Apple, Grape), Preserves Strawberry

Meijer Brand -

Fruit Spread (Apricot, Blackberry Seedless, Red Raspberry, Strawberry)

Grape Jam

Grape Jelly

Preserves (Apricot, Blackberry Seedless, Marmalade Orange, Peach, Red Raspberry, Red Raspberry w/Seeds, Strawberry)

O Organics - Preserves (Apricot, Blackberry, Blueberry, Raspberry, Strawberry)

Oskri Organics -

Preserves (Apricot, Cranberry, Nectarine, Peach, Pear, Plum, Raspberry)

Spread (Date, Fig, Sesame)

Peanut Butter & Co. - Awesome Apricot Preserves, Gorgeous Grape Jelly, Rip Roaring Raspberry Preserves, Seriously Strawberry Jam

Polaner▲ - All (Jam, Jellies, Preserves)

Publix - All (Jam, Jellies, Preserves)

Safeway Brand - All (Jams, Jellies, Preserves)

Safeway Select - All (Jams, Jellies, Preserves)

Santa Cruz - Fruit Spread (All Varieties)

Shiloh Farms - Apple Butter

J

Smucker's▲ - All (Fruit Butter, Jams, Jellies, Low Sugar, Marmalades, Orchard's Finest Preserves, Organic, Preserves, Simply Fruit, Squeeze, Sugar Free w/NutraSweet, Sugar Free w/Splenda)

Spartan Brand -
Grape Jam
Jelly (Apple, Currant, Grape, Strawberry)
Orange Marmalade
Preserves (Apricot, Blackberry, Cherry, Peach, Red Raspberry, Strawberry)

Stop & Shop Brand -
Concord Grape Jelly (Spreadable, Squeezable)
Jelly (Apple, Currant, Mint)
Orange Marmalade
Preserves (Apricot, Grape, Peach, Pineapple, Red Raspberry, Seedless Blackberry, Strawberry)
Simply Enjoy Preserves (Blueberry, Raspberry Champagne Peach, Spiced Apple, Strawberry)
Spread (Apricot, Blueberry, Strawberry)
Squeezable Grape Jelly
Sugar Free Preserves (Apricot, Blackberry, Red Raspberry, Strawberry)

Taste Of Inspiration - All Flavors!

Trader Joe's -
Organic Fruit Spread (Blueberry, Strawberry, Superfruit)
Organic Preserves Reduced Sugar (Blackberry!!, Blueberry!!, Raspberry!!, Strawberry!!)
Preserves (Apricot!!, Blackberry!!, Blueberry!!, Boysenberry!!, Raspberry!!)

Walden Farms - Spread (Apple Butter, Apricot, Blueberry, Grape, Orange, Raspberry, Strawberry)

Wegmans Brand -
Fruit Spread (Apricot/Peach/Passion Fruit, Blueberry/Cherry/Raspberry, Raspberry/Strawberry/Blackberry, Strawberry/Plum/Raspberry, Sugar Free Raspberry/Wild Blueberry/Blackberry)

Jelly (Apple, Cherry, Concord Grape, Currant, Mint, Red
   Raspberry, Strawberry)

Nature's Marketplace Organic Fruit Spread (Jammin' Red
   Raspberry, Jammin' Strawberry)

Preserves (Apricot, Cherry, Concord Grape, Peach, Pineapple,
   Red Raspberry, Seedless Blackberry, Strawberry)

Sugar Free Fruit Spread (Apricot/Peach/Passion Fruit, Raspberry/
   Wild Blueberry/Blackberry, Strawberry/Plum/Raspberry)

Welch's - All Jam, Jellies & Preserves

Winn Dixie - All Jams, All Jellies, All Preserves

Jell-O... see Gelatin

Jerky/Beef Sticks

Buffalo Guys - Buffalo Jerky (Mild, Old Style)

Dietz & Watson▲ - Dried Beef●

Gary West - All Certified Angus Beef Steak Strips Varieties *(Except
   Teriyaki)*, All Original Steak Strips Varieties *(Except Teriyaki)*,
   Buffalo & Elk Strips, Silver Fork Natural Steak Strips

Hormel - Dried Beef

Hy-Vee - Original Jerky

Old Wisconsin - Snack Bites (Beef, Pepp, Turkey), Snack Sticks
   (Beef, Pepp, Turkey)

Organic Prairie - Organic Beef Jerky 2 oz. (Prairie Classic!, Smoky
   Chipotle!, Spicy Hickory!)

Wellshire Farms - Snack Sticks (Hot N' Spicy!!, Matt's Beef
   Pepperoni!!, Turkey Tom Tom!!)

Juice Mix... see Drink Mix

Juice... see Drinks/Juice

K

Kale

   ... *All Fresh Kale Is Gluten/Casein/Soy Free*

Pictsweet - Cut Leaf

K Kasha
    Bob's Red Mill▲ - Organic
    Shiloh Farms - Organic
    Wolff's - Regular
  Ketchup
    Albertsons
    Annie's Naturals - Organic!!
    Bakers & Chefs - Fancy Ketchup
    Full Circle - Regular
    Great Value Brand (Wal-Mart) - Regular
    Hannaford Brand - Regular
    Heinz - Easy Squeeze Regular, Hot & Spicy, Hot & Spicy Kick'rs, No Salt Added, Organic, Organic Tomato, Reduced Sugar, Regular
    Hy-Vee - Regular, Squeezable Thick & Rich Tomato, Thick & Rich Tomato
    Kroger Value
    Kurtz - Regular
    Lowes Foods Brand - Regular
    Meijer Brand - Regular, Squeeze, Tomato Organic
    Midwest Country Fare - Regular
    O Organics - Regular
    Organicville - Organic●
    Publix - Regular
    Publix GreenWise Market - Organic
    Safeway Brand - Regular
    Spartan Brand - Regular
    Trader Joe's - Organic
    Walden Farms - Regular
    Wegmans Brand - Organic, Regular
    Westbrae - Unsweetened
    Winn Dixie - Regular
    Woodstock Farms - Organic
  Kielbasa... see Sausage

Kipper Snacks
   Crown Prince - Naturally Smoked
   Ocean Prince - In Mustard, Naturally Smoked
Kiwi
   ... **All Fresh Kiwi Is Gluten/Casein/Soy Free*
Kohlrabi
   ... **All Fresh Kohlrabi Is Gluten/Casein/Soy Free*
Korma
   Amy's - Indian Vegetable!

L

Lamb
   ... **All Fresh Meat Is Gluten/Casein/Soy Free (Non-Marinated, Unseasoned)*
   Kirkland Signature - Fresh Rib Roast
   Sweet Bay - All Fresh Lamb
Lasagna Noodles... see Pasta
Leeks
   ... **All Fresh Lemons Are Gluten/Casein/Soy Free*
   Trader Joe's - Frozen Sliced Leeks
Lemonade... see Drinks/Juice
Lemons
   ... **All Fresh Lemons Are Gluten/Casein/Soy Free*
   Nuts Online - Dried●
   Sunkist
Lentils... see also Beans
   GoGo Rice - On The Go Cooked Rice Bowls Tasty & Healthy
     Harvest
   Tasty Bite - Bengal!, Lentil Magic!
Lettuce
   ... **All Fresh Lettuce Is Gluten/Casein/Soy Free*
Licorice... see Candy/Candy Bars
Limeade... see Drinks/Juice
Limes
   ... **All Fresh Limes Are Gluten/Casein/Soy Free*

L

M

Liverwurst
  Jones Dairy Farm -
    Chub Braunschweiger Liverwurst (Bacon & Onion●, Light●,
      Mild & Creamy●, Original●)
    Chunk Braunschweiger (Light●, Original●)
    Sliced Braunschweiger (Cracker Size●, Sandwich Size●)
  Kayem - Old World Style
  Old Wisconsin - Spreadable Pate (Onion & Parsley, Original)
Lobster
  ... *All Fresh Shellfish Is Gluten/Casein/Soy Free (Non-Marinated, Unseasoned)*
Lunch Meat... see Deli Meat

M

Macaroni & Cheese
  Amy's - Rice Macaroni w/Non Dairy Cheeze **!**
  Ian's - Wheat Free Gluten Free Mac & No Cheese
  Namaste Foods▲ - Say Cheez
  Road's End Organics - Dairy Free (Organic Mac & Chreese Alfredo
    Style, Organic Penne & Chreese Cheddar Style)
Macaroons... see Cookies
Mackerel... see also Fish
  ... *All Fresh Fish Is Gluten/Casein/Soy Free (Non-Marinated, Unseasoned)*
  Bumble Bee - Jack Mackerel
  Chicken Of The Sea - All Mackerel Products
  Crown Prince - Jack Mackerel In Water
Mandarin Oranges
  ... *All Fresh Mandarin Oranges Are Gluten/Casein/Soy Free*
  Albertsons - Regular
  Del Monte - Canned/Jarred Fruit (All Varieties), Fruit Snack Cups
    (Metal, Plastic)
  Dole - All Fruits (Bowls *(Except Fruit Crisps)*, Canned, Dried, Frozen,
    Jars
  Great Value Brand (Wal-Mart) - Plastic Cups In Light Syrup

Hy-Vee -
Fruit Cups (Light Syrup, Orange Gel)
Light Syrup
Mandarin Oranges
Kroger Brand - Fruit (Canned, Cups)
Lowes Foods Brand - In Lite Syrup
Meijer Brand - Light Syrup
Native Forest - Organic Mandarins
Publix - In Gel, In Light Syrup
Spartan Brand - Canned, Fruit Cups
Trader Joe's - In Light Syrup
Wegmans Brand - Regular, Whole Segment In Light Syrup
Winn Dixie - Regular

Mango
  ... *All Fresh Mangos Are Gluten/Casein/Soy Free
C & W - All Plain Frozen Fruit
Del Monte - Canned/Jarred Fruit (All Varieties), Fruit Snack Cups
  (Metal, Plastic)
Gluty Free - Dried (Diced●, Organic●, Regular●, Unsulphured●)
Meijer Brand - Frozen (Chunks, Sliced)
Native Forest - Organic Mango Chunks
Nuts Online - Dried Mango (Diced●, Less Sugar Added●, Organic●,
  Regular●, Simply●)
Stop & Shop Brand - Frozen
Trader Joe's - Frozen (Mango Chunks, Sweet Mango Halves), Mango
  On Sticky Rice **!**
Winn Dixie - Frozen Mango Chunks
Woodstock Farms - Organic Frozen Mango
Maple Syrup... see Syrup
Maraschino Cherries... see Cherries
Margarine... see Spread and/or Butter
Marinades
A.I. - Classic, New York Steakhouse
Adolph's - Marinade In Minutes (Meat **!!**, Meat Sodium Free **!!**)

M Drew's -
    10 Minute Marinades
       Honey Dijon
       Italian Garlic Vinaigrette
       Kalamata Olive & Caper
       Poppy Seed
       Raspberry
       Roasted Garlic & Peppercorn
       Rosemary Balsamic
       Smoked Tomato
House Of Tsang - Sweet & Sour Marinade
Kroger Brand - Bourbon Peppercorn, Caribbean Jerk, Chipotle,
    Grill Time Southwest, Herb & Garlic, Tequila Lime
Lawry's -
    Baja Chipotle!!
    Caribbean Jerk!!
    Havana Garlic & Lime!!
    Herb & Garlic!!
    Louisiana Red Pepper!!
    Mesquite!!
    Tuscan Sun Dried Tomato!!
McCormick -
    Grill Mates
       Marinade Mix (Caribbean Citrus Seafood, Lemon Pepper Seafood)
       Marinade Packets (25% Less Sodium Montreal Steak, Baja
          Citrus, Chipotle Pepper, Mesquite, Mojito Lime, Montreal Steak,
          Peppercorn & Garlic, Southwest)
       Mexican Fiesta
Mr. Spice Organic - Sauce & Marinade (Ginger Stir Fry, Honey BBQ,
    Indian Curry, Sweet & Sour, Thai Peanut)
Sweet Baby Ray's - Steakhouse
Weber Grill Creations - Chipotle Marinade
Wild Thymes - Chili Ginger Honey, New Orleans Creole
Winn Dixie - Mojo

Wright's - Liquid Smoke (Hickory Seasoning, Mesquite)

Marmalade... see Jam/Jelly

Marshmallow Dip

    Marshmallow Fluff - Original, Raspberry, Strawberry

    Walden Farms - Calorie Free Marshmallow Dip

Marshmallows

    Albertsons - Mini, Regular

    AllerEnergy▲ - Marshmallow Creme, Regular

    Eylon - Natural Vanilla (Mini, Regular)

    Ginger Evans - Regular

    Great Value Brand (Wal-Mart) - Marshmallows (Flavored, Miniature, Regular)

    Hannaford Brand - Miniature, Regular

    Hy-Vee - Colored Marshmallows, Miniatures, Regular

    Jet-Puffed - FunMallows, Miniatures, Regular, StrawberryMallows, SwirlMallows

    Kroger Brand - Colored, Cream, Large, Miniature

    Marshmallow Fluff - Original, Raspberry, Strawberry

    Meijer Brand - Mini, Mini Flavored, Regular

    Publix - Regular

    Safeway Brand - Large, Mini

    Spartan Brand - Miniature, Regular

    Winn Dixie - Miniature, Regular

Masala

    Loyd Grossman - Tikka Masala

    Tasty Bite - Channa**!**

Mashed Potatoes

    Edward & Sons - Organic (Chreesy, Home Style, Roasted Garlic)

    Hy-Vee - Real Russet

    Meijer Brand - Instant

    Ore-Ida - Steam N' Mash (Cut Russet Potatoes, Cut Sweet Potatoes)

    Potato Buds▲ - Gluten Free 100% Real Potatoes

    Safeway Brand - Instant Regular

    Spartan Brand - Box Instant

MMayonnaise
> **Best Foods** - Canola
> **Hellmann's** - Canola
> **Simply Delicious** - Organic Mayonnaise (Garlic, Original)
> **Spectrum** - Canola (Regular), Squeeze Bottle Canola (Regular)
> **Walden Farms** - Mayo

Meals
> **Chi-Chi's** - Fiesta Plates Salsa Chicken
> **Dinty Moore** - Microwave Meals Rice w/Chicken
> **Ethnic Gourmet** - Chicken Korma, Eggplant Bhartha,
>   Vegetable Korma
> **Free Choice Foods▲** -
>> Chickpea & Potato Curry w/Roasted Peanuts●
>> Chili Non Carne●
>> Creole Red Bean Jambalaya Rice & Bean Mix●
>> Cuban Style Black Beans & Rice●
>> Hearty Vegetable Stew w/Buckwheat & Quinoa●
>> Middle Eastern Lentil Pilaf w/Cashews & Raisins●
>> Quinoa Lentil Pilaf w/Almonds & Raisins●
>> Quinoa Vegetable Pilaf●
>> Red Quinoa & Black Bean Salad Starter●
>> Taboule Style Quinoa Salad Starter●
>> Tuscan Style White Beans & Rice Mix●
>> Wild Rice Pilaf Mix w/Roasted Pecans●
> **Garden Of Eatin'** - Yellow Corn Taco Dinner Kit
> **Gluten Free Cafe** - Savory Chicken Pilaf●
> **Glutino▲** - Frozen Meals (Chicken Ranchero, Pomodoro Chicken)
> **Hormel** -
>> Compleats Santa Fe Style Chicken
>> Compleats Microwave 10 oz. Meals
>>> Chicken & Rice
>>> Santa Fe Chicken & Rice
> **Ian's** - Wheat Free Gluten Free (Mac & Meat Sauce, Mac &
>   No Cheese)

Kid's Kitchen - Beans & Wieners
Mixes From The Heartland▲ -
  Meal Mix
    BBQ Beef & Pasta●
    Beef Skillet●
    Cheeseburger Pie●
    Garden Meat Loaf●
    Green Chili●
    Mexican (Chicken N' Rice●, Style Casserole●)
    Sausage Casserole●
    Southwest Potato Casserole●
    Sweet Corn Casserole●
    Taco Rice Skillet●
    Tex Mex Meat Loaf●
    Texas (Bean Bake●, Goulash●)
My Own Meals - Beef Stew, Chicken & Black Bean, Mediterranean
  Chicken Meal, My Kind Of Chicken, Old World Stew
Namaste Foods▲ - Pasta Meals (Pasta Pisavera, Say Cheez, Taco)
Orgran▲ - Spaghetti In A Can
Pure Market Express▲ -
  Baked Macaroni & Cheese●
  Black Bean Burgers●
  Garlic Alfredo Pasta●
  Hemp Tabouli●
  Lasagna●
  Pad Thai Kit●
  Pad Thai●
  Portabella Herb Steak & Red Pepper Corn Salsa●
  Ravioli●
  Salmon & Hollandaise●
  Stir Fry Less Sauce●
  Tostadas●
  Walnut Pesto Pasta w/Shrimp Bites Kit●

Tambobamba - Mojo Bowls Peruvian Rice & Beans

Tasty Bite -
   Aloo Palak **!**
   Bombay Potatoes **!**
   Channa Masala **!**
   Chunky Chickpeas **!**
   Kerala Vegetables **!**
   Mushroom Takatak **!**
   Punjab Eggplant **!**
   Zesty Lentils and Peas **!**

Thai Kitchen - Microwave Rice Noodles & Sauce Original Pad Thai,
   Stir Fry Rice Noodles Original Pad Thai

Melon
   ... *All Fresh Melons Are Gluten/Casein/Soy Free*

Milk Alternative
   Better Than Milk - Rice Milk Powder (Original, Vanilla)
   Dari Free - Non Dairy Milk Alternative (Chocolate, Original)
   Good Karma - Original Ricemilk (Chocolate, Original,
      Unsweetened, Vanilla)
   Grainaissance -
      Almond Shake
      Amazing Mango
      Banana Appeal
      Chocolate (Almond, Cool Coconut)
      Gimme Green
      Go (Go Green, Hazelnuts)
      Oh So Original
      Rice Nog
      Tiger Chai
      Vanilla Pecan Pie
   Growing Naturals - Rice Milk (Creamy Vanilla, Silky Smooth
      Original, Velvety Chocolate)
   Living Harvest - Tempt Hempmilk (All Varieties)
   MimicCreme - Sugar Free Sweetened, Sweetened, Unsweetened

Pacific Natural Foods -
  Almond (Chocolate, Unsweetened Original, Unsweetened Vanilla)
  Hazelnut Chocolate
  Hemp Milk (Original, Vanilla)
  Low Fat Almond (Original, Vanilla)
  Original Hazelnut
  Ricemilk (Low Fat Plain, Low Fat Vanilla)
Pure Market Express▲ - Brazil Nut Milk●
Rice Dream - Refrigerated & Shelf Stable Rice Beverages (All
  Varieties)
Wegmans Brand - Organic Ricemilk (Original, Vanilla)
Millet
  Arrowhead Mills - Hulled Millet, Millet Flour
  Bob's Red Mill▲ - Flour, Grits/Meal, Hulled Millet
  Gluty Free - Organic●
  GoGo Rice - On The Go Cooked Rice Bowls (Exotic & Spicy Thai
    Peanut, Sweet & Mild Hawaiian)
Mints... see also Candy/Candy Bars
  Altoids -
    Curiously Strong Mints Large Tin
      Cinnamon
      Crème De Menthe
      Peppermint
      Wintergreen
  Eclipse - All Flavors
  St. Claire's Organics - Organic (Peppermint, Spearmint,
    Wintermint), Premium
  Vermints - Cafe Express, Chai, Cinnamint, Gingermint, Peppermint,
    Wintermint
Miso
  South River - Azuki Bean **! !**, Chick Pea **! !**, Garlic Red Pepper **! !**
Mixed Fruit
  *... *All Fresh Mixed Fruit Is Gluten/Casein/Soy Free*
  C & W - All Plain Frozen Fruit

Del Monte - Canned/Jarred Fruit (All Varieties), Fruit Snack Cups (Metal, Plastic)

Dole -
  All Fruits
    Bowls *(Except Fruit Crisps)*
    Canned
    Dried
    Frozen
    Jars *(Except Real Fruit Bites)*

Great Value Brand (Wal-Mart) -
  Canned (Fruit Cocktail, No Sugar Added Fruit Cocktail, Triple Cherry Fruit Mix In Natural Flavored Cherry, Tropical Fruit Salad In Light Syrup & Fruit Juices)
  Frozen Berry Medley
  Frozen Strawberries Peaches Pineapples & Mangoes
  Plastic Cups (Cherry Fruit Mix, No Sugar Added Mixed, Regular, Tropical)

Hannaford Brand - All (Canned, Frozen)

Hy-Vee - Fruit Cups (Mixed, Tropical), Mixed Fruit (Lite Chunk, Regular)

Kroger Value - All Fresh Fruit Canned

Lowes Foods Brand - Canned Fruit Cocktail (In Heavy Syrup, In Juice)

Meijer Brand - Frozen Tropical Fruit Blend, Mixed Fruit (Individually Quick Frozen, Regular)

Private Selections - All Plain Fruit Organic

Publix - Canned (Chunky Mixed Fruit In Heavy Syrup, Fruit Cocktail In Heavy Syrup, Lite Chunky Mixed Fruit In Pear Juice, Lite Fruit Cocktail In Pear Juice), Frozen

S&W - All Canned/Jarred Fruits

Spartan Brand - Frozen (Berry Medley, Mixed Fruit), Fruit Cups, In Lite Syrup

Stop & Shop Brand - Fruit Mix In Heavy Syrup, Mixed Fruit, Very Cherry Fruit Mix In Light Syrup

M

Trader Joe's - Frozen (Berry Medley, Fancy Berry Medley)

Wegmans Brand - Fruit Cocktail (In Heavy Syrup, In Pear Juice, Regular)

Winn Dixie -

Canned Chunky Mixed Fruit (Heavy Syrup, Light Syrup)

Frozen (Berry Medley, Mixed Fruit)

Fruit Cocktail (Heavy Syrup, Light Syrup)

Woodstock Farms - Organic Tropical Delight Mix, Tropical Fruit Mix

Mixed Vegetables

... *All Fresh Mixed Vegetables Are Gluten/Casein/Soy Free*

Albertsons - Plain Frozen Mixed Vegetables *(Except Edamame, Sweet Onion Rounds & Soybeans)*

Birds Eye - All Plain Mixed Vegetables *(Except Edamame & Soybeans)*

C & W - All Plain Mixed Vegetables *(Except Edamame & Soybeans)*

Del Monte - All Canned Mixed Vegetables *(Except Edamame & Soybeans)*

Freshlike - Frozen Plain Vegetables

Full Circle - Organic Frozen 4 Vegetable Blend

Grand Selections - Frozen Vegetables (Caribbean Blend, Normandy Blend, Riviera Blend)

Green Giant - Frozen Mixed Vegetables, Valley Fresh Steamers Mixed Vegetables

Hannaford Brand - All Frozen Mixed Vegetables *(Except Edamame & Soybeans)*

Hy-Vee -

Canned Mixed Vegetables

Frozen (California Mix, Country Trio, Fiesta Blend, Italian Blend, Mixed Vegetables, Oriental Vegetables, Stew Vegetables, Winter Mix)

Kirkland Signature - Frozen (Normandy Style Vegetable Blend, Stir Fry Vegetable Blend)

Kroger Brand - All Plain Vegetables (Canned, Frozen) *(Except Edamame & Soybeans)*

Lowes Foods Brand - Frozen (California Blend, Italian Blend, Mixed Vegetables, Vegetables For Soup)

Meijer Brand -
Canned Mixed
Frozen (California Style, Fiesta, Florentine Style, Italian, Mexican, Mixed Vegetables (Organic, Regular), Oriental, Parisian Style, Stew Mix, Stir Fry)

Mezzetta -
California Hot Mix
Chicago Style Italian Sandwich Mix (Hot Giardiniera, Mild Giardiniera)
Italian Mix Giardiniera
Mexi Mix Hot N' Spicy

Midwest Country Fare - Canned, Frozen (California Blend, Mixed Vegetables, Winter Mix)

Nuts Online - Simply Organic Mixed Veggies Freeze Dried●

O Organics - Frozen (California Style Vegetables, Mixed Vegetable Blend)

Pictsweet -
All Plain Frozen Mixed Vegetables *(Except Edamame & Soybeans)*
Baby California
Baby Mixed Vegetables
Cracked Pepper Seasoned (Okra & Squash, Seasoned Summer Vegetables)
Fiesta Chicken & Rice
Ground Peppercorn Seasoned Garden Vegetables
Seasoned (Corn & Black Beans, Blend)
Spring Vegetables

Publix - Canned, Frozen Blends (Alpine, California, Del Oro, Gumbo, Italian, Japanese, Mixed Vegetable, Oriental, Peas & Carrots, Roma, Soup Mix w/Tomatoes, Succotash)

S&W - All Canned Mixed Vegetables *(Except Edamame & Soybeans)*

Safeway Brand -
Frozen Blends (Asian Style, California Style, Santa Fe Style, Stew Vegetables, Stir Fry, Tuscan Style Vegetables, Winter Blend)
Mixed Vegetables (Canned, Frozen)

Spartan Brand -
  Canned Mixed Vegetables
  Frozen (Baby Corn Blend, Baby Pea Blend, California Vegetables,
     Fiesta Vegetables, Italian Vegetables, Mixed Vegetables, Oriental
     Vegetables, Pepper Stir Fry, Stew Mix Vegetables, Vegetables For
     Soup, Winter Blend)

Tasty Bite - Kerala Vegetables**!**

Trader Joe's - Frozen Harvest Hodgepodge**!!**, Frozen Organic
  Foursome

Wegmans Brand -
  Mix (Santa Fe, Southern, Spring)
  Mixed Vegetables (Canned, Frozen)

Winn Dixie - Canned No Salt Added, Frozen Mixed Vegetables
  (Organic, Regular)

Woodstock Farms - Organic Frozen Mixed Vegetables

Mochi

Grainaissance - Cashew Date, Chocolate Brownie, Original, Pizza,
  Raisin Cinnamon, Super Seed

Molasses

Brer Rabbit - Molasses (Blackstrap, Full Flavor, Mild)

Grandma's - Original, Robust

Oskri Organics - Regular

Mousse

Orgran▲ - Chocolate Mousse Mix

Muffins/Muffin Mix

1-2-3 Gluten Free▲ - Meredith's Marvelous Muffin/Quickbread Mix●

Andrea's Fine Foods▲ - Banana, Pumpkin

Augason Farms▲ - Gluten Free Muffin Mix Almond Poppy Seed●

Authentic Foods▲ - Blueberry Muffin Mix

Breads From Anna▲ - Pancake & Muffin Mix (Apple, Cranberry,
  Maple)

Breakaway Bakery▲ - Muffin Batter (Banana●, Coffee Cake●,
  Pumpkin●)

Canyon Bakehouse▲ - Cranberry Crunch Muffins

Cause You're Special▲ - Classic Muffin & Quickbread Mix, Lemon Poppy Seed Muffin Mix, Sweet Corn Muffin Mix

Ener-G▲ - Brown Rice English Muffins w/Flax, English Muffins

Flax4Life▲ - Flax Muffins Hawaiian Pineapple Coconut●

Flour Nut - Muffin Mix (Austin's Maple Cinnamon, Maple Walnut)

Foods By George▲ - Muffins (Cinnamon Currant English, English, No Rye)

Gifts Of Nature▲ - Mix (Basic, Cinnamon Spice, Cranberry Orange, Vanilla Poppy Seed)

Gluten-Free Creations▲ - Chocolate Zucchini●, Cranberry Orange Pecan●, Lemon Poppyseed●

Gluten-Free Essentials▲ - Lemon Poppy Seed Bread & Muffin Mix●, Spice Cake & Muffin Mix●

Heaven Mills▲ - Muffins (Blueberry●, Carrot●, Cinnamon●)

Hodgson Mill▲ - Gluten Free Apple Cinnamon Muffin Mix

Katz Gluten Free▲ - Honey Muffins●

King Arthur Flour▲ - Gluten Free Muffin Mix●

Kinnikinnick▲ -
Jumbo Muffins (Harvest Crunch, Lemon Poppy Seed)
Regular Muffins (Blueberry, Carrot)
Tapioca Rice English Muffin

Kneaded Specialties▲ - Banana Muffins●, Blueberry Streusel●, Double Chocolate Chip Banana●, Raspberry Swirl●, Vegan Pumpkin●, Vegan Very Berry●

Longevity Bean Muffins - Muffins (Almond, Banana, Blueberry, Cherry, Cinnamon, Cranberry, Original)

Marion's Smart Delights▲ - Cookie & Muffin Mix●

Mixes From The Heartland▲ - Streusel Muffin Mix (Apple Cinnamon●, Blueberry●, Cranberry●, Raspberry●, Spring●)

Mrs. Crimble's - Muffin Mix

Namaste Foods▲ - Muffin Mix, Sugar Free

Only Oats - Muffin Mix (Cinnamon Spice●, Decadent Chocolate●)

Orgran▲ - Muffin Mix (Chocolate, Lemon & Poppyseed)

Pamela's Products▲ - Cornbread and Muffin Mix

Really Great Food Company▲ - Muffin Mix (Apple Spice, Cornbread, English, Maple Raisin, Sweet, Vanilla)

Silly Yak Bakery - CFGF Muffins (Apple Sorghum●, Blueberry Sorghum●)

The Cravings Place▲ - Create Your Own

Udi's Gluten Free Foods▲ - Gluten Free Muffins (Blueberry, Double Chocolate, Lemon Streusel)

Whole Foods Market Gluten Free Bakehouse▲ - Morning Glory Muffins

Mushrooms

... *All Fresh Mushrooms Are Gluten/Casein/Soy Free*

Albertsons - Pieces & Stems (No Salt, Regular)

Birds Eye - All Plain Frozen Mushrooms

Eden Organic - Maitake Dried, Shiitake (Dried Sliced, Dried Whole)

Fungus Among Us - All Dried!

Great Value Brand (Wal-Mart) - Canned Mushrooms (Pieces & Stems, Sliced)

Green Giant - Canned Mushrooms (Pieces & Stems, Sliced, Whole)

Hannaford Brand - Stems & Pieces (No Salt, Regular)

Hy-Vee - Sliced, Stems & Pieces

Ka-Me - Stir Fry!, Straw!

Kroger Value - All Plain Canned Mushrooms

Lowes Foods Brand - Canned Sliced

Meijer Brand -
Canned (Sliced, Whole)
Canned Stems & Pieces (No Salt, Regular)

Midwest Country Fare - Mushrooms & Stems (No Salt Added, Regular)

Native Forest - Organic Pieces & Stems

Nuts Online - Simply Mushrooms Freeze Dried Vegetables●

Pennsylvania Dutchman - Chunky Style Portabella, Sliced, Stems & Pieces, Whole

Publix GreenWise Market - Portabella, Regular

Safeway Brand - Canned Button Sliced

M

Spartan Brand - Buttons Sliced, Canned (Buttons Whole, No Salt Added Pieces & Stems, Pieces & Stems)

Trader Joe's - Marinated w/Garlic

Wegmans Brand - Button, Pieces & Stems, Sliced

Woodstock Farms - Organic Frozen (Mixed, Shiitake)

Mustard

Albertsons - Dijon, Regular

Annie's Naturals - Organic (Dijon**!!**, Honey**!!**, Horseradish**!!**, Yellow**!!**)

Best Foods - Deli Brown, Honey

Bone Suckin' Sauce - Regular, Sweet & Hot

Di Lusso - Chipotle, Cranberry Honey, Deli Style, Dijon, Honey Sweet & Hot, Jalapeno

Dietz & Watson▲ - Champagne Dill●, Chipotle●, Jalapeno●, Spicy Brown●, Sweet & Hot●, Wasabi●, Whole Grain Dijon●, Yellow●

Eden Organic - Organic (Brown, Yellow)

Emeril's - Dijon, Kicked Up Horseradish, New York Deli Style, Smooth Honey

Fischer & Wieser - Smokey Mesquite, Sweet Heat

French's - Classic Yellow, Honey, Honey Dijon, Horseradish, Spicy Brown

Frontera - Chipotle Honey Mustard Grilling Sauce

Full Circle - Organic (Spicy Brown, Yellow)

Great Value Brand (Wal-Mart) - All Natural Yellow, Coarse Ground, Dijon, Honey, Southwest Spicy, Spicy Brown

Grey Poupon - Country Dijon, Deli, Dijon, Harvest Coarse Ground, Hearty Spicy Brown, Mild & Creamy, Savory Honey

Hannaford Brand - Dijon, Honey, Spicy Brown, Yellow

Heinz - Spicy Brown

Hellmann's - Deli Brown, Honey

Hy-Vee - Dijon, Honey, Regular, Spicy Brown

Jack Daniel's - Honey Dijon, Stone Ground Dijon

Kroger Brand - Honey, Horseradish, Regular, Spicy Brown

Kurtz - Honey Mustard, Spicy Brown, Yellow

noodles

M

Meijer Brand - Honey Squeeze, Hot & Spicy, Salad Squeeze, Spicy Brown Squeeze
Midwest Country Fare - Yellow

N

O Organics - Dijon
Publix - Classic Yellow, Deli Style, Dijon, Honey, Spicy Brown
Publix GreenWise Market - Creamy Yellow, Spicy Yellow, Tangy Dijon
Royal Food Products - Slender Select Fat Free
Ruth's Hemp Power - Hemp & Honey Mustard
Safeway Brand - Coarse Ground Dijon, Dijon, Honey Mustard, Spicy Brown, Stone Ground Horseradish, Sweet & Spicy, Yellow
Safeway Select - Stoneground w/Horseradish
Spartan Brand - Deli Style w/Horseradish, Dijon, Honey, Southwestern Sweet & Hot, Yellow
Taste Of Inspiration - Maine Maple!, Raspberry!, Roasted Garlic!
Texas Pete - Honey Mustard
Trader Joe's - Dijon!!, Organic Yellow!!
Wegmans Brand - Dijon (Honey, Traditional), Horseradish, Smooth & Tangy, Spicy Brown, Yellow
Winn Dixie - Dijon, Honey, Horseradish, Spicy Brown, Yellow
Woodstock Farms - Organic (Dijon, Stoneground, Yellow)

N

Nectars... see also Drinks/Juice
    Bionaturae - Organic (Apple, Apricot, Bilberry, Carrot Apple, Peach, Pear, Plum, Sicilian Lemon, Sour Cherry, Strawberry, Wildberry)
Noodles... see also Pasta
    A Taste Of Thai - Rice Noodles (Regular, Thin, Vermicelli Rice, Wide)
    Annie Chun's - Rice Noodles (Maifun Brown, Pad Thai Brown Rice)
    Grandma Ferdon's▲ - Chow Mein●
    Mixes From The Heartland▲ - Noodle Mix (Pesto●, Plain●, Spinach●)
    Seitenbacher - Gluten Free Rigatoni, Gourmet Noodles Gluten Free Golden Ribbon

N

Thai Kitchen -
    Rice Noodles (Stir Fry Rice Noodles, Thin Rice Noodles)
    Stir Fry Rice Noodle Meal Kit (Original Pad Thai)
    Take Out Boxes (Original Pad Thai)

Nut Beverages

Pacific Natural Foods -
    Almond (Chocolate, Unsweetened Original, Unsweetened Vanilla)
    Hazelnut Chocolate
    Low Fat Almond (Original, Vanilla)
    Original Hazelnut

Nut Butter... see Peanut Butter

Nutritional Supplements

Fruit Advantage - Dietary Supplement (All Varieties)

Meijer Brand - Gluco Burst Artic Cherry

MLO - Brown Rice Protein Powder

Pedialyte - Freezer Pops!, Hospital Sized Bottles!, One Liter
    Bottles!, Powder Packs!, Single Juice Boxes!

Salba - Ground Salba Seed●, Salba Seed Oil Gelcaps●, Salba Seed
    Oil●, Whole Salba Seed●

Nuts

Back To Nature -
    Sea Salt Roasted California Almonds
    Sea Salt Roasted Cashew Almond Pistachio Mix
    Sea Salt Roasted Jumbo Cashews
    Tuscan Herb Roasts
    Unroasted Unsalted California Almonds
    Unroasted Unsalted Walnuts

Blue Diamond -
    Almonds
        100 Calorie Packs (Cinnamon Brown Sugar, Dark Chocolate,
            Lightly Salted, Sea Salt, Whole Natural)
        Bold Flavors (Blazin' Buffalo Wing, Carolina Barbeque,
            Chocolate Mint, Cinnamon Brown Sugar, No Salt, Sea Salt)
        Cooking & Baking (Sliced, Slivered, Whole)

Oven Roasted (Dark Chocolate, Honey Roasted)
Traditional Flavors (Honey Roasted, Lightly Salted, Roasted
Salted, Whole Natural)

Don Enrique's - Chile Pistachio**!**

Emerald - Dry Roasted Lightly Salted Peanuts, On The Go Canisters
(Cashews Halves & Pieces, Cocktail Peanuts, Deluxe Mix Nuts,
Whole Cashews)

FritoLay - Honey Roasted Peanuts**!!**, Salted Cashews**!!**, Salted
Peanuts**!!**, Whole Cashews**!!**

Gluty Free -
Almonds
Blanched Whole●
No Shell Raw Organic●
Raw (In Shell●, No Shell●)
Salted●
Sliced (Natural●, Regular●)
Slivered●
Unsalted●
Blanched Hazelnuts/Filberts●
Brazil Nuts
In Shell●
No Shell Raw Organic●
Raw (No Shell●, Pieces●)
Salted●
Unsalted●
Cashews
Raw●
Raw Organic●
Raw Organic Pieces●
Raw Pieces●
Salted●
Unsalted●
Cilantro Lime Pistachios & Pepitas●

N

Hazelnuts
  In Shell●
  No Shell Raw●
  Raw Organic No Shell●
  Salted●
  Unsalted●
Macadamia Nuts
  Raw●
  Raw Organic●
  Raw Pieces●
  Salted●
  Unsalted●
Mixed Nuts In Shell●
Peanuts
  Blanched●
  Cajun Salted In Shell●
  In Shell Salted●
  No Shell Salted Organic●
  No Shell Salted●
  Raw (In Shell●, Redskin●, Spanish●)
  Raw Organic (In Shell●, No Shell●)
  Roasted (In Shell●, In Shell Organic●)
  Salted Jumbo No Shell●
  Unsalted (Jumbo No Shell●, No Shell●, Organic No Shell●)
  Wild Organic Jungle●
Pecans
  Hard Shell●
  No Shell Raw Organic●
  Paper Shell●
  Raw (No Shell●, Pieces●)
  Salted●
  Unsalted●
Pignolia Nuts
  In Shell Raw●
  Mediterranean●

No Shell Raw Organic●
Pistachios
   In Shell Salted Organic●
   In Shell Salted●
   No Shell Raw Organic●
   No Shell Salted●
   Raw (In Shell●, No Shell●)
   Red●
   Siirt Turkish●
   Sweet & Spicy Chipotle●
   Unsalted (In Shell●, No Shell●)
   Unsalted Organic In Shell●)
Walnuts
   In Shell●
   Raw (Halves No Shell●, No Shell●, Pieces●)
   Raw Organic (No Shell●, Pieces●)
   Salted●
   Unsalted●
Just Almonds - All Varieties
Katy Sweet▲ - Nuts (Glazed Pecans●, Holy Mole●, Peppered
   Pecans●, Sugar & Spice Pecans●)
Kirkland Signature - Pecans, Pistachios, Walnuts
Kroger Brand -
   All Baking Varieties
   Cashews (Lightly Salted, Salted)
   Mixed (Deluxe, Lightly Salted, Natural, Unsalted w/Peanuts)
   Peanuts (Honey Roasted, In Shell (Raw, Salted, Unsalted), Lightly
      Salted, Salted, Salted Spanish, Unsalted)
   Salted Pistachios
Mareblu Naturals▲ -
   Crunch Bags (Almond●, Cashew●, Cashew Coconut●,
      CranMango Cashew●, Pecan Cinnamon●, Pecan Cranberry
      Cinnamon●)
   Dry Roasted Nuts (Almonds●, Cashews●, Pistachios●)
   Glazed Whole Nuts Pecans w/Cranberry & Cinnamon●

N

Trail Mix Crunch Bags (Blueberry Pomegranate●, Cranberry Pomegranate●, Cranblueberry●, Cranstrawberry●, Pecan●, Pistachio●)

Meijer Brand -

Almonds (Blanched Sliced, Blanched Slivered, Natural Sliced, Slivered, Whole)

Blanched (Regular, Slightly Salted)

Cashews (Halves w/Pieces, Halves w/Pieces Lightly Salted, Whole)

Dry Roasted (Lightly Salted, Regular, Unsalted)

Honey Roasted, Mixed (Deluxe, Lightly Salted, Regular)

Nut Topping

Peanuts

Pecan (Chips, Halves)

Pine

Spanish

Walnuts (Black, Chips, Halves & Pieces)

Nut Harvest - Lightly Roasted Almonds **! !**, Sea Salted Whole Cashews **! !**

Nuts Online -

Almonds (Organic (Blanched●, Dry Roasted Salted●, Natural Sliced●, Natural Slivered●, Raw No Shell●, Roasted Unsalted●), Raw (In Shell●, No Shell●), Roasted (Salted●, Unsalted●), Sliced Natural●, Sliced●, Slivered●, Sprouted●, Whole Blanched●)

Brazil Nuts (In Shell●, No Shell●, Organic Raw No Shell●, Pieces●, Roasted (Salted●, Unsalted●)

Cashews (Organic (Pieces●, Raw●), Pieces●, Raw●, Roasted (Salted●, Unsalted●), Salted Organic Dry Roasted●, Supreme Raw●, Supreme Roasted (Salted●, Unsalted●), Thai Coconut Curry●),

Cilantro Lime Pistachios & Pepitas●

Hazelnuts (Blanched●, Organic Raw No Shell●)

Hazelnuts/Filberts (In Shell●, Raw No Shell●, Roasted (Salted●, Unsalted●))

Macadamia Nuts (In Shell●, Organic●, Pieces●, Raw●, Roasted (Salted●, Unsalted●))

Mixed Nuts In Shell●

Peanuts (Blanched●, Cajun Roasted Salted In Shell●, In Shell (Jumbo Raw●, Jumbo Roasted●), Organic Dry Roasted (Salted No Shell●, Unsalted No Shell●), Organic Raw (In Shell●, No Shell●), Organic Roasted (In Shell●, Salted In Shell●), Organic Wild Jungle●, Raw Redskin●, Raw Spanish●, Roasted Salted In Shell●, Roasted Super Jumbo Virginia (Salted No Shell●, Unsalted No Shell●), Roasted Virginia (Salted No Shell●, Unsalted No Shell●), Super Jumbo Blanched●)

Pecans (Georgia Raw No Shell●, Hard Shell●, Organic (Pieces●, Raw No Shell●), Paper Shell●, Pieces●, Roasted (Salted●, Unsalted●))

Pine Nuts (Mediterranean Pignolias●, Organic Raw No Shell●, Pignolias●, Raw In Shell●)

Pink Salt & Cracked Pepper Mixed Nuts & Seeds●

Pistachios (Chili Lime●, Dry Roasted (Salted●, Unsalted●), Organic Raw No Shell●, Raw (In Shell●, No Shell●), Red●, Roasted (Salted In Shell●, Salted No Shell●, Unsalted In Shell●, Unsalted No Shell●), Roasted Organic (Salted In Shell●, Unsalted In Shell●), Sweet & Spicy Chipotle●, Turkish Siirt●)

Raw Cacao Almonds & Raisins●

Raw Cacao Brazil Nuts & Mulberries●

Rosemary Garlic Pistachios & Almonds●

Sesame Teriyaki Almonds & Cashews●

Walnuts (Black●, English (Halves Raw No Shell●, In Shell, Raw No Shell●), Maple Mesquite Pod●, Organic (Pieces●, Raw No Shell●), Pieces●, Roasted Salted●)

White Chocolate Chip Almonds Cashews & Cacao Nibs●

Planters -

Almonds Dry Roasted

Baking

Almond (Slices, Slivers, Whole)

Black Walnuts

N

    Pecan (Chips, Halves, Pieces)
    Walnut Pieces
    Cashews (Halves & Pieces, Halves & Pieces Lightly Salted, Jumbo,
        Whole (Honey Roasted, Lightly Salted, Regular))
    Flavor Grove
        Almonds (Chili Lime, Cracked Pepper w/Onion & Garlic, Sea
            Salt & Olive Oil)
        Cashews (Chipotle, Sea Salt & Cracked Pepper)
    Mixed (Cashew Lovers, Deluxe (Lightly Salted, Regular), Honey
        Roasted, Lightly Salted, Macadamia Lovers, Pecan Lovers,
        Pistachio Lovers, Regular, Select (Cashews Almonds & Pecans,
        Macadamia Cashew & Almonds), Unsalted)
    Nut Rition (Almonds, Antioxidant, Heart Healthy, South Beach
        Diet Recommended)
    Peanuts (Cocktail (Honey Roasted, Lightly Salted, Regular,
        Unsalted), Dry Roasted (Honey Roasted, Lightly Salted w/Sea
        Salt, Unsalted, w/Sea Salt), Kettle Roasted, Redskin Spanish)
Private Selections - Cashews, Macadamia, Mixed, Pecans, Select
    Brand Mixed, Shell Pistachios
Safeway Brand - Baking (Almonds, Pecan, Walnut)
Shiloh Farms - Whole Almonds
Spartan Brand - Peanuts Dry Roasted (Lightly Salted, No Salt,
    Regular)
Sunkist - Pistachios (Dry Roasted, Kernels)
Trader Joe's - Cinnamon Almonds
True North - Clusters (Almond!!, Almond Pecan Cashew!!, Pecan
    Almond Peanut!!), Pistachios/Walnuts/Pecans/Almonds!!
Wegmans Brand -
    Dry Roasted (Macadamias Salted, Seasoned Sunflower Kernels)
    Peanuts (Salted In Shell, Unsalted In Shell)
    Peanuts Dry Roasted (Lightly Salted, Seasoned, Unsalted)
    Pine Nuts Italian Classics
Winn & Lovett - Coconut Almonds

N

O

Woodstock Farms -
Almonds (Non Pareil Supreme, Roasted & No Salt, Roasted & Salt, Thick Slice)
Brazil
Cashew (Large Whole, Large Whole Roasted & Salted)
Deluxe Mixed Nuts Roasted & Salted
Extra Fancy Mixed Nuts Roasted & Salted
Hazelnut Filberts
Honey Roasted Peanuts
Organic Brazil
Organic Nuts (Brazil, Cashew (Large Whole, Large Whole Roasted & Salted, Pieces), Pecan Halves, Pine, Pistachios (No Salt, Roasted & Salt), Walnuts Halves & Pieces)
Pecan Halves
Pine
Walnuts Halves & Pieces

O

Oatmeal
GlutenFreeda▲ - Instant Oatmeal (Apple Cinnamon w/Flax, Banana Maple w/Flax, Maple Raisin w/Flax, Natural)
PrOatina Gluten Free - Gluten Free Oat Bran●, Gluten Free Old Fashioned Oatmeal●
Pure Market Express▲ - French Toast Oatmeal●
Oats
Augason Farms▲ - Gluten Free Regular Rolled Oats●
Bob's Red Mill▲ - Gluten Free Quick Rolled Oats, Gluten Free Rolled Oats, Gluten Free Steel Cut Oats
Chateau Cream Hill Estates - Lara's Rolled Oats●
Gifts Of Nature▲ - Old Fashioned Rolled Oats, Whole Oat Groats
Gluten Free Oats▲ - Old Fashioned Rolled Oats●
Gluty Free - Steel Cut●

Montana Monster Munchies - Whole Grain (Quick Oats●,
Rolled Oats)

Montina▲ - Rolled Oats●

Only Oats - Oat Flakes (Quick●, Regular●), Steel Cut Oat Pearls●

Tom Sawyer▲ - Gluten Free

Oil

Albertsons - Canola Oil, Olive Oil, Peanut

Annie's Naturals -
Olive Oil (Basil!!, Dipping!!, Roasted Pepper!!)
Olive Oil Extra Virgin Roasted Garlic!!

Bakers & Chefs - 100% Pure Peanut Oil

Bertolli - All Olive Oils

Bionaturae - Organic Extra Virgin Olive Oil

Carapelli - Olive Oil

Consorzio - Olive Oil (Basil, Cilantro, Roasted Garlic, Roasted
Pepper, Rosemary)

Crisco -
Canola w/Omega 3 DHA
Olive (100% Extra Virgin, Light Tasting, Pure)
Pure (Canola, Corn, Peanut)

Eden Organic -
Olive Oil Spanish Extra Virgin
Organic (Hot Pepper Sesame Oil, Safflower Oil, Sesame Oil
Extra Virgin)
Toasted Sesame Oil

Filippo Berio - Extra Virgin Olive

Foods Alive - Organic (Hemp, High Lignan Golden Flax)

Full Circle - Organic Extra Virgin Olive Oil

Fungus Among Us - Certified Organic Olive Infused w/White
Truffle!

Grand Selections - 100% Pure & Natural Olive Oil, Extra Virgin Olive
Oil, Olive Oil Lemon

Great Value Brand (Wal-Mart) - Olive Oil (Extra Light, Extra Virgin),
Pure Olive Oil

Hannaford Brand - Canola Oil, Corn Oil, Olive (Extra Virgin, Extra Virgin Imported, Light Pure)

Hollywood - Enriched (Canola, Expeller Pressing Safflower, Gold Peanut)

House Of Tsang - Oil (Hot Chili Sesame, Mongolian Fire, Sesame, Wok)

Hy-Vee - 100% Pure Oil (Canola, Corn)

Ka-Me - Pure Sesame!

Kirkland Signature - Canola, Peanut, Pure Olive

Kroger Brand - Canola, Corn, Olive, Peanut, Sunflower

Lee Kum Kee - Oil Pure Sesame

Living Harvest - Hemp Oil

Manitoba Harvest - Hemp Seed Oil (Organic, Regular)

Mazola - Canola Oil, Corn Oil, Corn Oil Plus, Olive Oil (Extra Virgin, Pure)

Meijer Brand -
  Canola
  Corn
  Oil Olive Infused (Garlic & Basil Italian, Roasted Garlic Italian, Spicy red Pepper Italian)
  Olive (100% Pure Italian Classic, Extra Virgin (Italian Classic, Regular), Italian Select Premium Extra Virgin, Milder Tasting, Regular)
  Peanut
  Sunflower

Member's Mark - 100% Pure Olive Oil

Mezzetta - Extra Virgin Olive Oil

Newman's Own Organics - Extra Virgin Olive Oil

Nutiva - Organic (Extra Virgin Coconut Oil, Hemp Oil)

Nuts Online - Organic Hemp Oil●

O Organics - Extra Virgin Olive

OmegaMontana - Virgin Camelina Oil●

Peter Paul - Virgin Coconut

Phildesco - Virgin Coconut

Planters - Peanut
Private Selections - All Varieties *(Except Vegetable Oil)*
Publix - Canola, Corn, Olive, Peanut
Ruth's Hemp Power - Hemp
Safeway Brand - Canola, Peanut
Safeway Select - Olive Oil (Extra Light, Extra Virgin, Regular)
Santa Barbara Olive Co. - Chili, Cuvee 60/40 Blend, Geno's Garlic
    Nectar, Olive Oil (Chili Fajita, Extra Virgin), Rosemary
Smart Balance - Olive Oil (Extra Virgin, Light Taste, Pure)
Spartan Brand - Canola, Corn, Olive (Extra Virgin, Pure)
Star - Extra Light Olive, Extra Virgin Garlic Olive, Extra Virgin Olive,
    Originale Garlic Olive, Originale Olive, Special Reserve Organic
    Extra Virgin Olive
Stop & Shop Brand - Canola, Extra Light Olive, Pure Olive
Tassos - Olive Oil (Extra Virgin, Fine, Organic Extra, Peza Crete Extra)
Toscano - Extra Virgin Olive
Tropical Traditions - Organic Virgin Palm Oil
Wegmans Brand -
    Basting w/Garlic & Herbs
    Canola
    Corn
    Extra Virgin (Black Truffle, Campania Style, Olive, Sicilian Lemon,
        Sicilian Style, Tuscany Style)
    Grapeseed
    Mild Olive
    Organic (Extra Virgin, Sunflower Oil)
    Organic High Oleic Sunflower Oil
    Peanut
    Pumpkin Seed
    Pure Olive
Winn & Lovett - Olive Oil (Balsamic, Extra Virgin, Garlic,
    Mediterranean, Roasted Garlic, Zesty Italian)
Winn Dixie - Canola, Corn, Olive, Peanut

Okra

... *All Fresh Okra Is Gluten/Casein/Soy Free*

Meijer Brand - Frozen (Chopped, Whole)

Mezzetta - Hors D'Oeuvres Gourmet, Marinated Hot

Pictsweet -

All Plain Frozen Okra

Cracked Pepper Seasoned Okra & Squash

Publix - Frozen (Cut, Whole Baby)

Safeway Brand - Frozen

Spartan Brand - Cut, Whole

Trappey's - Cocktail Okra

Winn Dixie - Frozen (Cut, Diced, Whole)

Olive Oil... see Oil

Olives

B&G - Black, Green

Di Lusso - Green Ionian, Mediterranean Mixed, Pitted Kalamata

Great Value Brand (Wal-Mart) - California Chopped Ripe, California
Medium Pitted Ripe, California Sliced Ripe, Jumbo Pitted Ripe,
Large Pitted Ripe, Minced Pimento Stuffed Manzanilla, Sliced
Salad

Hannaford Brand - Pitted Ripe (Extra Large, Large, Medium, Small),
Sliced Ripe, Sliced Salad, Stuffed (Manzanilla, Queen)

Hy-Vee - Chopped Ripe, Manzanilla Olives, Medium Ripe Black,
Queen, Ripe Black (Jumbo, Large), Sliced (Ripe Black, Salad)

Krinos - Imported (Black, Green Cracked, Kalamata Olives)

Kroger Brand - Green Pimento Stuffed, Not Stuffed (Black, Green)

Kurtz - Salad Olives, Small Pitted Black Olives, Spanish Olives

Meijer Brand -

Manzanilla Stuffed (Placed, Thrown, Tree)

Queen (Stuffed Placed, Whole Thrown)

Ripe (Large, Medium, Pitted Jumbo, Pitted Small, Sliced)

Salad

Salad Sliced

Mezzetta -
- Calamata Greek
- Castelvetrano Whole Green
- Colossal Spiced Sicilian
- Fancy Colossal Green
- Garlic (Queen, Regular)
- Home Style Cured Pitted
- Jalapeno (Garlic, Garlic Queen w/Minced Pimento)
- Marinated Cracked Deli
- Mediterranean Nicoise Style
- Napa Valley Bistro (Applewood Smoked Olives, Garlic Stuffed Olives, Italian Olive Antipasto, Jalapeno Stuffed Olives, Olive Medley, Pitted Kalamata Olives, Roasted Garlic Stuffed Olives)
- Organics (Pitted Kalamata, Whole Kalamata)
- Pitted Calamata
- Salad
- Sliced Calamata
- Spanish (Colossal Queen w/Minced Pimento, Manzanilla w/ Minced Pimento, Queen Martini In Dry Vermouth)
- Stuffed Olives (Anchovy, Garlic, Jalapeno)

Midwest Country Fare - Large Ripe Black, Sliced Ripe Black

Peloponnese - Antipasto Party, Country Gourmet Mixed, Cracked Gourmet Green, Halved Kalamata Gourmet Black, Ionian Gourmet Green, Kalamata Olive Spread, Pitted Kalamata Gourmet Black

Private Selections - All Varieties

Publix - Colossal, Green, Large, Ripe, Small

Safeway Brand - All Varieties

Santa Barbara Olive Co. - Canned (#10, Green, Large, Medium), Sun Dried (Black, Organic California, Pitted Black)

Spartan Brand - Manzanilla, Queen, Ripe Pitted Olives (Jumbo, Large, Medium, Sliced Salad, Small), Sliced Spanish Salad

Tassos - Black Olives In Extra Virgin Olive Oil & Red Wine, Blonde Olives In Extra Virgin Olive Oil & Red Wine, Evian Olives In Sea

O

Salt Brine, Kalamata In Tassos Extra Virgin Olive Oil & Red Wine, Stuffed Almond In Sea Salt Brine

Trader Joe's - Colossal Olives Stuffed w/(Garlic Cloves, Jalapeño Peppers)

Wegmans Brand -
Greek Mix
Kalamata (Pitted, Whole)
Pitted Ripe (Colossal, Extra Large, Medium)
Sliced Ripe
Spanish (Manzanilla, Queen, Salad)
Stuffed w/(Almonds, Garlic, Red Peppers)

Winn Dixie - Green (All Varieties), Ripe (All Varieties)

Onions

... *All Fresh Onions Are Gluten/Casein/Soy Free*

Birds Eye - All Plain Frozen Vegetables

C & W - All Plain Frozen Vegetables

Meijer Brand - Frozen Chopped

Mezzetta - Hors D'Oeuvres Onions, Imported Cocktail Onions

Ore-Ida - Chopped Onions

Publix - Frozen Diced

Trader Joe's - Frozen Peeled & Ready To Use Pearl Onions

Wegmans Brand - Whole Onions In Brine

Winn Dixie - Frozen Pearl Onions

Orange Juice... see Drinks/Juice

Oranges

... *All Fresh Oranges Are Gluten/Casein/Soy Free*

Nuts Online - Organic Dried Oranges●

Sunkist

Oyster Sauce

Choy Sun - Oyster Flavored Sauce (Glass Bottles & Metal Cans)

Panda Brand - Lo Mein Oyster Flavored Sauce, Oyster Flavored Sauce *(Green Label Only)*

Wok Mei - All Natural Oyster Flavored

O Oysters

... *All Fresh Seafood Is Gluten/Casein/Soy Free

P

Bumble Bee - Fancy Smoked, Fancy Whole

Chicken Of The Sea - Smoked In Oil, Whole

Crown Prince - Fancy Whole Smoked In Cottonseed Oil, Natural (Smoked Oysters In Olive Oil, Whole Boiled In Water)

Great Value Brand (Wal-Mart) - Canned Smoked Oysters

Ocean Prince - Fancy Whole Smoked In Cottonseed Oil, Whole Boiled

P

Pancakes/Pancake Mix & Waffles/Waffle Mix

1-2-3 Gluten Free▲ - Allie's Awesome Buckwheat Pancake Mix●

Andrea's Fine Foods▲ - Pancake Mix

Arnel's Originals - Pancake Mix

Arrowhead Mills - Gluten Free Pancake & Waffle Mix

Authentic Foods▲ - Pancake & Baking Mix

Better Batter - Pancake & Biscuit Mix

Bob's Red Mill▲ - Gluten Free Pancake Mix

Breads From Anna▲ - Pancake & Muffin Mix (Apple, Cranberry, Maple)

Breakaway Bakery▲ - Pancake Batter●

Cause You're Special▲ - Hearty Pancake & Waffle Mix

Cherrybrook Kitchen - Gluten Free Pancake Mix *(Box Must Say Gluten Free)*

El Peto▲ - Waffles Belgium Milk Free Corn Free

Full Circle - Gluten Free Waffle & Pancake Mix

Gluten Free Mama▲ - Mama's Pancake Mix●

Gluten Free Sensations▲ - Pancake & Waffle Mix

Gluten-Free Creations▲ - Buckwheat Pancake Mix●, Mighty Mesquite Pancake Mix●

Gluten-Free Essentials▲ - Pancake & Waffle Mix●

Grandma Ferdon's▲ - Pancake/Waffle Mix●

parmesan cheese

P

Hodgson Mill▲ - Gluten Free Pancake & Waffle Mix w/Flaxseed
Hol Grain▲ - Pancake & Waffle Mix●
King Arthur Flour▲ - Gluten Free Pancake Mix●
Kinnikinnick▲ - Homestyle Waffles (Cinnamon & Brown Sugar, Original)
Laurel's Sweet Treats▲ - Bulk Pancake Mix, Pancake & Waffle Mix
Linda's Gourmet Latkes - Potato Pancake Latkes
Mixes From The Heartland▲ - Pancake Mix (Apple Cinnamon●, Blueberry●, Country●, Cranberry●)
Mrs. Crimble's - Pancake Mix
Namaste Foods▲ - Waffle & Pancake Mix
Nuts Online - Gluten Free Pancake Mix●
Only Oats - Whole Oat Pancake Mix●
Orgran▲ -
   Apple & Cinnamon Pancake Mix
   Buckwheat Pancake Mix
Pure Market Express▲ - Blueberry Pancake Dippers w/Honey●
Really Great Food Company▲ - Pancake Mix (Brown Rice Flour, Classic, Jumbo Classic)
Ruby Range - Southwest Pancakes Gluten Free Baking Mix●
Simply Organic▲ - Pancake & Waffle Mix
The Cravings Place▲ - All Purpose

Papaya

*... *All Fresh Papaya Is Gluten/Casein/Soy Free*

Gluty Free - Dried (Chunks●, Diced●, Natural●, Regular●)
Native Forest - Organic Papaya Chunks
Nuts Online - Dried Papaya (Chunks●, Diced●, Dried●, Natural●, Organic●)
Woodstock Farms - Organic Frozen Papaya Chunks, Spears Low Sugar Unsulphured

Paprika... see Seasonings
Parmesan Cheese... see Cheese

P Pasta

Allegaroo - Chili Mac, Spaghetti, Spyglass Noodles

Ancient Harvest Quinoa - Elbows, Garden Pagodas, Linguine, Rotelle, Shells, Spaghetti, Veggie Curls

Andean Dream - Quinoa (Fusilli, Macaroni, Spaghetti)

Annie Chun's - Rice Noodles (Maifun Brown, Pad Thai Brown Rice)

Bi-Aglut - Bucatini, Ditalini, Fusilli, Gemmini, Maccheroncini, Micron, Penne, Pipe, Sedani, Spaghetti, Stelline

Conte's Pasta - Gnocchi●, Pierogies Potato Onion●

Cornito - Elbow Macaroni, Mystic Flames Noodles, Rainbow Rotini, Rigatoni (Penne), Rotini, Sea Waves (Mini Lasagna), Spaghetti

DeBoles -
  Corn Pasta (Elbow Style●, Spaghetti●)
  Gluten Free Multi Grain (Penne●, Spaghetti●)
  Gluten Free Rice (Angel Hair & Golden Flax●, Spirals & Golden Flax●)
  Rice Pasta (Angel Hair●, Fettucini●, Lasagna●, Penne●, Spaghetti●, Spirals●)

Eden Organic - Bifun, Kuzu, Mung Bean

Ener-G▲ - White Rice (Lasagna, Macaroni, Small Shells, Spaghetti, Vermicelli)

Gillian's Foods▲ - Fetuccini, Fusilli, Penne, Spaghetti

Glutano▲ - Fusilli, Penne, Spaghetti

Grandma Ferdon's▲ - Brown Rice (Chow Mein Noodles●, Elbows●, Fettuccini●, Lasagna●, Spaghetti●)

Hodgson Mill▲ - Gluten Free Brown Rice (Angel Hair, Elbow, Lasagna, Linguine, Penne, Spaghetti)

Jovial▲ - Brown Rice (Capellini ●, Caserecce ●, Fusilli ●, Penne Rigate ●, Spaghetti ●)

Le Veneziane - Anellini, Ditalini, Eliche, Fettucce, Penne, Pipe Rigate, Rigatoni, Spaghetti

Lundberg▲ - Organic Brown Rice Pasta (Elbow, Penne, Rotini, Spaghetti)

Mrs. Leeper's - Corn Pasta (Elbows, Rotelli, Spaghetti, Vegetable

Radiatore), Rice Pasta (Alphabets, Elbows, Kids Shapes, Penne, Spaghetti, Vegetable Twists)

Namaste Foods▲ - Pasta Meals (Pasta Pisavera, Say Cheez, Taco)

Notta Pasta - Fettuccine, Linguine, Spaghetti, Vermicelli

Orgran▲ -

Buontempo Rice Pasta (Penne, Shells, Spirals)

Canned (Spaghetti In Tomato Sauce, Spirals In Tomato Sauce)

Corn & Spinach Rigati

Corn & Vegetable Pasta Shells

Corn Pasta Spirals

Essential Fibre (Penne, Spirals)

Garlic & Parsley Rice Pasta Shells

Italian Style Spaghetti

Pasta & Sauce Tomato Basil

Rice & Corn (Herb Pasta, Macaroni, Mini Lasagne Sheets, Penne, Risoni Garlic Herb, Spaghetti, Spirals, Tortelli, Vegetable Animal Shapes, Vegetable Corkscrews)

Rice & Millet Spirals

Rice Pasta Spirals

Super Grains Multigrain Pasta (w/Amaranth, w/Quinoa)

Tomato & Basil Corn Pasta

Vegetable Rice (Penne, Spirals)

Pastariso▲ -

All Natural Rice (Brown Rice Elbows●, Brown Rice Penne●, Brown Rice Rotini●, Brown Rice Spaghetti●)

Organic Brown Rice (Angel Hair●, Elbows●, Fettuccine●, Lasagna●, Linguine●, Penne●, Rotini●, Spaghetti●, Spinach Spaghetti●, Vegetable Rotini●, Vermicelli●)

Rizopia -

Brown Rice (Elbows, Fettuccine, Fusilli, Lasagne, Penne, Shells, Spaghetti, Spirals)

Organic Brown Rice (Elbows, Fantasia, Fettuccine, Fusilli, Penne, Spaghetti)

Organic Wild Rice (Elbows, Fusilli, Penne, Radiatore, Shells, Spaghetti)

P

    Spinach Brown Rice Spaghetti
    Vegetable Brown Rice Fusilli
    White Rice Spaghetti
Sam Mills▲ - Corn Pasta (Conchiliette, Cornetti Rigati, Fusilli, Lasagna, Penne Rigate, Rigatoni, Tubetti Rigati)
Schar▲ - Anellini, Fusilli, Multigrain Penne Rigate, Penne, Spaghetti, Tagliatelle
Seitenbacher - Gluten Free Rigatoni, Gourmet Noodles Gluten Free Golden Ribbon
Tinkyada▲ -
    Brown Rice (Elbows, Fettuccini, Fusilli, Grand Shells, Lasagne, Little Dreams, Penne, Shells, Spaghetti, Spinach Spaghetti, Spirals, Vegetable Spirals)
    Organic Brown Rice (Elbows, Lasagne, Penne, Spaghetti, Spirals)
    White Rice Spaghetti
Westbrae - Corn Angel Hair Pasta
Pasta Sauce... see Sauces
Pastrami
    Boar's Head - All Varieties
    Carl Buddig - Deli Cuts, Extra Thin Original, Original
    Castle Wood Reserve - Deli Meat Turkey Pastrami
    Dietz & Watson▲ - Pastrami Brisket●, Spiced Beef Pastrami●
    Eckrich - Deli Meat Pastrami
    Hormel - Bread Ready
    Hy-Vee - Thin Sliced
    Jennie-O Turkey Store - Refrigerated Dark Turkey
    Kayem - Extra Lean Black, New England Red, New York Style Black
Pastry Mix
    Mrs. Crimble's - Pastry Mix
    Orgran▲ - All Purpose
Pate
    Kootenay Kitchen - Vege Pate (Curry, Herb, Jalapeno)
    Old Wisconsin - Spreadable Pate (Onion & Parsley, Original)

Tartex -
> Cremisso (Champignon, Chardonnay Cote D'or, Delicacy, Exquisite, Green Pepper, Herbs, Horseradish Apple, Hungarian, Mediterrana, Mexicana, Olivera, Peppers Chili, Pesto, Pomodoro d'Italia, Provence Herbs, Ratatouille, Shiitake, Tomato Basil, Truffle Champagne, Zucchini Curry)
> Organic Pate In Tubes (Classic, Green Olive, Herb & Garlic, Herbs, Mushroom, Roasted Onion & Pink Peppercorn)
> Pate Creme (Basil, Italian Olives, Rocket & Mustard, Sundried Tomato & VanDouvan)

Pea Pods... see also Peas
> ... *All Fresh Pea Pods Are Gluten/Casein/Soy Free*
> **Meijer Brand -** Frozen Chinese

Peaches
> ... *All Fresh Peaches Are Gluten/Casein/Soy Free*
> **Albertsons -** All Canned Peaches, Frozen
> **C & W -** All Plain Frozen Fruits
> **Del Monte -** Canned/Jarred Fruit (All Varieties), Fruit Snack Cups Metal, Plastic
> **Dole -** All Fruits (Bowls *(Except Fruit Crisps)*, Canned, Dried, Frozen, Jars *(Except Real Fruit Bites)*)
> **Gluty Free -** Dried White●, Dried●
> **Great Value Brand (Wal-Mart) -** Frozen, No Sugar Added Yellow Cling Peaches (Halves In Pear Juice From Concentrate, Sliced), Yellow Cling Sliced Peaches In Heavy Syrup
> **Hy-Vee -** Diced, Diced Fruit Cups, Halves, Lite (Diced, Halves, Slices), Peaches In Strawberry Gel, Slices
> **Kirkland Signature -** Sliced
> **Kroger Brand -** Fruit (Canned, Cups)
> **Kroger Value -** All Fresh Fruit Canned
> **Lowes Foods Brand -** Slices (In Heavy Syrup, In Juice)
> **Meijer Brand -** Cling Halves (In Heavy Syrup, In Juice Lite, In Pear Juice Lite), Cling Sliced (In Heavy Syrup, In Juice, In Pear Juice Lite), Frozen (Organic, Sliced), Yellow Sliced in Heavy Syrup

P

Midwest Country Fare - Lite Peaches (Halves, Slices), Slices, Yellow Cling (Halves In Light Syrup, Slices (In Heavy Syrup, In Light Syrup))

Native Forest - Organic Sliced Peaches

Nuts Online - Dried Fruit (Diced●, Dried●, Natural●, Organic●, Simply●, White●)

Publix - Canned (Lite Yellow Cling Peaches In Pear Juice Halves & Slices, Yellow Cling Peaches In Heavy Syrup Halves & Slices), Frozen Sliced

S&W - All Canned/Jarred Fruits

Safeway Brand - Canned Peaches (Halves, Halves Lite, Sliced, Sliced Lite), Frozen

Spartan Brand - Cling Halves (Heavy Syrup, Lite Syrup), Cling Slices (Heavy Syrup, Lite Syrup), Diced (Heavy Syrup, Lite Syrup), Frozen, Fruit Cups

Wegmans Brand - Halved Yellow Cling, Sliced Yellow Cling (In Heavy Syrup, In Light Syrup Raspberry Flavored, Regular)

Winn Dixie - Frozen Sliced, Yellow Cling Halves & Slices (Heavy Syrup, Light Syrup)

Woodstock Farms - Organic Frozen Peach Slices

Peanut Butter

... (includes Nut Butters)

Arrowhead Mills -
Almond Butter Creamy
Cashew Butter Creamy
Organic Valencia Peanut Butter (Creamy, Crunchy)
Valencia Peanut Butter (Creamy, Crunchy)

Bell Plantation - PB2 Powdered (Chocolate●, Original●)

Blue Diamond - Almond Butter (Homestyle (Creamy, Crunchy, Honey), Ready Spread (Creamy, Crunchy, Honey))

Earth Balance▲ - Natural Almond Butter Creamy, Natural Peanut Butter (Creamy, Crunchy)

Emmy's Organics▲ - Raw (Cashew, Macadamia Cashew)

Full Circle - Organic Creamy

Gluty Free -
Almond Butter (Crunchy●, Raw Organic (Crunchy●, Smooth●), Smooth●, Smooth●)

P

Organic Sunflower Butter●
Peanut Butter Organic (Crunchy●, Smooth●)
Smooth Organic Cashew Butter●
Jif - Natural (Creamy, Crunchy)
Kirkland Signature - Organic Creamy
MaraNatha -
  All Natural Almond Butter (Natural (Honey!, No Salt Creamy!, No
    Salt Crunchy!, Raw!), No Stir (Creamy!, Crunchy!))
  Natural Cashew Butter!
  Organic Almond Butter (Raw (No Salt Creamy!, No Salt
    Crunchy!), Roasted (No Salt Creamy!, No Salt Crunchy!))
  Peanut Butter (All Varieties)
Meijer Brand - Creamy, Crunchy, Natural (Creamy, Crunchy)
Nuts Online -
  Almond Butter (Organic (Raw Crunchy●, Roasted Smooth●),
    Roasted Crunchy●, Roasted Smooth●)
  Almond Paste●
  Hazelnut Praline Paste●
  Organic Peanut Butter (Crunchy Unsalted●, Smooth Unsalted●)
  Organic Sunflower Butter●
  Pistachio Nut Paste●
  Roasted Smooth Organic Cashew Butter●
O Organics - Old Fashioned (Creamy, Crunchy)
Peanut Butter & Co. - Cinnamon Raisin Swirl, Crunch Time, Mighty
  Maple, Old Fashioned Crunchy, Old Fashioned Smooth, Smooth
  Operator, The Bees Knees, The Heat Is On
Private Selections - Organic (Creamy, Crunchy)
Publix - All Natural (Creamy, Crunchy), Deli Fresh Ground!!
Santa Cruz - All Varieties
Smart Balance - Rich Roast (Chunky, Creamy)
Smucker's▲ - Goober (Grape, Strawberry), Natural (Chunky,
  Creamy, Honey, No Salt Added Creamy, Reduced Fat Creamy),
  Organic (Chunky, Creamy)

P

Sunland - Organic Peanut Butter (Creamy Cherry Vanilla, Creamy Dark Chocolate, Creamy Valencia, Crunchy Chipotle Chile, Crunchy Valencia, Italian Thai Ginger & Red Pepper)

Trader Joe's -
Almond Butter (Creamy w/Salt **!!**, Crunchy Unsalted **!!**, Raw Crunchy Unsalted **!!**)
Organic Creamy **!**
Organic Crunchy **!**
Salted (Creamy **!!**, Crunchy **!!**)
Sunflower Seed Butter
Unsalted (Creamy **!!**, Crunchy **!!**)

Tropical Traditions - Coconut Peanut Butter

Walden Farms - Creamy Peanut Spread Sugar Free

Wegmans Brand -
Natural Peanut Butter (Creamy, Crunchy)
Organic No Stir (Creamy, Crunchy)

Woodstock Farms -
Non Organic Nut Butters (Almond Butter (Crunchy Unsalted, Smooth Unsalted), Cashew Butter Unsalted, Raw Almond, Tahini Unsalted)
Organic Nut Butters (Almond Butter (Crunchy Unsalted, Smooth Unsalted), Classic Peanut Butter (Crunchy Salted, Smooth Salted), Easy Spread Peanut Butter (Crunchy Salted, Crunchy Unsalted, Smooth Salted, Smooth Unsalted), Peanut Butter (Crunchy Salted, Crunchy Unsalted, Smooth Salted, Smooth Unsalted), Raw Almond, Tahini Unsalted)

Peanut Sauce
A Taste Of Thai - Peanut Satay Sauce
Mr. Spice Organic - Thai Peanut Sauce & Marinade
Thai Kitchen - Peanut Satay

Peanuts... see Nuts

Pears
... *All Fresh Pears Are Gluten/Casein/Soy Free*
Albertsons - Canned

Del Monte -
  Canned/Jarred Fruit (All Varieties)
  Fruit Snack Cups (All Varieties)
Dole - All Fruits (Bowls *(Except Fruit Crisps)*, Canned, Dried, Frozen, Jars *(Except Real Fruit Bites)*)
Full Circle - Organic (Halves In Juice, Sliced In Juice)
Gluty Free - Dried●
Great Value Brand (Wal-Mart) -
  Bartlett Pears In Heavy Syrup (Halves, Sliced)
  Fruit Cocktail
  No Sugar Added Bartlett Chunky Mixed Fruits
  Pear Halves In Pear Juice From Concentrate & Water
Hy-Vee -
  Bartlett Pears (Halves, Sliced)
  Diced Bartlett Pears Cups
  Lite Pears
Kroger Brand - Fruit (Canned, Cups)
Lowes Foods Brand - Halves (In Heavy Syrup, In Juice)
Meijer Brand - Halves (Heavy Syrup, In Juice, In Juice Lite, Lite), Slices (Heavy Syrup, In Juice Lite)
Midwest Country Fare - Bartlett Pear Halves In Light Syrup
Native Forest - Organic Sliced Asian Pears
Nuts Online - Dried Fruit (Diced●, Dried●, Natural●, Organic●, Simply●)
Publix - Canned (Barlett Pears In Heavy Syrup (Halves, Slices), Lite Barlett Pear Halves In Pear Juice)
S&W - All Canned/Jarred Fruits
Safeway Brand - Canned Pears (Halves, Halves Lite, Sliced, Sliced Lite)
Spartan Brand - Fruit Cups, Halves (Heavy Syrup, Lite Syrup), Slices (Heavy Syrup, Lite Syrup)
Stop & Shop Brand - Bartlett Pear Halves (Heavy Syrup, Light Syrup, Pear Juice)

P **Wegmans Brand -**
Halved (In Heavy Syrup, In Pear Juice From Concentrate)
Sliced (In Heavy Syrup, In Pear Juice From Concentrate)
Winn Dixie - Bartlett Halves & Slices (Heavy Syrup, Light Syrup)

Peas
... *All Fresh Peas Are Gluten/Casein/Soy Free*
Albertsons - All Plain Peas Canned & Frozen
Birds Eye - All Plain Frozen Peas
Bush's Best - Black Eye, Crowder, Field Peas w/Snaps, Purple Hull
C & W - All Plain Frozen Peas
Del Monte - All Plain Canned Peas
Food Club Brand - Dried Peas Blackeyed
Freshlike - Select Petite Sweet Peas, Sweet Peas & Carrots, Tender
Garden
Full Circle - Organic (Frozen Peas, Sweet Peas)
Gluty Free - Freeze Dried●
Grand Selections - Frozen (Petite Green, Sugar Snap)
Great Value Brand (Wal-Mart) - Canned (Blackeye Peas, No Salt
Added Sweet Peas, Peas & Carrots, Sweet Peas), Microwaveable
Plastic Cups Sweet Peas
Green Giant -
Canned Sweet Peas
Frozen (Simply Steam (Baby Sweet Peas, Sugar Snap Peas), Sweet
Peas)
Valley Fresh Steamers (Select Baby Sweet Peas, Select Sugar Snap
Peas, Sweet Peas)
Hannaford Brand - No Salt, Petite, Sweet
HealthMarket - Organic Sweet
Hy-Vee - Black Eyed, Dry Green Split, Frozen Sweet, Steam In A Bag
Frozen Peas, Sweet
Kroger Brand - All Plain Peas (Canned, Frozen)
Kroger Value - All Plain Peas (Canned, Frozen)
Lowes Foods Brand - Frozen (Black Eyed, Crowder, Green, Tiny
Peas), Peas, Split Green Peas

Meijer Brand -
Canned (Blackeye, Peas & Sliced Carrots, Small, Sweet, Sweet No Salt, Sweet Organic)
Frozen Peas (Green, Green Petite, Organic Green, Peas & Sliced Carrots)

Midwest Country Fare - Frozen Green, Sweet

Nuts Online - Simply Peas Freeze Dried Vegetables●

O Organics - Frozen Sweet Peas

Pictsweet - All Plain Frozen Peas

Private Selections - All Plain Peas Frozen

Publix -
Canned Sweet Peas (Regular, Small)
Frozen (Blackeye, Butter, Crowder, Field Peas w/Snap, Green, Original, Petite, Purple Hull)

Publix GreenWise Market - Organic Canned Sweet Peas

S&W - All Canned Vegetables

Safeway Brand - Frozen, Steam In Bag

Safeway Select - Frozen (Blackeyed, Green, Peas & Carrots, Petite), Steam In Bag (Peas & Onions, Petite Green, Pod)

Spartan Brand -
Canned (Green, Peas & Carrots, Sweet)
Dried (Blackeyed, Green Split)
Frozen (Blackeyed, Peas & Sliced Carrots, Petite, Plain, Sugar Snap, w/Snaps)

Trader Joe's - Frozen (Organic Naturally Sweet, Petite Peas)

Wegmans Brand - Blackeyed, Regular (Sweet Canned, Sweet Frozen), Small Sweet, Sugar Snap Frozen, Sweet No Salt Added, Sweet Petite Frozen, w/Pearl Onions Frozen

Westbrae - Sweet Peas

Winn Dixie -
Canned Green Peas (Large, Medium, No Salt Added, Small, Tiny)
Frozen (Field w/Snaps, Green, Organic Green, Peas & Carrots, Petite Green, Purple Hull)

P   Woodstock Farms - Organic Frozen (Green Peas, Peas & Carrots, Petite Peas, Sugar Snap)

Pectin
Certo - Premium Liquid Fruit Pectin

Pepper Rings
B&G - Hot
Meijer Brand - Banana Pepper Rings (Hot, Mild)
Mezzetta - Deli Sliced (Hot, Mild)
Publix - Banana Pepper Rings (Mild)
Spartan Brand - Hot, Pepper Rings Mild

Pepper Sauce... see Chili Sauce and/or Hot Sauce

Pepperoni... see Sausage

Peppers
... *All Fresh Peppers Are Gluten/Casein/Soy Free
B&G -
  Giardiniera
  Hot
    Cherry Peppers (Regular, w/Oregano & Garlic)
    Chopped Roasted
    Jalapenos
    Pepper Rings
  Pepperoncini
  Roasted (w/Balsamic Vinegar, w/Oregano & Garlic)
  Sandwich Toppers (Hot Chopped Peppers, Hot Peppers, Sweet Bell Bepper, Sweet Pepper)
  Sweet Salad w/Oregano & Garlic
Birds Eye - All Plain Frozen Peppers
C & W - All Plain Frozen Peppers
Di Lusso - Roasted Red
Dietz & Watson▲ - Pepperoncini●, Sliced Jalapeno●, Sweet Roasted Red Pepper●
Earthbound Farm - Organic Bell
Hannaford Brand - Whole Pepperoncini
Hy-Vee - Diced Green Chilies, Green Salad Pepperoncini, Hot

Banana Peppers, Mild Banana Peppers, Salad Peppers, Sliced Hot Jalapenos, Whole Green Chilies

La Victoria - Diced Jalapenos, Nacho Jalapenos (Sliced)

Meijer Brand - Frozen Green Peppers (Chopped)

Melissa's - Fire Roasted Sweet Bell

Mezzetta -

Deli Sliced (Hot Jalapeno Peppers, Hot Pepper Rings, Mild Pepper Rings, Roasted Sweet Bell Pepper Strips, Sweet Bell Pepper Sandwich Strips, Tamed Jalapeno Peppers)

Deli Style (Sweet Bell Pepper Relish, Zesty Hot Bell Pepper Relish)

Garlic & Dill Golden Peperoncini

Golden Peperoncini

Gourmet Deli

Mild Rosemary & Garlic Pepper Rings

Roasted Red Bell Pepper & Caramelized Onions

Sweet & Hot (Jalapeno Pepper Rings, Pepper Rings)

Tamed (Diced Jalapeno Peppers, Fire Roasted Jalapeno Peppers w/Chipotle Pep)

Tri Color Roasted Bell Pepper Strips

Habanero Peppers

Hot (Banana Wax Peppers, Cherry Peppers, Chili Peppers, Chili Peppers Mexican Style En Escabeche, Jalapeno Peppers En Escabeche, Serrano Chili Peppers)

Italian Wax Peppers

Organics

Fire Roasted Red Bell Peppers

Sliced Hot Jalapeno Peppers

Roasted

Bell Peppers

Marinated Yellow & Red Sweet Peppers

Yellow & Red Sweet Peppers

Sliced (Golden Peperoncini, Hot Cherry Peppers)

Sweet Banana Wax Peppers

Sweet Cherry Peppers

Tamed Jalapeno Peppers En Escabeche

P

Mt. Olive - Diced Jalapeno Peppers, Hot Banana Pepper Rings, Jalapeno Slices, Marinated Roasted Red Peppers, Mild Banana Pepper Rings, Pepperoncini, Roasted Red Peppers, Sliced Pepperoncini, Sweet 'N Hot Salad Peppers

Nuts Online - Simply Red Peppers Freeze Dried Vegetables●

Peloponnese - Florina Whole Sweet Peppers

Peppadew - Goldew, Peppadew Hot, Peppadew Mild

Pictsweet - Chopped Green

Publix - Frozen Green Peppers Diced

Safeway Select - Fire Roasted, Frozen Pepper Strips

Spartan Brand - Jalapeno

Stop & Shop Brand - Chopped Green

Trader Joe's - Artichoke Red Pepper Tapenade**!!**, Frozen Fire Roasted Bell Peppers & Onions**!!**, Frozen Melange A Trois, Red Pepper Spread w/Garlic & Eggplant

Trappey's - Banana, Hot Jalapenos, In Vinegar, Torrido

Vlasic - All Varieties

Wegmans Brand - Clean and Cut Peppers & Onions (Diced, Sliced), Pepper & Onions Mix, Roasted Red Peppers Whole

Winn Dixie - Pepperoncini, Sliced Banana Peppers

Woodstock Farms - Organic Frozen Tri Colored Peppers

Pesto

   Fischer & Wieser - Sicilian Tomato

   Mezzetta - Napa Valley Bistro Homemade Style Basil Pesto

Picante Sauce

   Albertsons - Medium, Mild

   Chi-Chi's

   Hy-Vee - Hot, Medium, Mild

   Winn Dixie - Medium, Mild

Pickled Beets... see Beets

Pickles

   Albertsons - All Varieties

   Boar's Head - All Varieties

pickles

P

B&G - Bread & Butter, Dill, Hamburger Dill, Kosher Dill (Gherkins, Original), NY Deli Dill, Pickle In A Pouch, Sandwich Toppers (Bread & Butter, Hamburger Dill, Kosher Dill, N Y Deli, Polish Dill), Sweet (Gherkins, Mixed)

Dietz & Watson▲ - Kosher Spear●, New Half Sours●, Sour Garlic●

Full Circle - Kosher Baby Dill, Sweet Bread & Butter

Hannaford Brand -
  Bread & Butter (Chips, Sandwich Slices)
  Kosher (Baby Dills, Dill, Dill Sandwich Slices, Dill Spears, Petite)
  Polish Dill Spears
  Sour Dill
  Sugar Free Bread & Butter (Chips, Spears)
  Sugar Free Sweet Gherkins
  Sweet (Gherkins, Midgets, Mixed Chips, Relish, Relish Squeeze)

Hy-Vee -
  Bread & Butter (Sandwich Slices, Sweet Chunk Pickles, Sweet Slices)
  Dill (Cocktail, Hamburger Slices, Kosher (Baby, Fresh Pack Baby, Sandwich Slices, Spears), Pickles, Polish (Pickles, Spears))
  Refrigerated Kosher Dill (Halves, Sandwich Slices, Spears, Whole Pickles)
  Special Recipe (Baby Dills, Bread & Butter Slices, Hot & Spicy Zingers, Hot & Sweet Zinger Chunks, Jalapeno Baby Dills, Sweet Garden Crunch)
  Sweet Gherkins
  Whole (Dill, Sweet)
  Zesty (Kosher Dill Spears, Sweet Chunks)

Kroger Brand - All Varieties

Kroger Value - All Varieties

Kurtz - Bread & Butter, Hamburger Dill Slices, Kosher Dill Spears, Sweet, Whole Dill

Lowes Foods Brand - Bread & Butter Chips, Dill (Kosher, Kosher Spears), Kosher Baby Dill, Sweet Midgets, Sweet Salad Cubes

P

Meijer Brand -
> Bread & Butter (Chips (Regular, Sugar Free), Sandwich Slice)
> Dill (Hamburger, Kosher (Baby, Spears, Whole), Polish, Sandwich
>   Slice Polish, Spears (No Garlic, Polish, Zesty), Whole)
> Kosher (Baby Dill, Sandwich Slices, Whole)
> Sweet (Gherkin, Midgets, Sugar Free)

Mezzetta - Whole Kosher Style Dill Pickles

Midwest Country Fare - Dill, Hamburger Dill Pickle Slices, Kosher
> Dill, Whole Sweet

Mrs. Renfro's - Green Tomato Pickles

Mt. Olive -
> Bread & Butter (Chips, Spears)
> Dill (Hamburger Chips, Jalapeno Flavored Baby, Kosher
>   (Baby, Hamburger Chips, Hamburger Stuffers, Hot 'N Spicy, Hot
>   Sauce Flavored Baby, Petite, Petite Snack Cruncher), Polish Spears,
>   Regular)
> No Sugar Added (Bread & Butter Chips, Bread & Butter Sandwich
>   Stuffers, Sweet Gherkins, Sweet Petites PicklePAK)
> PicklePAK (Hamburger Dill Chips, Kosher Dill Petites, Sweet
>   Petites)
> Sour
> Sweet Petite Snack Crunchers

Publix - All Varieties

Safeway Brand - All Varieties

Spartan Brand -
> Bread & Butter Slices (Sandwich, Sweet)
> Kosher Dill (Baby, Slices (Hamburger, Sandwich), Spears, Whole)
> Polish Dill (Spears, Whole)
> Sweet (Gherkin Whole, Slices, Whole)

Trader Joe's - Organic (Kosher Sandwich Pickles, Sweet Butter Pickles!)

Vlasic - All Varieties

Wegmans Brand -
> Hamburger Dill Slices
> Kosher Dill (Baby Dills, Halves, Sandwich Slices, Spears, Spears
>   Reduced Sodium, Whole)

Polish Dill (Spears, Whole)
Sweet (Gherkins, Midgets)
Sweet Bread & Butter Chips (No Salt Added, Regular)
Sweet Sandwich Slices
Winn Dixie -
Dill (All Varieties)
Sweet Pickles (All Varieties)
Sweet Relish
Woodstock Farms - Organic (Kosher Dill (Baby, Sliced, Whole), Sweet Bread & Butter)

Pie
Amy's - Mexican Tamale Pie**!**
Fabe's Bakery - 8" Gluten Free Vegan Apple Pie●, Mini Gluten Free Vegan Apple Pie●
Pure Market Express▲ - Apple Pie●, Banana Cream Pie●, Pumpkin Pie●

Pie Crust/Pie Crust Mix
Arnel's Originals - Pie Crust Mix
Augason Farms▲ - Gluten Free Pie Crust Mix●
Authentic Foods▲ - Pie Crust Mix
Breads From Anna▲ - Piecrust Mix
Cause You're Special▲ - Homestyle Pie Crust
El Peto▲ - Pie Crust
Gluten Free Mama▲ - Mama's Pie Crust Mix●
Grandma Ferdon's▲ - Frozen 8" Crust w/Tin●, Pie Crust Mix●
Mixes From The Heartland▲ - Impossible Coconut Pie Mix●, Pie Crust Mix●
Really Great Food Company▲ - Flaky Pie Crust Mix

Pie Filling
Comstock - All Varieties
Fischer & Wieser -
Fredericksburg Golden Peach
Harvest Apple & Brandy Pie
Hy-Vee - More Fruit Pie Filling/Topping (Apple, Cherry)

P

Jell-O -
- Regular Cook N Serve (Banana Cream, Chocolate (Fudge, Regular), Coconut Cream, Vanilla)
- Regular Instant Pudding & Pie Filling (Cheesecake, Chocolate (Fudge, Regular), Coconut Cream, Devil's Food, French Vanilla, Lemon, Pistachio, Pumpkin Spice, Vanilla Regular, White Chocolate)

Kroger Brand - Canned Pie Filling

Lowes Foods Brand - Apple, Blueberry

Lucky Leaf -
- Apple
- Apricot
- Banana Crème
- Blueberry
- Cherries Jubilee
- Cherry
- Chocolate Crème
- Coconut Crème
- Dark Sweet Cherry
- Key Lime Pie Crème
- Lemon (Crème, Regular)
- Lite (Apple, Cherry)
- Peach
- Pineapple
- Premium (Apple, Blackberry, Blueberry, Cherry, Red Raspberry)
- Raisin
- Strawberry

Meijer Brand - Apple, Blueberry, Cherry, Cherry Lite, Peach

Midwest Country Fare - Apple, Cherry

Musselman's -
- Apple
- Apricot
- Banana Crème
- Blackberry
- Blueberry

Cherries Jubilee
Cherry
Chocolate Crème
Coconut Crème
Dark Sweet Cherry
Key Lime Crème Pie
Lemon (Crème, Regular)
Lite (Apple, Cherry)
Peach
Pineapple
Raisin
Strawberry (Glaze, Regular)
Supreme (Blueberry & Crème, Cherries & Crème, Peaches & Crème)

Nuts Online - Filling (Almond●, Chocolate●, Cinnamon●, Poppy Seed●)
Private Selections - All Varieties
Spartan Brand - Apple, Blueberry, Cherry (Lite, Regular), Pumpkin
Wilderness - All Varieties
Winn Dixie - Apple, Blueberry, Cherry

Pimentos
Meijer Brand - Pieces, Sliced

Pineapple
... *All Fresh Pineapple Is Gluten/Casein/Soy Free*
Albertsons - All Varieties
Del Monte - Canned/Jarred Fruit (All Varieties), Fruit Snack Cups (Metal, Plastic)
Dole - All Fruits (Bowls *(Except Fruit Crisps)*, Canned, Dried, Frozen, Jars *(Except Real Fruit Bites)*)
Gluty Free - Dried (Diced●, Natural●, Organic●, Regular●)
Great Value Brand (Wal-Mart) - Chunks, Pineapple In Unsweetened Pineapple Juice (Crushed, Slices, Tidbits), Plastic Cups Tidbits
Hy-Vee - Chunk, Crushed, In Lime Gel, Sliced, Tidbit Fruit Cup
Kroger Brand - Fruit (Canned, Cups)

P

Lowes Foods Brand - Chunks In Juice, Crushed In Juice, Sliced In Juice

Meijer Brand - Chunks (Heavy Syrup, In Juice), Crushed (Heavy Syrup, In Juice), Frozen Chunks, Sliced In (Heavy Syrup, Juice)

Midwest Country Fare - Chunks, Crushed, Slices, Tidbits

Native Forest - Organic (Chunks, Crushed, Slices)

Nuts Online - Dried Fruit (Chunks●, Diced●, Dried●, Natural●, Organic●, Organic Chunks●, Simply●)

Publix - All Varieties

Safeway Brand - Chunks, Crushed, Sliced

Spartan Brand - Chunks, Crushed, Sliced, Tidbits

Stop & Shop Brand - Frozen Pineapple

Trader Joe's - Frozen Pineapple Tidbits

Wegmans Brand - Chunk In Heavy Syrup, In Pineapple Juice (Chunk, Crushed, Sliced, Tidbits)

Winn Dixie - Chunks, Crushed, Sliced, Tidbits

Pistachio Nuts... see Nuts

Pizza

Pure Market Express▲ - Pepperoni Pizza●, Sausage Pizza●

Pizza Crust/Pizza Mix

Andrea's Fine Foods▲ - Pizza Crust (12", 6")

Bob's Red Mill▲ - GF Pizza Crust Mix

Cause You're Special▲ - Famous Pizza Crust Mix

Dad's▲ - Gluten Free Pizza Crust

El Peto▲ - Pizza Crust (Basil, Millet, White)

Ener-G▲ -
  Rice Pizza Shell (10", 6")
  Yeast Free Rice Pizza Shell (10", 6")

Foods By George▲ - Pizza Crusts

Food-Tek Fast & Fresh▲ - Dairy Free Minute Pizza Crust Mix

Gifts Of Nature▲ - French Bread & Pizza Crust Mix

Gluten-Free Creations▲ - Italian Seasoned Crust●, Simply Pizza Crust Mix●, Simply Pizza Crust●

Grandma Ferdon's▲ - Pizza Crust Mix●

Heaven Mills - Pizza Crust
Hodgson Mill▲ - Gluten Free Pizza Crust Mix
King Arthur Flour▲ - Gluten Free Pizza Crust Mix●
Kinnikinnick▲ - Pizza Crust (10", Personal Size), Pizza Crust Mix
Kneaded Specialties▲ - Pizza Crust●
Laurel's Sweet Treats▲ - Pizza Dough Mix
Namaste Foods▲ - Pizza Crust Mix
Orgran▲ - Pizza & Pastry Multi Mix
PaneRiso▲ - White Rice Pizza Crust●
Really Great Food Company▲ - French Bread/Pizza Crust, Pizza Crust Mix
Rose's Bakery▲ - Pizza Crusts (14", 9", Parbaked)
Silly Yak Bakery▲ - CFGF 8" Pizza Crusts●
Still Riding Pizza▲ - Gluten Free Pizza Crust
Udi's Gluten Free Foods▲ - Gluten Free Pizza Crust
Pizza Sauce... see also Sauces
Dei Fratelli - Presto Pizza Sauce
Eden Organic - Organic Pizza Pasta Sauce
Meijer Brand
Sauces 'N Love - Marinara & Pizza Sauce
Trader Joe's - Fat Free **! !**
Plum Sauce
Sharwood's
Wok Mei - All Natural Plum
Plums
... *All Fresh Plums Are Gluten/Casein/Soy Free*
Gluty Free - Dried Pluots●
Kirkland Signature - Pitted Dry Plums
Safeway Brand
Stop & Shop Brand - Whole Plums In Heavy Syrup
Winn Dixie - Canned Whole Plums
Polenta
Beretta - Gran Polenta Express
Bob's Red Mill▲ - Gluten Free Corn Grits/Polenta

P

Food Merchants Brand - Ancient Harvest (Basil & Garlic, Chili & Cilantro, Mushroom & Onion, Quinoa Heirloom Red & Black, Sun Dried Tomato & Garlic, Traditional Italian)

Melissa's - Organic (Italian Herb, Original, Sun Dried Tomato)

San Gennaro Foods - Basil & Garlic, Sundried Tomato & Garlic, Traditional

Pomegranate
*... *All Fresh Pomegranate Is Gluten/Casein/Soy Free*

Trader Joe's - Frozen Pomegranate Seeds

Pop... see Soda Pop/Carbonated Beverages

Popcorn

Albertsons - Microwavable Kettle, Yellow

Eden Organic - Organic Yellow Popping Kernels

Farmer Steve's - Organic Microwave, Super Pop Kernels

Hannaford Brand - Microwavable (Kettle, Natural)

Hy-Vee - Microwave (Kettle, Natural Flavor), Regular (White, Yellow)

Jolly Time - Kernel Corn (American's Best, Organic Yellow, White, Yellow)

Kroger Brand - Natural, Plain Popcorn Kernels (White, Yellow)

Meijer Brand - Microwave (Kettle Sweet & Salty, Natural Lite), Regular (White, Yellow)

Mini Pops▲ - Popped Sorghum (Hot N' Chilly Chili●, Little Lemon Pepper●, Petite Plain●, Subatomic Sea Salt●)

Newman's Own - Regular Raw Popcorn

Newman's Own Organics - Microwave Pop's Corn No Butter/No Salt 94% Fat Free

Old Dutch - Gourmet White

Pirate's Booty - Barbeque!

Publix - Microwave (Kettle!, Natural!)

Safeway Brand - White, Yellow

Skeete & Ike's - Organic (BBQ!!, Kettle Corn!!, Sea Salt!!)

Spartan Brand - Microwave (Kettle, Natural), White, Yellow

Trader Joe's - Gourmet White, Kettle, Lite Popcorn 50% Less Salt!, Organic w/Olive Oil!

pork

Wegmans Brand - Microwave (94% Fat Free Butter Flavor, Organic), Regular Yellow

Winn Dixie - Yellow

Pork

... *All Fresh Meat Is Gluten/Casein/Soy Free (Non-Marinated, Unseasoned)*

Coleman's Natural Foods - Hampshire (Chops●, Loin●, Ribs (Baby Back●, St. Louis●), Tenderloins●)

Dietz & Watson▲ -
Boneless Pork Chops w/Natural Juices●
Canadian Center Cut Spare Ribs●
Cuban Roast Pork●
Italian Style Roast Pork●
Panchetta Sweet●
Pork Cello Butt●
Roast Sirloin Of Pork●
Souse Roll●
Spiced Luncheon Meat●

Farmer John - California Natural Pork (Boneless Loin, Ground Pork, Spareribs, Tenderloins)

Farmland - Sliced Salt Pork Belly, Smoked Pork Jowl

Hormel - Pork Roast Au Jus Fully Cooked Entrée

Jones Dairy Farm -
All Natural
Hearty Pork Sausage Links●
Light Pork Sausage & Rice Links●
Little Link Pork Sausage●
Maple Sausage Links●
Original Pork Roll Sausage●
Pork Sausage Patties●
Golden Brown All Natural Fully Cooked
Maple Sausage (Links●, Patties●)
Mild Sausage (Links●, Patties●)
Pork & Uncured Bacon Sausage Links●
Sausage & Rice Links●
Spicy Sausage Links●

P

Kirkland Signature - Fresh Sirloin Tip Roast, Smoked Pulled

Organic Prairie - Fresh Organic (Ground Pork 1 lb., Pork Chops, Pork Loin, Pork Loin Roast), Frozen Organic Pork Chops

Publix - All Natural Fresh Pork, Fresh Ground (Hot, Mild, Sage)

Saz's - Barbecue Pork Meat Tub, Barbecued Baby Back Ribs

Trader Joe's - BBQ Pulled Pork In Spicy BBQ sauce

Wegmans Brand - Canned Pork & Beans In Tomato Sauce

Potato Chips... see Chips

Potato Crisps... see Crisps

Potatoes

... *All Fresh Potatoes Are Gluten/Casein/Soy Free*

Albertsons - Canned (Sliced, Whole)

Alexia Foods -

Crispy Potatoes w/Seasoned Salt Waffle Fries **!**

Julienne Fries (Spicy Sweet Potato **!**, Sweet Potato **!**, w/Sea Salt Yukon Gold **!**)

Mashed Potatoes Yukon Gold Potatoes w/Sea Salt **!**

Olive Oil (& Sea Salt Oven Fries **!**, Rosemary & Garlic Oven Fries **!**)

Organic (Classic Oven Crinkles **!**, Oven Crinkles Onion & Garlic **!**, Oven Crinkles Salt & Pepper **!**, Seasoned Salt Hashed Browns **!**, Yukon Gold Julienne Fries w/Sea Salt **!**)

Yukon Gold Potatoes w/Seasoned Salt Potato Nuggets

Dr. Praeger's - Potato Littles **!**

Great Value Brand (Wal-Mart) - Canned (Diced, Sliced, Whole New)

Hannaford Brand - Diced, Frozen Hash Browns (Country, Southern Style), Instant Regular, Sliced, Whole

Hy-Vee - Canned (Sliced, Whole)

Ian's - Alphatots

Kroger Brand - Frozen (Hash Browns (Country Style, Southern Style), O'Brien)

Linda's Gourmet Latkes - Potato Pancake Latkes

Meijer Brand -

Canned White (Sliced, Whole)

Frozen Hash Browns (Original, Shredded, Southern Style, Western Style)

Midwest Country Fare - Whole White Potatoes

Nuts Online - Simply Potatoes Freeze Dried Vegetables●

Ore-Ida -
Hash Browns (Country Style, Southern Style)
Potatoes O'Brien
Steam N' Mash (Cut Russet Potatoes, Cut Sweet Potatoes)

Potato Buds▲ - Gluten Free 100% Real Potatoes

Publix - Canned White, Frozen Southern Style Hash Browns

S&W - All Canned Potatoes

Safeway Brand - Instant Mashed Potatoes Regular

Shiloh Farms - Potato Flakes

Spartan Brand -
Canned White (Sliced, Whole)
Frozen Hash Browns (O'Brien, Shredded, Southern Style)
Mashed Potatoes Box Instant

Stop & Shop Brand - Whole Potatoes (No Added Salt, Regular)

Tasty Bite - Aloo Palak!, Bombay!, Mushroom Takatak!

Wegmans Brand - Frozen Hash Browns (Country Style, Hash Browns O'Brien, Regular), White Potatoes (Sliced, Whole Peeled)

Winn Dixie -
Canned (Diced White, No Salt Added White, Sliced White, Sweet, Whole White)
Frozen (O'Brien, Southern Style Hashbrowns)
Instant (Regular, Roasted Garlic)

Woodstock Farms - Organic Frozen (Crinkle Cut Oven Fries, Shredded Hash Browns, Tastee Taters)

Preserves... see Jam/Jelly

Pretzels
Dutch Country - Soft Pretzel Mix
Ener-G▲ - Wylde Pretzels (Poppy Seed, Regular, Sesame)

P Protein

    Bob's Red Mill▲ - Hemp Protein Powder

    Gluty Free - Organic Hemp Protein Powder●

    Growing Naturals - Rice Protein Isolate Powder (Chocolate, Original, Vanilla)

    Living Harvest - Organic Hemp Protein Powder (All Varieties)

    MLO - Brown Rice Protein Powder

    Nutiva - Hemp Protein Shake (Amazon Acai, Berry Pomegrate, Chocolate), Protein Powder (Hemp, Hemp & Fiber)

    Nuts Online - Organic Hemp Protein Powder●

    Ruth's Hemp Power - Powders (Regular, w/Maca & E3Live, w/ Sprouted Flax & Maca)

Protein Shakes... see Shakes... see also Protein

Prunes

    Gluty Free - Dried Pluots●, Jumbo●, Organic Pitted●, Pitted●

    Great Value Brand (Wal-Mart) - Pitted Prunes

    Meijer Brand - Pitted (Canister, Carton)

    Nuts Online - Dried Fruit (Plums (Angelino●, Jumbo●, No Pit●, October Sun●, Organic Angelino●, Organic No Pit●), Pluots●)

    Spartan Brand - Prunes Pitted

Pudding

    Jell-O -

        Regular Cook N Serve (Banana Cream, Chocolate (Fudge, Regular), Coconut Cream, Vanilla)

        Regular Instant Pudding & Pie Filling (Banana Cream, Cheesecake, Chocolate (Fudge, Regular), Coconut Cream, Devil's Food, French Vanilla, Lemon, Pistachio, Pumpkin Spice, Vanilla Regular, White Chocolate)

    Mixes From The Heartland▲ - Pudding Mix (Apple Cinnamon Rice●, Chocolate Delight●)

    Royal - All Instant Varieties, Cook & Serve (Chocolate)

Pumpkin

    *... *All Fresh Pumpkin Is Gluten/Casein/Soy Free*

    Hy-Vee - Canned Pumpkin

P

Libby's - Canned (100% Pure Pumpkin, Easy Pumpkin Pie Mix)
Meijer Brand - Canned
Nuts Online - Pumpkin Seed Powder●
Spartan Brand - Canned
Wegmans Brand - Solid Pack

Q

Puppodums
  Sharwood's - Indian Puppodums (Plain, Spicy)

R

Q

Quinoa
  Ancient Harvest Quinoa - Inca Red Quinoa, Quinoa Flakes, Quinoa
    Flour, Quinoa Pasta (Elbows, Garden Pagodas, Linguine, Rotelle,
    Shells, Spaghetti, Veggie Curls), Traditional Quinoa Grain
  Arrowhead Mills - Quinoa
  Arzu - Chai●, Original●, Southwest●
  Gluty Free - Organic●
  GoGo Rice - Organic Steamed Quinoa Bowls (Regular)
  Shiloh Farms - Quinoa , Quinoa Flakes , Red Quinoa

R

Radishes
  ... *All Fresh Radishes Are Gluten/Casein/Soy Free*
Raisins
  Albertsons - Regular
  Full Circle - Organic (Canister, Regular)
  Gluty Free - Crimson●, Dark●, Flame●, Golden●, Organic●,
    Thompson Seedless●
  Great Value Brand (Wal-Mart) - 100% Natural California Sun Dried
    Raisins
  Hannaford Brand - Regular
  Hy-Vee - California Sun Dried Raisins (Regular)
  Kroger Brand - Regular

R
Kroger Value - Regular
Lowes Foods Brand - Canister, Seedless Carton
Meijer Brand - Canister, Seedless Carton
Nuts Online - Crimson●, Dark●, Jumbo (Flame●, Golden●, Golden Flame●, Thompson Seedless●), Midget●, Organic●
O Organics - Regular
Private Selections - Organic
Publix - Regular
Spartan Brand - Regular
Sun-Maid - Raisins (Baking, Golden, Natural California, Regular), Zante Currants
Wegmans Brand - Seedless
Woodstock Farms - Organic (Jumbo Flame, Jumbo Thompson, Select Thompson)

Raspberries
*... *All Fresh Raspberries Are Gluten/Casein/Soy Free*
C & W - All Plain Frozen Fruits
Full Circle - Organic Raspberries
Gluty Free - Dried Red●
Great Value Brand (Wal-Mart) - Frozen Red Raspberries
Hy-Vee - Frozen Red Raspberries
Meijer Brand - Frozen (Organic, Regular), Red Individually Quick Frozen
Nuts Online - Dried Fruit (Dried Red●, Organic Red●, Simply●)
Publix - Frozen
Safeway Brand - Frozen Red Raspberries
Spartan Brand - Frozen Red Raspberries
Stop & Shop Brand - Raspberries, Raspberries In Syrup
Trader Joe's - Frozen Organic Raspberries, Frozen Raspberries
Wegmans Brand - w/Sugar
Winn Dixie - Frozen Red Raspberries
Woodstock Farms - Organic Frozen Red Raspberries
Raspberry Vinaigrette... see Salad Dressing

R

Ravioli
  Everybody Eats▲ - Chicken
Refried Beans... see Beans
Relish
  Albertsons - Sweet
  B&G - Dill, Hamburger, Hot Dog, India, Sweet
  Full Circle - Sweet
  Hannaford Brand - Dill, Hot Dog
  Heinz - All Varieties
  Hy-Vee - Dill, Squeeze Sweet, Sweet
  Kurtz - Sweet Relish
  Lowes Foods Brand - Sweet Pickle
  Meijer Brand - Dill Relish, Sweet Relish Sugar Free
  Mezzetta - Deli Style (Sweet Bell Pepper Relish, Zesty Bell Pepper
    Relish Hot)
  Midwest Country Fare - Sweet Pickle
  Mrs. Renfro's - Corn, Hot Chow Chow, Hot Tomato, Mild Chow
    Chow, Mild Tomato
  Mt. Olive - Dill Relish, Dill Salad Cubes, Sweet India Relish, Sweet
    Relish, Sweet Salad Cubes
  Spartan Brand - Dill, Sweet
  Trader Joe's - Organic Sweet **! !**
  Vlasic - All Varieties
  Wegmans Brand - Dill, Hamburger, Hot Dog, Sweet
  Woodstock Farms - Organic (Spicy Chipotle Sweet, Sweet Relish)
Ribs
  *... *All Fresh Meat Is Gluten/Casein/Soy Free (Non-Marinated, Unseasoned)*
  Saz's - Barbecued Baby Back Ribs
Rice
  A Taste Of Thai - Rice (Jasmine, Soft Jasmine)
  Albertsons - Boil In A Bag, Brown, White (Instant, Regular)
  Annie Chun's - Sprouted Brown Rice, Sticky White Rice
  Arrowhead Mills - Brown Basmati, Long Grain Brown
  Beretta - Carnaroli Chef, Carnaroli Rice

R

Dinty Moore - Microwave Meal Rice w/Chicken

Eden Organic - Organic Canned (Curried Rice & Lentils, Mexican Rice & Black Beans, Moroccan Rice & Garbanzo Beans, Rice & Cajun Small Red Beans, Rice & Caribbean Black Beans, Rice & Garbanzo Beans, Rice & Kidney Beans, Rice & Lentils, Rice & Pinto Beans, Spanish Rice & Pinto Beans)

Fantastic World Foods - Arborio, Basmati, Jasmine

Full Circle - Organic (Basmati Brown, Basmati White, Long Grain Brown, Long Grain White)

Gluten-Free Essentials▲ - Side Kicks (Exotic Curry●, Italian Herb & Lemon●, Southwest Chipotle & Lime●)

GoGo Rice -
Brown Rice w/Thai Curry Sauce
On The Go Cooked Rice Bowls (Exotic & Spicy Thai Peanut, Sweet & Mild Hawaiian, Tasty & Healthy Harvest, Zesty & Spicy Mexican Green)
Organic
Rice Medley w/Wild Rice
Steamed Rice Bowls (Brown, White)
White Rice
Sprouted Brown

Golden Star - Jasmine Rice

Great Value Brand (Wal-Mart) - Boil In Bag, Brown, Enriched Long Grain Parboiled Rice

Hannaford Brand - Enriched Long Grain, Frozen Steam In Bag White Rice, Instant

Hormel - Compleats Microwaveable Meals (Chicken & Rice, Santa Fe Chicken & Rice)

Hy-Vee - Boil In Bag Rice, Enriched Extra Long Grain (Instant, Regular), Extra Long Grain, Instant Brown, Natural Long Grain Brown, Spanish

Konriko▲ - Brown Rice (Hot N' Spicy●, Original●), Wild Pecan Rice (Box Regular●, Burlap Bag Regular●)

Kroger Brand - Boil N Bag (Brown, White), Instant (Brown, White), Original (Brown, White)

Lotus Foods -
  Bhutanese Red
  Brown Kalijira
  Forbidden
  Madagascar Pink
  Organic (Brown Jasmine, Forbidden, Jade Pearl, Jasmine, Mekong Flower)
  Volcano

Lundberg▲ - All Varieties

Meijer Brand - Brown, Instant (Boil In Bag, Brown), Long Grain, Medium Grain

Midwest Country Fare - Pre Cooked Instant Rice

Minute Rice - Brown, Premium, Steamers (White, Whole Grain Brown), White

Mixes From The Heartland▲ - Instant Rice Mix (White●, Wild●)

Nishiki - Sushi Rice

O Organics - Long Grain (Brown, Thai Jasmine)

Ortega - Yellow Rice Mix

Publix - Long Grain (Brown, Enriched), Medium Grain White, Pre Cooked Instant (Boil In Bag, Brown, White), Yellow Rice Mix

Pure Market Express▲ - Basil Fried Rice●, Spanish Rice●

Royal - Basmati Rice

Safeway Brand - Brown, Instant, Long Grain, Rice Pouch Gently Milled Bran Rice, White

Shiloh Farms - Basmati Rice , California Wild Rice , Long Grain Brown Rice , Short Grain Brown Rice

Spartan Brand - 4% Broken Long Grain, Instant (Boil In Bag, Brown Box, Regular Box)

Stop & Shop Brand - Organic Long Grain Brown & White

Success - Boil In Bag (Jasmine Rice, White Rice, Whole Grain Brown Rice)

R

Tambobamba - Mojo Bowls Peruvian Rice & Beans, Side Dishes (Cuban Black Beans & Rice, Jamaican Rice & Beans, Mexican Rice & Beans)

Tasty Bite - Basmati **!**, Brown Rice (Garlic **!**, Regular **!**), Ginger Lentil **!**, Jasmine **!**, Jasmine Green Energy **!**, Long Grain **!**, Mexican Fiesta **!**

Thai Kitchen - Jasmine Rice Mixes Jasmine Rice

Trader Joe's - Biryani Curried Rice **! !**, Organic (All Varieties)

Uncle Ben's -
    Boil In Bag
    Fast & Natural Instant Brown Rice
    Instant Rice
    Natural Whole Grain Brown Rice
    Original Converted Brand Rice
    Ready Rice (Original Long Grain Rice 8.8 oz. & 14.8 oz., Whole Grain Brown Rice)

Wegmans Brand -
    Arborio (Italian Style, Regular)
    Basmati
    Boil In Bag
    Enriched (Long, Long Grain White, Medium)
    Instant (Brown, Regular)
    Jasmine
    Long Grain (Brown, White)
    Medium Grain White

Rice Beverages

Good Karma - Original Ricemilk (Chocolate, Original, Unsweetened, Vanilla)

Grainaissance -
    Almond Shake
    Amazing Mango
    Banana Appeal
    Chocolate (Almond, Cool Coconut)
    Gimme Green

R

Go (Go Green, Hazelnuts)
Oh So Original
Rice Nog
Tiger Chai
Vanilla Pecan Pie
Growing Naturals - Rice Milk (Creamy Vanilla, Silky Smooth
   Original, Velvety Chocolate)
Pacific Natural Foods - Low Fat Plain, Low Fat Vanilla
Rice Dream - Refrigerated & Shelf Stable Rice Beverages (All Varieties)
Wegmans Brand - Organic (Original, Vanilla)
Rice Cakes
   Hy-Vee - Lightly Salted
   Lundberg▲ -
      Eco Farmed (Brown Rice (Apple Cinnamon, Lightly Salted, Toasted
         Sesame), Honey Nut, Salt Free)
      Organic (Brown Rice Lightly Salted, Mochi Sweet, Rice w/
         Popcorn, Salt Free, Sweet Green Tea w/Lemon, Wild Rice)
   Mrs. Crimble's - Apple, Caramel, Honey, Slightly Salted, Unsalted
   Publix - Lightly Salted, Unsalted
   Quaker - Lightly Salted**!**
   Trader Joe's - Lightly Salted Rice Cakes**!!**
Rice Crackers... see Crackers
Rice Noodles... see Noodles... see also Pasta
Rice Syrup... see Syrup
Rice Vinegar... see Vinegar
Risotto
   Lundberg▲ - Organic (Florentine, Tuscan)
Roast Beef... see Beef
Rolls... see Bread
Rum
   ... *All Distilled Alcohol Is Gluten/Casein/Soy Free* [2]
Rutabaga
   ... *All Fresh Rutabaga Is Gluten/Casein/Soy Free*

S S

Salad

... **All Fresh Salad Is Gluten/Casein/Soy Free*

Earthbound Farm -
American Salad
Baby (Arugula, Arugula Blend, Lettuces, Romaine, Spinach, Spinach Blend)
Bibb Lettuce Leaves
Butter Lettuce Leaves
California Blend
Fancy Romaine Salad
Fresh (Herb Salad, Spinach)
Frisée
Frisée Blend
Harvest Blend
Hearts Of Romaine
Heirloom Lettuce Leaves
Iceberg Lettuce
Italian Salad
Mâche
Mâche Blend
Mixed Baby Greens
Romaine (Hearts, Salad)
Spring Mix

Hy-Vee - American Blend, Chopped Romaine, Cole Slaw, European Blend, Garden, Garden Supreme, Italian Blend, Riveria Blend, Shredded Lettuce, Spring Mix

Mixes From The Heartland▲ - Pasta Salad (Corn●, Cucumber Dill●, Dilled●)

Publix - Classic Blend, Cole Slaw Blend, European Blend, Italian Blend, Packaged Blends, Romaine Lettuce Heart, Spinach

Publix GreenWise Market - Organic Salad (Baby (Arugula, Lettuce, Mixed Greens, Romaine, Spinach), Fresh Herb, Romaine Hearts)

Pure Market Express▲ - Broccoli Salad●, Salad Kit (Big Greek●, Caesar Salad●), Thai Salad●

Salad Dressing

Albertsons - Raspberry Vinaigrette, Zesty Italian

Annie's Naturals -

Natural Dressings (Basil & Garlic!!, Fat Free (Mango Vinaigrette!!, Raspberry Balsamic Vinaigrette!!), Lemon & Chive!!, Lite Herb Balsamic!!, Lite Vinaigrette Raspberry!!, Roasted Red Pepper Vinaigrette!!, Tuscany Italian!!)

Organic (French!!, Green Garlic!!, Oil & Vinegar!!, Vinaigrette (Balsamic!!, Pomegranate!!, Roasted Garlic!!))

Briannas - Dijon Honey Mustard, New American, Rich (Poppy Seed, Santa Fe Blend), Vinaigrette (Blush Wine, Champagne Caper, Real French), Zesty French

Consorzio - Fat Free (Mango, Raspberry & Balsamic, Strawberry & Balsamic), Honey Mustard

Drew's - Garlic Italian Vinaigrette, Honey Dijon, Kalamata Olive & Caper, Poppy Seed, Raspberry, Roasted Garlic & Peppercorn, Rosemary Balsamic, Smoked Tomato

Emeril's - Caesar, Vinaigrette (Balsamic, House Herb, Italian, Raspberry Balsamic)

Fischer & Wieser - Citrus Herb & Truffle Oil Vinaigrette, Original Roasted Raspberry Chipotle Vinaigrette, Southwestern Herb & Tomato Vinaigrette, Spicy Lime & Coriander, Sweet Corn & Shallot

Follow Your Heart - Fresh & Naturals (Lemon Herb, Thousand Island, Vegan Caesar)

Foods Alive - Organic Golden Flax Oil (Mike's Special, Sweet & Sassy, Sweet Mustard), Organic Hemp Oil Sweet & Sassy

Fosse Farms▲ - Blackberry●, Cranberry●, Marionberry●, Organic (Blackberry●, Cranberry●, Provencal●, Raspberry●), Raspberry●

Hannaford Brand - Fat Free (Raspberry Vinaigrette, Sweet Herb Vinaigrette, Zesty Italian)

S

Henri's - Fat Free Honey Mustard

Ken's Steak House - Fat Free Dressings (Raspberry Pecan, Sun Dried Tomato), Regular Christo's Yasou Greek

Kraft - Free French, Light Balsamic Vinaigrette, Zesty Italian

Lily's Gourmet Dressings - Balsamic Vinaigrette

Maple Grove Farms Of Vermont -

All Natural (Blueberry Pomegranate, Champagne Vinaigrette, Ginger Pear, Maple Fig, Strawberry Balsamic)

Balsamic Maple

Fat Free (Cranberry Balsamic, Greek, Honey Dijon, Lime Basil, Vinaigrette (Balsamic, Raspberry))

Organic Vinaigrette (Balsamic, Dijon, Raspberry)

Sugar Free (Italian Balsamic, Vinaigrette (Balsamic, Raspberry))

Sweet 'N Sour

Marzetti - Shelf Stable (Honey Dijon Fat Free, Italian Fat Free, Sweet & Sour Fat Free)

Newman's Own - Regular (Parisienne Dijon Lime, Red Wine Vinegar & Olive Oil, Two Thousand Island), Salad Mist (Balsamic, Italian)

Oliv - Vinaigrette (Aged Balsamic, Herbs De Provence, Sundried Tomato & Garlic, White Balsamic)

Private Selections - Poppy Seed, Raspberry Vinaigrette

Royal Food Products - Slender Select French Fat Free Red

Seeds Of Change - Balsamic Vinaigrette!!, French Tomato!!, Italian Herb Vinaigrette!!, Roasted Red Pepper Vinaigrette!!

Teresa's Select Recipes - Lite Honey Dijon

Trader Joe's - Dressings Balsamic Vinaigrette Regular!!

Walden Farms -

Single Serve Packets (Creamy Bacon, Honey Dijon, Italian, Ranch, Thousand Island)

Sugar Free No Carb (Balsamic Vinaigrette, Blue Cheese, Caesar, Coleslaw, Creamy (Bacon, Italian), French, Honey Dijon, Italian (Regular, w/Sun Dried Tomato), Ranch, Raspberry Vinaigrette, Russian, Sweet Onion, Thousand Island, Zesty Italian)

Wegmans Brand - Fat Free (Red Wine Vinegar, Roasted Red Pepper), Tarragon Vinaigrette

Wild Thymes -

Salad Refresher (Black Currant, Mango, Meyer Lemon, Morello Cherry, Passion Fruit, Pomegranate, Raspberry, Tangerine)

Vinaigrette (Fig Walnut, Mandarin Orange Basil, Mediterranean Balsamic, Parmesan Walnut Caesar, Raspberry Pear Balsamic, Roasted Apple Shallot, Tahitian Lime Ginger, Tuscan Tomato Basil)

Salami... see Sausage

Salmon... see also Fish

... *All Fresh Fish Is Gluten/Casein/Soy Free (Non-Marinated, Unseasoned)

Bumble Bee - Blueback, Keta, Pink, Premium Wild Pink, Prime Fillet Atlantic, Red

Crown Prince - Natural (Alaskan (Coho Alderwood Smoked, Pink Salmon), Skinless & Boneless Pacific Pink Salmon)

Great Value Brand (Wal-Mart) - Canned Alaskan Pink Salmon

Henry & Lisa's - 4 oz Wild, Battered Salmon Filets, Canned Wild Alaskan Pink

Hy-Vee - Frozen

Kirkland Signature - Fresh Atlantic, Frozen Alaskan Fillets, Sockeye (Canned, Frozen Fillets)

Kroger Brand - Canned

Publix - Coho Salmon Fillets, Sockeye Salmon Fillets

Pure Market Express▲ - Salmon●

Trader Joe's - Premium Salmon Patties**!!**

Salsa

Albertsons - Chunky (Medium, Mild)

Amy's - Organic (Black Bean & Corn**!**, Medium**!**, Mild**!**, Spicy Chipotle**!**)

Bone Suckin' Sauce - Hot, Regular

Bravos - Hot, Medium, Mild

Chi-Chi's - Fiesta, Garden, Natural, Original

S

Dave's Gourmet - Insanity Salsa

Dei Fratelli - Black Bean 'N Corn (Medium), Casera (Medium Hot, Mild), Chipotle (Medium), Original (Medium, Mild)

Drew's - Organic (Black Bean Cilantro & Corn Medium, Chipotle Lime Medium, Double Fire Roasted Medium, Hot, Medium, Mild)

Eat Smart - Naturals Garden Style Sweet

Emeril's - Kicked Up Chunky Hot, Original Recipe Medium, Southwest Style Medium

Fischer & Wieser -
Artichoke & Olive
Chipotle & Corn
Cilantro & Olive
Das Peach Haus Peach
Havana Mojito
Hot Habanero
Salsa (A La Charra, Verde Ranchera)
Timpone's Organic Salsa Muy Rica

Frontera - Gourmet Mexican Salsa (Chipotle, Corn & Poblano, Double Roasted, Habanero, Jalapeno Cilantro, Mango Key Lime, Medium Chunky Tomato, Mild Chunky Tomato, Red Pepper & Garlic, Roasted Tomato, Spanish Olive, Tomatillo)

Full Circle - Organic (Medium, Mild)

Green Mountain Gringo▲ - All Varieties

Hannaford Brand - Medium, Mild, Southwestern (Medium, Mild)

HealthMarket - Organic (Medium, Mild, Pineapple)

Herdez - Salsa Casera

Herr's - Chunky (Medium, Mild)

Hy-Vee - Thick & Chunky (Hot, Medium, Mild)

Kirkland Signature - Organic Medium

Kroger Brand -
Picante Sauce (Hot, Medium, Mild)
Thick & Chunky (Hot, Medium, Mild)
Traditional (Hot, Medium, Mild)
Verde
Viva (Medium, Mild)

La Victoria -
 Cilantro (Medium, Mild)
 Jalapena Extra Hot (Green, Red)
 Salsa Ranchera Hot
 Suprema (Medium, Mild)
 Thick 'N Chunky (Medium, Mild)
 Verde (Medium, Mild)
 Victoria Hot

Lowes Foods Brand - Thick & Chunky (Medium, Mild)

Meijer Brand -
 Original (Hot, Medium, Mild)
 Restaurant Style (Hot, Medium, Mild)
 Santa Fe Style (Medium, Mild)
 Thick & Chunky (Hot, Medium, Mild)

Melissa's - Salsa Casera

Mezzetta - California Habanero Salsa Twist & Shout

Miguel's - Black Bean & Corn●, Chipotle●, Medium●, Mild●, Roasted Garlic●

Mixes From The Heartland▲ - Mix (Corn & Tomato●, Garden●, Kick N Hot●, Sun Dried Tomato●, Tex Mex●)

Mrs. Renfro's - Black Bean, Chipotle Corn, Garlic, Green, Mild, Peach, Raspberry Chipotle, Roasted

Newman's Own - All Natural (Hot, Medium, Mild), Black Bean & Corn, Mango, Peach

O Organics - Chipotle, Chunky Bell Pepper, Fire Roasted Tomato, Mild

Old Dutch - Restaurante Salsa (Medium, Mild)

Old El Paso - Salsa Thick N' Chunky (Hot, Medium, Mild)

On The Border - Hot, Medium, Mild

Organicville - Medium●, Mild●, Pineapple●

Ortega - Black Bean & Corn, Garden Vegetable (Medium, Mild), Original (Medium, Mild), Salsa Verde, Thick & Chunky (Medium, Mild)

Pace - Chunky (Medium, Mild), Picante Sauce (Hot, Medium, Mild), Pico De Gallo, Thick & Chunky (Medium, Mild)

S

Private Selections - Authentic Restaurant Style, Black Beans & Corn, Cilantro, Fire Roasted, Green Chile, Peach Mango, Peppery Sweet Corn, Tart Lime

Publix - All Natural (Hot, Medium, Mild)

Publix GreenWise Market - Organic (Medium, Mild)

Pure Market Express▲ - Red Pepper●, Sassy●

Safeway Select -
  3 Bean (Medium)
  Fiesta Fajita
  Garlic Lovers
  Peach Pineapple (Medium)
  Roasted Tomato (Medium)
  Southwest (Hot, Medium, Mild)
  Verde (Medium)

Salpica - Chipotle Garlic, Cilantro Green Olive, Fall Harvest, Grilled Pineapple Key Lime, Habanero Lime, Mango Peach, Roasted Corn & Bean, Rustic Tomato, Spring Break, Summer Of Love, Tomato Jalapeno

Santa Barbara -
  Black Bean & Corn
  Hot
  Mango & Peach
  Roasted (Chili, Garlic)

Signature Cafe - Creamy Tomatillo w/Avocado, Fresca, Triple Roasted, Verde

Taco Bell - Thick 'N Chunky (Medium, Mild)

Trader Joe's -
  Authentica!!
  Chunky!
  Corn & Chili Tomatoless!!
  Double Roasted!!
  Fire Roasted Tomato!!
  Fresh (All Varieties!!, Black Bean & Roasted Corn!!)
  Garlic Chipotle!!

Hot & Smoky Chipotle**!**
Pineapple**!!**
Spicy Smoky Peach**!!**
Verde**!!**
UTZ - Mt. Misery Mike's Salsa Dip, Sweet Salsa Dip
Wegmans Brand - Hot, Medium, Mild, Organic (Hot, Mango, Medium, Mild), Roasted (Chipotle, Salsa Verde, Sweet Pepper, Tomato), Santa Fe Style
Winn Dixie - Hot, Medium, Mild
Wise - Medium, Mild

Salt
Albertsons - Iodized, Regular
Gluty Free - Citric Acid●
Great Value Brand (Wal-Mart) - Iodized, Plain
Hannaford Brand - Iodized, Regular
Kroger Brand
Lawry's - Seasoned**!!**
Marcum Spices - Iodized Salt, Sea Salt, Seasoned Salt
Meijer Brand - Iodized, Plain
Morton - Coarse Kosher Salt, Iodized Table Salt, Lite Salt Mixture, Plain Table Salt, Salt Substitute, Sea Salt (Coarse, Fine)
No Salt - Salt Substitute
Nuts Online - Citric Acid●
Private Selections - Mediterranean Sea Salt
Publix
Safeway Brand - Iodized, Plain, Rock
Spartan Brand - Garlic, Iodized, Plain
Stop & Shop Brand - Iodized Salt, Plain
The Vegetarian Express - All Purpose Veggie Salt**!**
Victoria Gourmet - Sea Salt (Anglesey, Australian Flake, Celtic, Trapani)
Wegmans Brand - Iodized, Plain, Sea Salt (Coarse Crystals, Fine Crystals)

Sandwich Meat... see Deli Meat

S Sardines
   ... *All Fresh Fish Is Gluten/Casein/Soy Free (Non-Marinated, Unseasoned)*

Bumble Bee - Sardines In Water

Crown Prince -
   Crosspacked Brisling In Olive Oil
   In Water
   One Layer Brisling In Mustard
   Skinless & Boneless In Olive Oil
   Two Layer Brisling In Olive Oil

Ocean Prince - Sardines In (Tomato Sauce, Water)

Sauces
   ... *(includes Marinara, Pasta, Tomato, etc.)*

A Taste Of Thai - Curry Paste (Green, Red, Yellow), Fish Sauce, Garlic
   Chili Pepper, Peanut Satay, Sweet Red Chili

Amy's -
   Organic
      Low Sodium Marinara **!**
      Family Marinara (Light In Sodium **!**, Regular **!**)
      Tomato Basil (Light In Sodium **!**, Regular **!**)

Baxters - Bramley Apple Sauce, Mint Sauce

Bertolli - Marinara w/Burgundy Wine, Tomato & Basil, Vidalia Onion
   w/Roasted Garlic

Black Horse - Apricot Sauce, Chili Verde Sauce, Marionberry Pepper
   Sauce, Raspberry Mustard Sauce, Savory Sauce, Spicy Sauce

Bove's Of Vermont - All Natural (Marinara, Mushroom & Wine,
   Roasted Garlic)

Capa Di Roma - Arrustica, Fresh Basil, Marinara, Roasted Garlic

Choy Sun - Oyster Flavored Sauce (Glass Bottles & Metal Cans)

Classico -
   Bruschetta (All Varieties)
   Red Sauce (Fire Roasted Tomato & Garlic, Italian Sausage w/
      Peppers & Onions, Organic (Spinach & Garlic, Tomato Herbs &
      Spices), Spicy Tomato & Basil, Tomato & Basil, Traditional Sweet
      Basil)

sauces

S

Contadina - Sauce (Extra Thick & Zesty, Regular, w/Garlic & Onion, w/Italian Herbs) *(Paste w/Italian Herbs Is Not Gluten-Free)*

Cuisine Sante▲ - Brown Sauce Mix●

Daddy Sam's - Bar B Que Sawce (Medium Ginger Jalapeno, Original), Salmon Glaze

Dave's Gourmet - Pasta Sauce (Organic (Red Heirloom, Roasted Garlic & Sweet Basil, Spicy Heirloom Marinara), Wild Mushroom)

Dei Fratelli - Pizza Sauce, Presto (Italian Dip, Pizza Sauce), Sloppy Joe, Tomato

Del Monte - All Tomato Products *(Except Spaghetti Sauce Flavor)*

Di Lusso - Sweet Onion Sauce

Dietz & Watson▲ - Sweet Vidalia Onions In Sauce●

Eden Organic - Apple Cherry Sauce, Apple Strawberry Sauce, Spaghetti Sauce (Organic, Organic No Salt Added)

Emeril's - Pasta Sauce (Kicked Up Tomato, Roasted Red Pepper, Sicilian Gravy)

Ethnic Gourmet - Simmer Sauce Bombay Curry

Fischer & Wieser -
All Purpose Vegetable & Meat Marinade
Charred Pineapple Bourbon
Chipotle Sauce (Blackberry, Blueberry, Original Roasted Raspberry, Plum Chipotle BBQ, Pomegranate & Mango)
Granny's Peach 'N' Pepper Pourin'
Mango Ginger Habanero
Papaya Lime Serrano
Sweet (& Savory Onion Glaze, Sour & Smokey Mustard Sauce)

Frank's RedHot - Chile 'N Lime, Original, Sweet Chili, Xtra Hot

Frontera -
Barbeque Sauce (Original Sweet & Smoky, Roasted Chipotle Pineapple, Texas Black Pepper)
Cocktail & Ceviche Sauce (Cilantro Lime, Tomato Chipotle)
Cooking Sauce (Roasted Garlic & Chipotle, Roasted Tomato & Cilantro)
Grilling Sauce (Chipotle Honey Mustard, Red Pepper Sesame)

S

Hot Sauce (Chipotle, Habanero, Jalapeno, Red Pepper)

Taco Sauce (Chipotle Garlic, Roasted Tomato)

Full Circle - Organic Pasta Sauce (Portabella Mushroom, Roasted Garlic, Tomato Basil), Organic Tomato Sauce

Fungus Among Us - Truffle Gatherers**!**

Hannaford Brand - Cranberry Sauce, Hot Sauce, Sloppy Joe Sauce, Taco Sauce

Hargis House - Sloppy Joe Sauce

House Of Blues - Bayou Heat Hot Sauce

Hy-Vee - Tomato Sauce

Ka-Me - Duck**!**, Fish**!**, Hot Mustard**!**, Sriracha**!**, Sweet Chili**!**

Kroger Brand - Extra Hot, Hot

Kurtz - Steak Sauce

Las Palmas - Red Chile, Red Enchilada

Lee Kum Kee - Shrimp

Lowes Foods Brand - Tomato

McCormick - Marinade Mix (Caribbean Citrus Seafood, Lemon Pepper Seafood)

Meijer Brand -

Extra Chunky Spaghetti Sauce (Garden Combo, Mushroom & Green Pepper)

Pasta Sauce Select (Marinara, Mushroom & Olive, Onion & Garlic, Original)

Tomato Sauce (Organic, Regular)

Mezzetta - Napa Valley Bistro Pasta Sauce (Arrabbiata, Artichoke Marinara, Fire Roasted Marinara, Homemade Style Marinara, Porcini Mushroom, Puttanesca, Roasted Garlic, Tomato Basil)

Midwest Country Fare - Tomato Sauce

Moore's Marinade - Honey BBQ Wing

Mr. Spice Organic - Sauce & Marinade (Ginger Stir Fry, Honey BBQ, Sweet & Sour, Thai Peanut)

Newman's Own - Fra Diavolo

O Organics - Marinara, Mushroom, Roasted Garlic, Tomato Basil

Panda Brand - Lo Mein Oyster Flavored Sauce, Oyster Flavored Sauce *(Green Label Only)*

Prego -
> Chunky Garden (Combo, Mushroom & Green Pepper, Mushroom Supreme w/Baby Portobello, Tomato Onion & Garlic)
> Flavored w/Meat
> Fresh Mushroom
> Heart Smart (Mushroom, Roasted Red Pepper & Garlic, Traditional)
> Italian Sausage & Garlic
> Marinara
> Mushroom & Garlic
> Roasted Garlic & Herb
> Tomato Basil Garlic
> Traditional

Private Selections - Pasta (Artichoke Bruschetta, Bolognese & Arrabbiata, Tomato Bruschetta)

Publix - Tomato Sauce

Pure Market Express▲ - Pasta Sauce (Creamy Garlic Dill●, Garlic Alfredo●, Spicy Peanut●)

Ragu - Light (No Sugar Added Tomato & Basil, Tomato & Basil)

Rao's Specialty Foods - Homemade (Arrabbiata, Cuore DiPomodoro, Marinara, Puttanesca, Roasted Eggplant, Southern Italian Pepper & Mushroom), Pizza Sauce

S&W - Homestyle Tomato Sauce

Safeway Brand - Sloppy Joe

Safeway Select -
> Gourmet Dipping Sauces (Honey Mustard, Sweet & Sour)
> Pasta Sauce (Arrabiatta, Garlic Basil, Mushroom/Onion, Roasted Onion & Garlic, Spicy Red Bell Pepper)

Salpica - Texas Picante

Santa Barbara Olive Co. - Pasta Sauce (Roasted Garlic, Wine & Mushroom)

Sauces 'N Love - Chimichurri (Cilantro, Traditional Parsley), Original Sauces (Arrabbiata, Barely Bolognese, Fresh Marinara & Pizza, Pommodoro & Basilico, Puttanesca)

S

Scarpetta - Arrabbiata, Barely Bolognese, Bruschetta Toppings (Tomato & Artichoke, Tomato & Capers), Fresh Marinara & Pizza Sauces, Puttanesca, Tomato & Arugula

Seeds Of Change - Indian Simmer Sauce (Jalfrezi**!!**, Madras**!!**), Madras Sauce**!!**, Pasta Sauce (Arrabiatta di Roma**!!**, Marinara di Venezia**!!**, Tomato Basil Genovese**!!**, Tuscan Tomato & Garlic**!!**)

Senora Verde - Taco Sauce (Medium, Mild)

Sharwood's - Jalfrezi, Pineapple & Coconut, Plum Sauce, Thai Mussaman Curry, Two Step (Coconut & Curry Biryani, Mint & Coriander Biryani, Tomato & Cumin Biryani)

Simply Boulder - Culinary Sauce (Coconut Peanut●, Honey Dijon●, Lemon Pesto●, Pineapple Ginger●)

Spartan Brand - Chili, Sloppy Joe, Tomato Sauce

Steels Gourmet - Mango Curry

Stubb's - Bar-B-Q Sauce (Hickory Bourbon●, Honey Pecan●, Mild●, Original●, Smokey Mesquite●, Spicy●)

Sweet Baby Ray's - Grilling Sauce (Maple & Brown Sugar, Original), Marinade & Sauce Steakhouse

Taste Of Inspiration -
Barbeque (Maple Chipotle**!**, Spicy Mango**!**, Wild Maine Blueberry**!**)
Grilling (Caribbean Mango**!**, Chipotle**!**, Sweet Apple**!**)

Tasty Bite - Simmer (Good Korma**!**, Pad Thai**!**, Rogan Josh**!**, Satay Partay**!**)

Texas Pete - Garlic Hot Sauce, Hotter Hot Sauce, Original Hot Sauce, Pepper, Seafood

Thai Kitchen -
10 Minute Simmer Sauce (Green Curry, Panang Curry, Red Curry)
Peanut Satay
Premium Fish Sauce
Spicy Thai Chili
Sweet Red Chili

The Ginger People - Ginger Lemon Grass**!**, Ginger Wasabi**!**, Hot Ginger Jalapeno**!**, Sweet Ginger Chili**!**

Trader Joe's -
> Organic (Marinara Sauce No Salt Added!!, Spaghetti Sauce!!)
> Regular (Arrabiata!!, Bruschetta, Chili Pepper!!, Curry
> Simmer!!, Pizza Fat Free!!, Tuscano Marinara Low Fat!!,
> Whole Peeled Tomatoes w/Basil)

Walden Farms - Alfredo, Marinara, Scampi

Wegmans Brand - Bruschetta Topping (Roasted Red Pepper,
> Traditional Tomato), Lemon & Caper Sauce, Prepared Horseradish,
> Tomato Regular

Wild Thymes - Dipping Sauce (Indian Vindaloo, Moroccan Spicy
> Pepper, Thai Chili Roasted Garlic)

Winn Dixie - Classic (Fra Diavolo, Marinara, Tomato Basil), Select
> Recipe Double Garlic

Woodstock Farms - Organic Sauce (Original), Organic Tomato
> Sauce (No Salt, Original)

Sauerkraut

B&G

Boar's Head

Cortland Valley Organic

Dietz & Watson▲ - Sauerkraut●

Eden Organic - Organic

Great Value Brand (Wal-Mart) - Canned

Hannaford Brand

Krrrrisp Kraut - Bavarian, Regular

Meijer Brand

S&W

Safeway Brand

Silver Floss

Spartan Brand

Wegmans Brand

Willie's

Sausage

Abraham - Diced Prosciutto

S

Aidells -
  Apricot Ginger Breakfast Links
  Artichoke & Garlic
  Cajun Style Andouille
  Chicken & Apple Breakfast Links (Minis, Regular)
  Habanero & Green Chile
  Mango (Breakfast Links, Regular)
  Maple & Smoked Bacon Breakfast Links
  Organic (Andouille, Chicken & Apple, Sun Dried Tomato, Sweet
    Basil & Roasted Garlic)
  Roasted Pepper w/Corn
  Smoked Chorizo
  Whiskey Fennel

Al Fresco -
  Chicken Sausage
    Breakfast Sausage (Apple Maple, Country Style, Wild
      Blueberry)
    Dinner Sausage Fully Cooked (Buffalo Style, Chipotle Chorizo,
      Roasted Garlic, Spicy Jalapeno, Sundried Tomato, Sweet
      Apple, Sweet Italian Style)
    Fresh Dinner Sausage (Buffalo Style, Sweet Apple, Sweet
      Italian Style)

Albertsons - Beef Smoked, Polska Kielbasa, Smoked

Applegate Farms -
  Genoa Salami (Hot, Organic, Regular)
  Natural Uncured Hot Dogs (Beef, Big Apple, Chicken, Turkey)
  Organic Sausage (Andouille, Chicken & Apple, Fire Roasted Red
    Pepper, Smoked Pork Andouille, Smoked Pork Bratwurst,
    Smoked Pork Kielbasa, Sweet Italian)
  Organic Uncured Hot Dogs (Beef, Chicken, Stadium Style, The
    Great Organic, Turkey)
  Pancetta
  Pepperoni
  Sopressata (Hot, Regular)

The Greatest Little Organic Smokey Pork Cocktail Franks
Turkey Salami

Armour -
1877 Hard Salami
Cotto Salami
Deli Sandwich Style Pepperoni
Hard Salami
Hickory Smoked Summer Sausage
Novara Hard Salami
Pepperoni (Italian Style, Turkey)
Smoked Sausage (Bun Length (Fresh Bratwurst, Italian)
Pre Sliced (Regular, Turkey)

Busseto -
Coppa (Dry, Hot)
Dry Salami (Black Pepper, Italian, Rosette De Lyon)
Herbs De Providence
Pepper Coated Salami
Premium Genoa Salami

Butcher's Cut - Beef Smoked Sausage, Bratwurst, Breakfast, Bun Length (Beef Franks, Meat Franks), Italian Sausage (Mild, Regular), Jumbo Franks (Chicken, Pork, Turkey), Polska Kielbasa

Butterball - Premium Turkey Franks (Bun Size, Jumbo, Regular), Turkey Sausage (Dinner (Polska Kielbasa, Smoked), Fresh (Bratwurst, Breakfast, Hot Italian, Sweet Italian), Smoked, Smoked Hot)

Canino's - Bratwurst●, Breakfast Sausage●, German Brand Sausage●, Hot Chorizo●, Hot Italian Sausage●, Mild Italian Sausage●, Polish Sausage●, Spicy Cajun Style Sausage●, Sweet Italian Sausage●

Castle Wood Reserve - Deli Meat (Genoa Salami, Hard Salami)

Coleman's Natural Foods -
All Natural Uncured (Beef Hot Dog●, Beef/Pork Franks●)
Chicken Sausage (Mild Italian●, Spicy Andouille●, Spicy Chipotle●, Spicy Chorizo●, Spicy Italian●, Sun Dried Tomato & Basil●)

S

    Fully Cooked Bratwurst●

    Organic Chicken Sausage (Mild Italian●, Sun Dried Tomato
       & Basil●, Sweet Apple●)

    Polish Kielbasa●

Di Lusso - Beef Summer

Dietz & Watson▲ -

    Abruzzese (Hot●, Sweet●)

    Baby Genoa (Pepper Salami●, Salami●)

    Beef Franks (Gourmet Lite●, Mini Cocktail●, New York Brand●,
       New York Griddle●)

    Beef Summer Sausage●

    Beerwurst●

    Black Forest (Bauernwurst●, Bratwurst●, Cooked Fresh Liver
       Ring●, Hungarian Brand Bratwurst●, Wieners●)

    Black Forest Wieners●

    Blood Kiska●

    Blutwurst●

    Cacciatore●

    Capocolla (Hot●, Sweet●)

    Chicken (Andouille●, Brats●, Italian●, Jerk●, Pepper & Onion
       Sausage●)

    Gourmet Lite Franks●

    Honey Roll●

    Italian●

    Knockwurst●

    Krakow●

    Landjaeger●

    Lunch Roll●

    Mini Chorizo●

    Natural Casing Knockwurst●

    Pancetta●

    Pepperoni●

    Polska Kielbasa●

    Pork Roll Grillin' Links●

Salami (Hard●, Hot & Zesty●, Milano Paper Wrap●, Mini●)
Sopressata (Hot●, Sweet●)
South Philly Style Pepper & Onion●
Twin Stick Pepperoni●

Eckrich -
Angus Beef
Beef Franks (Jumbo, Regular)
Bun Length Original
Country Fresh Roll Sausage
Deli Meat (Hard Salami Regular, Pepperoni Regular, Regular
    Summer Sausage, Salami Genoa)
Franks (Bun Sized Beef, Regular Lite)
Grillers Smoked Sausage (Original, Polish)
Lunch Meat (Pepperoni, Salami (Cotto, Hard))
Original Meat Franks (Bun Sized, Franks, Jumbo)
Polska Kielbasa
Skinless Turkey
Smoked Sausage (Beef, Regular)
XL Skinless Angus Beef

Empire Kosher - Chicken Franks, Roll (Turkey Bologna, Turkey
Salami), Turkey Franks

Farmer John -
Breakfast Sausage Links & Patties (Old Fashioned Maple Skinless,
    Original Roll, Original Skinless, Premium PC Links Lower Fat,
    Premium Sausage Patties Lower Fat)
California Natural Chicken Sausage (Chicken Brat Smoked,
    Mango & Habanero Smoked)
Dinner Sausage (Beef Rope, Classic Polish, Hot Louisiana
    Smoked, Jalapeno Pepper Premium Smoked, Mild Jalapeno
    Pepper Premium Rope, Premium Beef Rope, Red Hots Extra Hot
    Premium Smoked)
Franks & Wieners (Dodger Dogs, Premium (Beef Franks, Jumbo
    Beef Franks, Jumbo Meat Wieners, Meat Wieners))
Lemon Cracked Pepper Chicken Smoked

S

Fratelli Beretta - Big Sopressata, Bresaola, Cacciatorino, Coppa, Dry Sausage, Milano, Nostrano, Pancetta, Sopressata

Garrett County Farms -
Andouille Sausage **!**
Chorizo Sausage **!**
Franks (4XL Big Beef **!**, Chicken **!**, Old Fashioned Beef **!**, Original Deli **!**, Premium Beef **!**, Turkey **!**)
Kielbasa (Polska **!**, Turkey **!**)
Sliced Beef (Bologna **!**, Salami **!**)
Sliced Uncured Pepperoni **!**

Great Value Brand (Wal-Mart) - Breakfast (Beef Patties, Fully Cooked Pork Links, Maple Pork Patties, Original Pork Patties), Canned Vienna Sausage

Habbersett - Pork Sausage (Hearty Link, Links), Pork Sausage Roll, Quick 'N Easy (Sausage Links, Sausage Patties)

Hannaford Brand - Hot Dogs (Beef Franks, Weiners)

Hans All Natural - Breakfast Links (Organic Chicken●, Skinless Chicken●)

Hargis House - Chicken Vienna

Heaven Mills▲ - Kishka (Cholent●, Vegetable●)

Hertel's - All Original Fresh Sausages *(Except British Bangers)*

Hillshire Farms - Lit'l Beef Franks, Lit'l Polskas, Lit'l Smokies (Beef, Cheddar, Regular, Turkey Breast), Lit'l Wieners, Summer Sausage (Beef, Regular, Yard O Beef)

Honeysuckle White -
Hardwood Smoked Turkey Franks
Hickory Smoked Cooked Turkey Salami
Turkey Sausage (Breakfast (Links, Patties)
Fully Cooked Smoked (Original Links, Original Rope, Polish Rope)
Italian (Hot Links, Sweet Links)
Mild Italian Roll
Poblano Pepper Links
Traditional Bratwurst

Hormel - Bread Ready (Deli Pastrami, Hard Salami), Hard Salami, Little Sizzlers (Links, Patties), Natural Choice (Hard Salami, Pepperoni), Pepperoni, Turkey Pepperoni, Wranglers Franks (Beef, Smoked)

Hy-Vee - Cooked Salami, Little Smokies (Beef, Regular), Thin Sliced Pastrami

Ian's - Wheat Free Gluten Free Recipe Popcorn Turkey Corn

Jennie-O Turkey Store -
Breakfast Lover's Turkey Sausage
Extra Lean Smoked Turkey Sausage (Kielbasa, Regular)
Fresh
    Dinner Sausage (Hot Italian, Lean Turkey Bratwurst, Sweet Italian, Lean Turkey Patties)
    Frozen Fully Cooked Sausage (Links, Patties)
    Turkey Franks

Jimmy Dean -
Fully Cooked
    Hearty Crumbles (Hot, Original, Turkey)
    Links (Maple, Original, Turkey)
    Patties (Hot, Maple, Original, Sandwich Size, Turkey)
Maple Fresh Sausage (Links, Patties)
Original Fresh Sausage (Links, Patties)
Pork Roll Sausage (All Natural Regular, Hot, Italian, Light, Maple, Mild Country, Regular, Sage)

Johnsonville -
Bratwurst (Hot 'N Spicy, Original, Patties, Smoked, Stadium Style)
Breakfast
    Brown Sugar & Honey Links
    Mild Country Sausage Roll
    Original (Links, Patties)
    Vermont Maple Syrup (Links, Patties)
Chorizo
Irish O'Garlic

S
    Italian Ground Sausage (Hot, Mild, Sweet)
    Italian Links (Hot, Mild, Sweet)
    Polish
    Sausage Roll (Hot, Regular)
    Summer Sausage
        Beef
        Deli Bites (Beef, Original, Salami)
        Garlic
        Old World
        Original

Jones Dairy Farm -
    All Natural
        Hearty Pork Sausage Links●
        Light Pork Sausage & Rice Links●
        Little Link Pork Sausage●
        Maple Sausage Links●
        Original Pork Roll Sausage●
        Pork Sausage Patties●
    Golden Brown All Natural Fully Cooked
        Beef Links●
        Maple Sausage (Links●, Patties●)
        Mild Sausage (Links●, Patties●)
        Pork & Uncured Bacon Links●
        Sausage & Rice Links●
        Spicy Links●
        Turkey Links●

Kayem -
    Bratwurst Original
    Franks
        Beef (Fenway Style, Hot Dogs, Minis)
        Fenway Style
        Hot Dogs
        Jumbo Hot Dogs
        Lower Sodium Hot Dogs

Minis
Old Tyme Natural (Casing, Casing Beef, Casing Reds)
Skinnies
Kielbasa (Fresh, Old World Style, Polish)
Natural (4 Pepper Hot Italian, Sweet Italian)

Kroger Brand - Links Maple Flavored Breakfast, Maple Flavored Pork Sausage Patties, Vienna (Barbecue, Chicken, Original)

Kroger Value - Cooked Salami, Country, Old Fashioned Loaf, P&P Loaf

Lou's Famous - Chicken Sausage (Apple, Peppers & Onion, Roasted Red Pepper & Garlic, Spicy Italian, Sundried Tomato)

Malone's - Vienna Sausages

Maluma - All Bison Sausage

Member's Mark - Chicken Sausage (Gourmet Chicken & Apple)

Mulay's -
Ground Sausage (Breakfast●, Mild Italian●, Original●, Original Italian●)
Links (Breakfast●, Killer Hot●, Mild Italian●, Original●, Original Italian●)

Old Wisconsin - Summer Sausage (Beef, Original)

Organic Prairie -
Frozen Organic (Beef Hot Dogs!!, Bratwurst!!, Brown N Serve Breakfast Links!!, Italian Sausage!!)
Organic Pork Fresh Sliced Pepperoni!

Oscar Mayer -
Beef Franks (Bun Length, Classic, Light, Premium)
Salami (Deli Fresh Beef, Hard)
Summer Sausage (Beef, Regular)
Turkey Franks (Bun Length, Classic)
Variety Pak Bologna/Ham/Salami
Wieners (98 % Fat Free, Bun Length, Classic, Light, Premium)
XXL Hot Dogs (Deli Style Beef, Hot & Spicy, Premium Beef)

Primo - Hot Italian, Mild Italian, Old World Bratwurst

S

Primo Naturale -
    Chorizo (Sliced Dried, Stick Dried)
    Chub Salami (Genoa, Original, w/Black Pepper, w/Herbs)
    Pepperoni (Pillow Pack, Sliced Dried, Stick, Whole Large Diameter)
    Sliced Salami (Hard, Original, Premium Genoa, w/Black Pepper,
      w/Herbs)
    Sopressata (Sliced, Sticks, Whole)
    Whole Chorizo
    Whole Salami (Black Pepper, Genoa, Hard, Herb, Original)
Private Selections - Bratwurst (Hot Italian, Sausage), Frozen Mild
    Country Patties, Maple Flavored Links
Publix - Beef Hot Dogs, Franks (Beef, Jumbo Beef, Jumbo Meat,
    Meat), Fresh (Bratwurst, Chorizo, Italian (Hot, Mild), Turkey Italian
    (Hot, Mild))
Pure Market Express▲ - Sausage●
Rocky Jr. - Rocky Dogs Uncured Chicken Hot Dog●
Safeway Brand - Beef Franks, Bratwurst, Hot Dogs
Safeway Select - Country Pork (Hot, Regular), Italian, Regular
    Hot Dogs
Shelton's -
    Franks (Smoked Chicken, Smoked Turkey, Uncured Chicken)
    Turkey Sausage (Breakfast, Italian, Patties)
    Turkey Sticks (Pepperoni, Regular)
    Uncured Turkey
Spartan Brand - Hot, Mild
Sweet Bay - All Fresh Sausage
Trader Joe's - Sliced Prosciutto, Uncured All Beef Hot Dogs
Wegmans Brand - Beef Hot Dogs Skinless, Pepperoni Italian
    Style Regular
Wellshire Farms -
    Beef Franks Hot Dogs
      4XL Big!!
        The Old Fashioned!!
        The Premium!!
    Cocktail Franks!!

Frozen
- Chicken Apple Sausage (Links!!, Patties!!)
- Original Breakfast Sausage (Links!!, Patties!!)
- Sunrise Maple Sausage (Links!!, Patties!!)
- Turkey (Burgers!!, Maple Sausage Links!!, Maple Sausage Patties!!)
- Morning Maple Turkey Breakfast Link Sausage!!
- Polska Kielbasa!!
- Pork Andouille Sausage!!
- Pork Sausage (Chorizo!!, Linguica!!)
- Sliced (Beef Pepperoni!!, Beef Salami!!)
- The Original Deli Franks!!
- Turkey (Andouille Sausage!!, Dinner Link Sausage Mild Italian Style!!, Franks!!, Kielbasa!!, Tom Toms (Hot & Spicy!!, Original!!))

Winn Dixie - Hot Dogs (Chicken, Jumbo Beef, Meat Franks, Turkey), Smoked (Hot, Original, Polish, Polish Kielbasa, Turkey)

Scallops

... *All Fresh Seafood Is Gluten/Casein/Soy Free (Non-Marinated, Unseasoned)*

Scones/Scone Mix

Breakaway Bakery▲ - Lemon Raisin Scone Dough●, Orange Cranberry Scone Dough●

Cause You're Special▲ - English Scone Mix

Gluten Free Mama▲ - Mama's Scone Mix●

Kneaded Specialties▲ - Scones (Blueberry Lemon●, Cranberry Orange●, Double Chocolate Chip●)

Silly Yak Bakery - GF Scone Mix

Simply Organic▲ - Chai Spice Scone Mix

Seafood Sauce... see also Cocktail Sauce

Frontera - Cocktail & Ceviche Sauce (Cilantro Lime, Tomato Chipotle)

Kroger Brand - Cocktail Sauce

McCormick - Cajun, Mediterranean, Original Cocktail Sauce, Santa Fe Style

S

    Safeway Brand - Cocktail

    Simply Delicious - Organic Seafood Sauce w/Lemon

    Texas Pete - Seafood Cocktail

    Walden Farms

Seasoning Packets... see Seasonings

Seasonings

    Accent - Flavor Enhancer (All Varieties)

    Adolph's - Original Tenderizer!!, Tenderizer Seasoned w/Spices!!

    Albertsons - Bay Leaves, Black Pepper, Chili Powder, Cinnamon, Garlic Powder, Garlic Salt, Ginger, Nutmeg, Onion, Onion Powder, Paprika, Parsley Flakes, Seasoned Salt

    American Natural & Organic Spices -

    Adobo Seas Sf●, All Purpose●, Allspice Ground●, Allspice Whole●, Anise Ground●, Anise Star Whole●, Anise Whole●, Annatto Ground●, Annatto Seed●, Apple Pie Spice●, Arrowroot●, Baharat Sf●, Barbeque Sf●, Basil●, Beef Burger Sf●, Bouquet Garni Sf●, Cajun Seasoning●, Caraway Seeds●, Cardamom Decorticated●, Cardamom Ground●, Cardamom Pods Green●, Cayenne Pepper●, Celery Ground●, Celery Salt●, Celery Seeds●, Chicken Kabob Sf●, Chili Ancho Ground●, Chili California Ground●, Chili Chipotle Ground Chili Con Carne Sf●, Chili Guajillo Ground●, Chili Habanero Ground●, Chili Jalapeno Ground●, Chili New Mexico Ground●, Chili Pepper Crushed●, Chili Pepper Whole●, Chili Powder●, Chimichurri Seas Sf●, Chinese Five Spice Sf●, Chives●, Cilantro Flakes●, Cinnamon Ground●, Cinnamon Sticks●, Cloves Ground●, Cloves Whole●, Coriander Ground●, Coriander Seeds●, Cream Of Tartar●, Cumin Ground●, Cumin Seed Whole●, Curry Powder Hot●, Curry Powder Salt Free●, Curry Powder●, Curry Thai Red Salt Free●, Dill Seed●, Dill Weed●, Dukka Seasoning●, Epazote●, Fajita Seasoning Sf●, Fennel Ground●, Fennel Seeds●, Fenugreek (Ground●, Seeds●), Fines Herbes Sf●, Fish Grill & Broil Sf●, Flaxseed●, French Four Spice Sf●, Galangal●, Garam Masala●, Garlic (Bread●, Granulates●,

Herbs●, Minced●, Pepper●, Sliced●, Toasted●), Ginger
Ground●, Greek Seasoning Sf●, Gumbo File●, Harisa Sf●,
Herbs De Provence●, Horseradish Powder●, Italian Seasoning●,
Jerk Seasoning Sf●, Juniper Berries●, Lamb Seasoning Sf●,
Lavender●, Lemon (Grass●, Peel●, Pepper●), Mace Ground●,
Marjoram (Ground●, Whole●), Meatloaf Seasoning Sf●,
Mediterranean Seas Sf●, Mexican Seasoning Sf●, Mint
(Peppermint●, Spearmint●), Mulling Spice Blend●, Mustard
(Ground●, Seeds Brown●, Seeds Yellow●), Nigella Seed●,
Nutmeg (Ground●, Whole●), Onion Granulates●, Orange
Peel●, Oregano (Ground●, Mediterranean●, Mexican●)
Organic (Allspice (Ground●, Whole●), Almond Extract●, Anise
Star Whole●, Basil●, Bay Leave Whole●, Cajun Seasoning●,
Caraway Seeds●, Cardamom (Green●, Ground●, Original●),
Cayenne Pepper●, Celery Seeds●, Chili (Ancho Ground●,
Chipotle Ground●, Pepper Crush●, Powder●), Chinese Five
Spice●, Cinnamon (Ground●, Sticks●), Cloves (Ground●,
Whole●), Coriander (Ground●, Seeds●), Cumin Ground●,
Cumin Seeds Whole●, Curry (Powder●, Thai Herb●), Dill
Weed●, Fennel Seeds●, Garam Masala●, Garlic Granulates●,
Ginger Ground●, Herbs De Provence●, Italian Season●,
Juniper Berries●, Lemon Extract●, Marjoram Whole●, Melange
Pepper●, Mexican Seasoning●, Mustard (Ground●, Seed
Brown●, Seed Yellow●), Nutmeg (Ground●, Whole●), Onion
Granulates●, Orange Extract●, Oregano Mediterranean●,
Panch Phoron Sf●, Paprika (Regular●, Smoked●), Parsley●,
Pasta Spaghetti Sf●, Pepper Black Long●, Pepper Ground
(Black●, White●), Peppercorn (Black●, Green●, Melange●,
Melody●, Pink●, Szechuan●, White●), Pickling Seasoning●,
Pizza Spice Sf●, Poppy Seeds●, Pork Chop Sf●, Poultry
Seasoning●, Pumpkin Pie Spice●, Rosemary Whole●, Saffron●,
Sage (Ground●, Rubbed●, Whole●), Sesame (Seed Black●,
Seed White●), Tarragon●, Thyme●, Turmeric●, Vanilla Extract●),
Ras El Hanout Sf●, Rib Eye Steak Sf●, Rice Seasoning Sf●,

S

Rosemary (Ground●, Whole●), Safflower●, Saffron●, Sage (Ground●, Rubbed●, Whole●), Sambal Ulek Sf●, Savory Ground●, Savory●, Sesame Seed (Black●, White●), Shawarma Seas Sf●, Shish Kabob Sf●, Shrimp/Crab Gr&Bl Sf●, Sumac●, Taco Seasoning Sf●, Tandoori Masala Sf●, Tarragon●, Thai Spice Blend Sf●, Thyme Ground●, Thyme●, Turmeric●, Vanilla (Bean●, Extract●), Vegetable Seas Sf●, Vindaloo Seasoning Sf●, Wasabi Powder Sf●, Zatar Sf●)

Arora Creations - Organic Seasoning Packets (Bhindi Masala, Gobi, Punjabi Chole, Rajmah, Tandoori Chicken), Regular Seasoning Packets (Bhindi Masala, Chicken Tikka Masala, Goan Shrimp Curry, Gobi, Punjabi Chole, Tandoori Chicken)

Bone Suckin' Sauce - Seasoning & Rub (Hot, Regular)

Cali Fine Foods▲ - Gourmet Seasoning Packets (Dill Delight●, Garlic Gusto●, Herb Medley●, Spicy Fiesta●, Sweet & Spicy BBQ●)

Chi-Chi's - Fiesta Restaurante Seasoning Mix

Dave's Gourmet - Insanity Spice

Durkee - All Food Coloring, All Liquid Extracts, All Liquid Flavorings, All Pepper Black/White, Allspice, Alum, Anise Seed, Apple Pie Spice, Arrowroot, Basil, Bay Leaves, Caraway Seed, Cardamom, Cayenne Pepper, Celery Flakes, Celery Seed, Chicken & Rib Rub, Chicken Seasoning, Chili Powder, Chives, Cilantro, Cinnamon, Cloves, Coriander, Crazy Dave's Salt & Spice, Cream Of Tartar, Crushed Red Pepper, Cumin, Curry Powder, Dill Seed/Weed, Fennel, Garlic Minced, Garlic Pepper, Garlic Powder, Garlic Salt, Ginger, Italian Seasoning, Jamaican Jerk Seasoning, Lemon Pepper, Lime Pepper, Mace, Marjoram, Meat Tenderizer, Mint Leaves, MSG, Mustard, Nutmeg, Onion Minced, Onion Powder, Onion Salt, Orange Peel, Oregano, Paprika, Parsley, Pepper Green Bell, Pickling Spice, Poppy Seed, Poultry Seasoning, Pumpkin Pie Spice, Rosemary, Sage, Salt Free Garden Seasoning, Salt Free Garlic & Herb, Salt Free Lemon Pepper, Salt Free Original All Purpose Seasoning, Salt Free Vegetable Seasoning, Seasoned Pepper,

Sesame Seed, Six Pepper Blend, Spaghetti/Pasta Seasoning, Spicy Spaghetti Seasoning, Steak Seasoning, Tarragon, Thyme, Turmeric

Emeril's - Essence (Bayou Blast, Italian, Original, Southwest), Rub (Chicken, Steak, Turkey), Rubs (Fish, Rub)

Full Circle - All Varieties

Gaylord Hauser - Spike Magic (5 Herb, Garlic)

Grandma Ferdon's▲ - Chili Powder●, Pure Spices (Basil Leaves●, Caraway Seeds●, Garlic Flakes●, Ground (Allspice●, Black Peppercorns●, Cinnamon●, Cloves●, Coriander●, Ginger●, Nutmeg●), Italian●, Lemon Peel Granules●, Onion Flakes●, Onion Powder●, Paprika●, Whole Marjoram●, Whole Thyme●), Taco Seasoning Mix●

Hannaford Brand - Basil Leaves, Bay Leaves, Celery Salt, Chili Powder, Crushed Red Pepper, Garlic Powder, Garlic Salt, Ground Black Pepper, Ground Cinnamon, Ground Ginger, Ground Mustard, Ground Nutmeg, Minced Onion, Oregano Leaves, Paprika, Taco Seasoning Mix

Hy-Vee - Basil Leaf, Bay Leaves, Black Pepper, Chicken Grill Seasoning, Chili Powder, Chopped Onion, Dill Weed, Garlic Powder, Garlic Salt, Grinders (Black Peppercorn, Peppercorn Melange, Sea Salt), Ground Cinnamon, Ground Cloves, Ground Mustard, Iodized Salt, Italian Seasoning, Lemon Pepper, Meat Tenderizer, Oregano Leaf, Paprika, Parsley Flakes, Plain Salt, Red Crushed Pepper, Rosemary, Salt & Pepper Shaker, Seasoned Salt, Steak Grilling Seasoning, Thyme

Kirkland Signature - California Garlic, Chopped Onion, Cinnamon, Garlic Salt, Malabar Black Pepper, Organic No Salt, Sea Salt (Mediterranean Grinder, Pure), Sweet Mesquite, Tellicherry Pepper (Grinder, Whole Peppercorns)

Konriko▲ - Chipotle All Purpose Seasoning●, Creole Seasoning●

Kootenay Kitchen - Traditional Gomashio

Kroger Brand - Seasoning Mixes (Enchilada, Pork Chop, Stir Fry Oriental, Swiss Steak)

S

Lawry's - Garlic Pepper!!, Lemon Pepper!!, Salt Free 17!!, Seasoned Pepper!!, Seasoned Salt (25% Less Sodium!!, Black Pepper!!, Regular!!), Seasoning Mixes (Chimichurri Burrito Casserole!!, Guacamole!!, Mediterranean Sundried Tomato & Garlic Chicken!!, Tenderizing Beef Marinade!!)

Litehouse - Dried (Basil, Chives, Cilantro, Dill, Garlic, Italian Herb Blend, Mushrooms, Oregano, Parsley, Poultry Herb Blend, Red Onion, Salad Herb Blend, Spring Onion)

Marcum Spices - Barbeque Pork Seasoning Mix, Basil, Bay Leaves, Black Peppercorn, Chicken Seasoning, Chili Powder, Chili Seasoning Mix, Cinnamon Sugar, Coarse Ground Black Pepper, Crushed Oregano, Crushed Red Pepper, Cumin, Garlic Powder, Iodized Salt, Italian Seasoning, Lemon Pepper, Minced Onion, Onion Powder, Paprika, Parsley Flakes, Pure Ground Black Pepper, Pure Ground Cinnamon, Sea Salt, Seasoned Meat Tenderizer, Seasoned Salt, Soul Seasoning, Taco Seasoning Mix, Whole Peppercorns

Mayacamas - Chicken BBQ, Curry Blend, Salad Delight, Savory Salt

McCormick -

Bag 'N Season (Chicken, Herb Roasted Pork Tenderloin, Pork Chops, Swiss Steak)

Blends (Bon Appetite, Cajun Seasoning, Celery Salt, Chinese Five Spice, Curry Powder, Garam Masala, Garlic Salt, Greek Seasoning, Herbes De Provence, Hot Madras Curry Powder, Jamaican Jerk, Lemon & Pepper, Mediterranean Spiced Sea Salt, Poultry Seasoning, Poultry Seasoning, Red Curry Powder)

Grill Mates Dry Rub (Applewood, Chicken, Pork, Seafood, Steak, Sweet & Smoky)

Grill Mates Grinders (Montreal Chicken, Montreal Steak)

Grill Mates Marinade Packets (Brown Sugar Bourbon, Mexican Fiesta)

Grill Mates Seasoning Blends (25% Less Sodium Montreal Chicken, 25% Less Sodium Montreal Steak, Barbecue, Garlic & Onion Medley, Hamburger, Lemon Pepper w/Herbs, Mesquite,

Montreal Chicken, Montreal Steak, Roasted Garlic & Herb, Smokehouse Maple, Spicy Montreal Steak)

Gourmet Collection

100% Organic (Basil Leaves, Cayenne Red Pepper, Celery Seed, Chinese Ginger, Coarse Ground Black Peppercorn, Crushed Red Pepper, Crushed Rosemary, Curry Powder, Dill Weed, Fennel Seed, Garlic Powder, Ground Cloves, Ground Coriander Seed, Ground Cumin, Ground Mustard, Ground Nutmeg, Ground White Pepper, Herbes De Provence, Italian Seasoning, Marjoram Leaves, Oregano Leaves, Paprika, Parsley Flakes, Poppyseed, Rosemary Leaves, Rubbed Sage, Saigon Cinnamon, Sesame Seed, Tellicherry Black Peppercorns, Thyme Leaves, Turkish Basil Leaves)

Spices

California Lemon Peel, Caraway Seed, Cardamom Seed, Celery Seed, Chevril Leaves, Chipotle Chili Pepper, Chopped Chives, Cilantro Leaves, Cinnamon Stick, Coarse Ground Black Peppercorn, Coriander Seed, Cracked Black Pepper, Cream Of Tartar, Crushed Red Pepper, Crushed Rosemary, Crystallized Ginger, Cumin Seed, Cumin Seed, Diced Jalapeno Pepper, Dill Seed, Dill Weed, Fennel Seed, Garlic Powder, Green Peppercorns, Ground Allspice, Ground Cardamom, Ground Cayenne Red Pepper, Ground Cloves, Ground Coriander Seed, Ground Cumin, Ground Ginger, Ground Mace, Ground Marjoram, Ground Mediterranean Oregano, Ground Mustard, Ground Nutmeg, Ground Savory, Ground Thyme, Ground Turmeric, Ground White Pepper, Italian Seasoning, Lemongrass, Madagascar Vanilla Beans, Marjoram Leaves, Mediterranean Oregano Leaves, Mexican Oregano Leaves, Mexican Style Chili Powder, Mint Flakes, Onion Powder, Paprika, Parsley Flakes, Peppercorn Melange, Poppyseed, Roasted Ground Coriander, Roasted Ground Cumin, Roasted Ground Ginger, Roasted Saigon Cinnamon, Rosemary Leaves, Rubbed Sage, Sage Leaves,

S

Saigon Cinnamon, Sesame Seed, Sicilian Sea Salt, Smoked Paprika, Spanish Saffron, Tarragon Leaves, Tellicherry Black Peppercorns, Thyme Leaves, Toasted Sesame Seed, Valencia Orange Peel, Wasabi Powder, Whole Allspice, Whole Cloves, Whole Nutmeg, Yellow Mustard Seed)

Roasting Rub (Cracked Peppercorn Herb, French Herb, Savory Herb)

Seafood Rubs (Herb w/Lemon, Seafood Steamers Shrimp & Crab Boil, Sweet Citrus & Spice Salmon)

Seasoning Packets (Fajitas, Hickory Barbeque Buffalo Wings, Salsa, Sloppy Joes, Tex Mex Chili, Thick & Zesty Spaghetti Sauce)

Slow Cookers (Barbeque Pulled Pork, Chili)

Spices (Alum, Anise Seed, Apple Pie Spice, Basil Leaves, Bay Leaves, Black Peppercorns, Caraway Seed, Celery Flakes, Celery Salt, Celery Seed, Chives, Chopped Onions, Cilantro Leaves, Cinnamon Sticks, Cinnamon Sugar, Coarse Ground Black Pepper, Cream Of Tartar, Crushed Red Pepper, Cumin Seed, Curry Powder, Dill Seed, Dill Weed, Fennel Seed, Garlic & Italian Herb, Garlic Powder, Garlic Salt, Garlic w/Extra Virgin Olive Oil, Ground Allspice, Ground Black Pepper, Ground Cinnamon, Ground Cloves, Ground Cumin, Ground Ginger, Ground Mace, Ground Marjoram, Ground Mustard, Ground Nutmeg, Ground Oregano, Ground Red Pepper, Ground Sage, Ground Thyme, Ground White Pepper, Hot Mexican Style Chili Powder, Hot Shot Black & Red Pepper Blend, Italian Seasoning, Marjoram Leaves, Minced Garlic, Minced Onions, Mixed Pickling Spice, Mustard Seed, Onion Powder, Onion Salt, Oregano Leaves, Paprika, Parsley Flakes, Poppy Seed, Poultry Seasoning, Pumpkin Pie Spice, Roasted Garlic Blend, Rosemary Leaves, Rubbed Sage, Sesame Seed, Sliced Garlic, Smokehouse Ground Black Pepper, Tarragon Leaves, Texas Style Chili Powder, Thyme Leaves, Turmeric, Whole Allspice, Whole Cloves, Whole Mexican Oregano)

Meijer Brand - Black Pepper, Chili Powder, Cinnamon, Garlic Powder, Garlic Salt, Mild Taco Seasoning Packet, Minced Onion,

Onion Salt, Oregano Leaves, Paprika, Parsley Flakes, Seasoned Salt, Spaghetti Mix, Taco Seasoning Packet

Melissa's - Garlic In Pure Olive Oil

Midwest Country Fare - Chili Powder, Chopped Onion, Cinnamon, Garlic Powder, Garlic Salt, Ground Black Pepper, Italian, Onion Powder, Parsley Flakes, Pure Ground Black Pepper, Seasoned Salt

Morton - Canning & Pickling Salt, Hot Salt, Lite Salt Mixture, Nature's Seasons Seasoning Blend, Popcorn Salt, Salt & Pepper Shakers, Seasoned Salt, Smoke Flavored Sugar Cure, Sugar Cure, Tender Quick

Mrs. Dash - Caribbean Citrus, Extra Spicy, Fiesta Lime, Garlic & Herb, Grilling Blend Chicken, Italian Medley, Lemon Pepper, Onion & Herb, Original Blend, Southwest Chipotle, Table Blend, Tomato Basil Garlic

Nantucket Off-Shore - Garden, Rub (Bayou, Dragon, Mt. Olympus, Nantucket, Prairie, Pueblo, Rasta, Renaissance), Shellfish Boil, St. Remy

Nielsen-Massey - Madagascar Bourbon Pure Vanilla Powder●

Nuts Online - Chamomile Flowers●, Garam Masala●, Ground Sumac●, Hibiscus Flowers●, Mahlab●, Mixed Syrian Spices●, Spearmint●, Whole Licorice Root●

O Organics - Basil Leaves, Bay Leaves, Cayenne Peppers, Chili Powder, Ground (Cinnamon, Cloves, Cumin, Nutmeg), Paprika

Old Bay - 30% Less Sodium, Blackened Seasoning, Garlic & Herb, Lemon & Herb, Original, Rub, Seafood Steamer

Ortega - Taco Seasoning Mix (40% Less Sodium, Chipotle, Hot & Spicy, Jalapeno & Onion, Original)

Polaner▲ - Ready To Use Wet Spices (All Varieties)

Private Selections - All Varieties, Rubs (Asian, Kicked Up Poultry, Peppercorn, Sweet & Spicy)

Publix - Adobo Seasoning w/o Pepper, Adobo Seasoning w/Pepper, Black Pepper, Chili Powder, Cinnamon, Garlic Powder, Garlic Powder w/Parsley, Garlic Salt, Ground Cumin, Ground Ginger,

S

Ground Red Pepper, Italian Seasonings, Lemon & Pepper, Minced Onion, Onion Powder, Paprika, Parsley Flakes, Salt, Seasoned Salt, Taco Seasoning Mix, Whole Basil Leaves, Whole Bay Leaves, Whole Oregano

Rancher's Reserve - Rubs (Classic Steak, Cowboy Blend w/Coffee, Roast)

Safeway Brand - All Spices & Seasonings, Fajita Seasoning Mix, Meat Marinade Mix

Sharwood's - Curry Powder (Hot, Medium, Mild)

Spartan Brand - Black Pepper, Brine Salt Black Sleeve, Chili Powder, Cinnamon, Garlic Powder, Garlic Salt, Ground Nutmeg, Imitation Vanilla, Iodized Salt, Iodized Salt Crystals, Minced Onion, Oregano Leaves, Paprika, Parsley Flakes, Salt, Vanilla Extract

Spice Islands - All Food Coloring, All Liquid Extracts, All Liquid Flavorings, All Pepper Black/White, All Steak Seasonings, Allspice, Alum, Anise Seed, Apple Pie Spice, Arrowroot, Basil, Bay Leaves, Caraway Seed, Cardamom, Cayenne Pepper, Celery Flakes, Celery Seed, Chicken & Rib Rub, Chicken Seasoning, Chili Powder, Chives, Cilantro, Cinnamon, Cloves, Coriander, Crazy Dave's Lemon Pepper, Crazy Dave's Salt & Spice, Cream Of Tartar, Crushed Red Pepper, Cumin, Curry Powder, Dill Seed/Weed, Fennel, Garlic Minced, Garlic Pepper, Garlic Powder, Garlic Salt, Ginger, Italian Seasoning, Jamaican Jerk Seasoning, Lemon Pepper, Lime Pepper, Mace, Marjoram, Meat Tenderizer, Mint Leaves, MSG, Mustard, Nutmeg, Onion Minced, Onion Powder, Onion Salt, Orange Peel, Oregano, Paprika, Parsley, Pepper Green Bell, Pickling Spice, Poppy Seed, Poultry Seasoning, Pumpkin Pie Spice, Rosemary, Sage, Salt Free Garden Seasoning, Salt Free Garlic & Herb, Salt Free Lemon Pepper, Salt Free Original All Purpose Seasoning, Salt Free Veg. Seasoning, Seasoned Pepper, Sesame Seed, Six Pepper Blend, Spaghetti/Pasta Seasoning, Spicy Spaghetti Seasoning, Tarragon, Thyme, Turmeric

Spice Islands Salt-Free - All Varieties

seasonings

S

Spice Islands Specialty - Beau Monde, Crystallized Ginger, Fine Herbs, Garlic Pepper Seasoning, Italian Herb Seasoning, Old Hickory Smoked Salt, Saffron, Summer Savory, Vanilla Bean

Spicely▲ - 100% Certified Organic Extracts (All Varieties)●, Natural Spices (All Varieties)●, Organic Spices (All Varieties)●, Seasoning Blends (All Varieties)●

Stubb's - Spice Rub (Bar BQ●, Chile Lime●, Rosemary Ginger●)

Tones - All Food Coloring, All Liquid Extracts, All Liquid Flavorings, All Pepper Black/White, All Steak Seasonings, Allspice, Alum, Anise Seed, Apple Pie Spice, Arrowroot, Basil, Bay Leaves, Caraway Seed, Cardamom, Cayenne Pepper, Celery Flakes, Celery Seed, Chicken & Rib Rub, Chicken Seasoning, Chili Powder, Chives, Cilantro, Cinnamon, Cloves, Coriander, Crazy Dave's Salt & Spice, Cream Of Tartar, Crushed Red Pepper, Cumin, Curry Powder, Dill Seed/Weed, Fennel, Garlic Minced, Garlic Pepper, Garlic Powder, Garlic Salt, Ginger, Italian Seasoning, Jamaican Jerk Seasoning, Lemon Pepper, Lime Pepper, Mace, Marjoram, Meat Tenderizer, Mint Leaves, MSG, Mustard, Nutmeg, Onion Minced, Onion Powder, Onion Salt, Orange Peel, Oregano, Paprika, Parsley, Pepper Green Bell, Pickling Spice, Poppy Seed, Poultry Seasoning, Pumpkin Pie Spice, Rosemary, Sage, Salt Free Garden Seasoning, Salt Free Garlic & Herb, Salt Free Lemon Pepper, Salt Free Original All Purpose Seasoning, Salt Free Veg. Seasoning, Seasoned Pepper, Sesame Seed, Six Pepper Blend, Spaghetti/Pasta Seasoning, Spicy Spaghetti Seasoning, Tarragon, Thyme, Turmeric

Victoria Gourmet - 7 Seed Crust, Brining Blend (Asian, Smoky, Spicy, Traditional), Chipotle Pepper Flakes, Cinnamon Chili Rub, Fire Roasted Tomatoes, Jalapeno Pepper Flakes, Pepper (Lemon, Mill Mix), Peppercorns (Tellicherry, White), Red Bell Peppers, Red Pepper Flakes, Roasted Garlic Slices, Shallots, Toasted Sesame Ginger

Watkins - Garlic Salt, Seasoning (All Purpose, Chicken, Coleslaw, Grill, Ground Beef, Omelet Souffle, Potato Salad, Poultry, Soup & Vegetable)

S

Weber Grill Creations - Club Pack Seasoning Smokey Mesquite, Grinders (Chicago Steak, Roasted Garlic & Herb, Six Pepper Fusion, Twisted Citrus Garlic, Zesty Lemon Seasoning), Seasoning (Chicago Steak, Kick 'N Chicken, Mango Lime, N'Orleans Cajun, Seasoning Salt, Smokey Mesquite, Veggie Grill)

Wegmans Brand - Bay Leaves, Black Pepper, Cracked Pepper Blend, Fleur De Sel Sea Salt, Garlic & Sea Salt, Oregano, Parsley, Sage

Wright's - Liquid Smoke (Hickory Seasoning, Mesquite)

Seaweed

Eden Organic - Agar Agar Bars, Agar Agar Flakes

Nagai's - Sushi Nori Roasted Seaweed

Yaki - Sushi Nori Roasted Seaweed

Yamamotoyama - Roasted Nori, Temaki Party Toasted

Seeds

Arrowhead Mills - Flax, Mechanically Hulled Sesame, Organic Golden Flax, Sunflower, Unhulled Sesame

Durkee - Anise, Celery, Dill, Poppy, Sesame

Eden Organic - Organic Pumpkin Dry Roasted & Salted

FritoLay - Sunflower Kernels!!

Gerbs Pumpkin Seeds - Raw Kernel Pumpkin Seeds●, Sunflower Seeds w/Sea Salt●, Whole Roasted Pumpkin Seeds Homestyle Onion & Garlic●

Gluty Free -

Hemp●

Organic Golden Flax Seed●

Pumpkin Seeds

Organic No Shell●

Raw (In Shell●, No Shell●)

Salted (No Shell●, Organic No Shell●)

Unsalted (In Shell●, No Shell●)

Raw (Chia●, White Chia●)

Raw Organic (Chia●, Hemp●)

Sesame (Hulled)●

Sunflower Seeds
- Raw (In Shell●, No Shell●)
- Raw Organic No Shell●
- Salted (In Shell●, No Shell●)
- Unsalted (In Shell●, Israeli In Shell●, No Shell●)

Watermelon Seeds●

Goraw▲ - Seed Mix (Simple●, Spicy●), Seeds (Sprouted Pumpkin●, Sprouted Sunflower●)

Hy-Vee - Dry Roasted Sunflower Kernels

Kaia Foods - Sprouted Sunflower Seeds (Cocoa Mole, Garlic & Sea Salt●, Sweet Curry●, Teriyaki●)

Meijer Brand - Sunflower (Plain, Salted In Shell)

Nuts Online -
- Chia Seeds (Organic●, Regular●, White●)
- Hemp●
- Hulled Sesame Seeds●
- Organic Raw No Shell Hemp●
- Pepitas
  - Organic Dry Roasted Salted No Shell Pumpkin Seeds●
  - Organic No Shell Pumpkin Seeds●
  - Raw No Shell Pumpkin Seeds●
  - Roasted (Salted No Shell Pumpkin Seeds●, Unsalted No Shell Pumpkin Seeds●
- Pumpkin Seeds (Raw In Shell●, Sprouted●)
- Roasted Squash Seeds Unsalted In Shell●
- Sunflower Seeds
  - Israeli Unsalted In Shell●
  - Organic Raw No Shell●
  - Organic Roasted Salted No Shell●
  - Raw (In Shell●, No Shell●)
  - Roasted (Salted In Shell●, Salted No Shell●, Unsalted In Shell●, Unsalted No Shell●)
- Watermelon Seeds●

S

Publix - Sunflower Seeds

Pure Market Express▲ - Spicy Pepitos●

Purely Chia▲ - White Chia Seed (Micro Milled●, Whole●)

Running Food▲ - Chia Seed (Milled●, Whole●)

Ruth's Hemp Power - Raw Goodness Chia Seed, Soft Hemp Shelled

Shiloh Farms - Black Sesame Seeds , Chia Seeds

Spice Islands - Anise, Caraway, Celery, Dill, Poppy, Sesame

Spitz -
  Seasoned Pumpkin**!!**
  Sunflower (Chili Lime**!!**, Cracked Pepper**!!**, Dill Pickle**!!**,
    Salted**!!**, Seasoned**!!**, Smoky BBQ**!!**, Spicy**!!**)

Tones - Anise, Caraway, Celery, Dill, Poppy, Sesame

Tropical Traditions - Whole Golden Flax Seeds

Woodstock Farms - Non Organic Seeds (Pumpkin (Regular, Roasted
  & Salted), Sunflower Hulled (Regular, Roasted & Salted, Roasted
  No Salt)), Organic Seeds (Flax, Hulled Sesame, Pumpkin Regular,
  Sunflower (Hulled, Hulled Roasted No Salt), White Quinoa)

Sesame Oil... see Oil

Sesame Seeds... see Seeds

Shakes... see also Smoothies

  Amazake -
    Almond
    Amazing Mango
    Banana Appeal
    Chocolate Almond
    Cool Coconut
    Go (Go Green, Hazelnuts)
    Oh So Original
    Rice Nog
    Tiger Chai
    Vanilla Pecan Pie
  Gluty Free -
    Organic Cacao Powder●
    Powder Raw Organic (Acai●, Maca●, Red Maca●)
    Raw Cacao Powder●

Nuts Online -
   Organic Powder
      Acai●
      Hemp Protein●
      Lucuma●
      Maca●
      Mesquite●
      Noni●
      Pomegranate●
      Raw (Strawberry●, Vita Cherry●)
      Red Maca●
      Wild Blueberry●
      Yumberry●
   Powder
      Apple Cider Vinegar●
      Camu Camu●
      Chamomile●
      Chlorella●
      Dandelion Root●
      Echinacea●
      Ginkgo Leaf●
      Goji Berry●
      Green Tea●
      Mangosteen●
      Pumpkin Seed●
      Spirulina●
      Stevia●
      Tomato●

Shortening
   Tropical Traditions - Organic Palm Shortening

Shrimp
   ... *All Fresh Seafood Is Gluten/Casein/Soy Free (Non-Marinated, Unseasoned)
   Bumble Bee - Broken, Deveined Shrimp (Large, Medium, Small), Jumbo, Large, Small, Tiny

S

Captain's Choice - Cooked Tail On Shrimp
Chicken Of The Sea - All Shrimp Products
Crown Prince - Broken, Tiny
Great Value Brand (Wal-Mart) - Canned Tiny Shrimp
Henry & Lisa's - Uncooked Natural
Hy-Vee - Frozen Cooked, Platter
Kirkland Signature - Frozen (Cooked, Raw)
Port Side - Frozen Cooked Salad, Frozen Shrimp (Cooked Medium, Ready To Eat)
Publix - All Sizes (Cooked, Fresh)
Sweet Bay - All Frozen
Wegmans Brand - Shrimp From Belize Uncooked

Shrimp Sauce... see Cocktail Sauce and/or Seafood Sauce

Sloppy Joe/Sloppy Joe Sauce
Hannaford Brand
Heinz - Sloppy Joe Sauce
Hormel - Not So Sloppy Joe
Hy-Vee
Kroger Brand
Meijer Brand - Sloppy Joe Mix, Sloppy Joe Sauce
Safeway Brand
Spartan Brand - Mix, Sauce
Winn Dixie - Original

Smoke
Wright's - Liquid Smoke (Hickory Seasoning, Mesquite)

Smoked Sausage... see Sausage

Smoked Turkey... see Turkey

Smoothies... see also Shakes
Ella's Kitchen - Smoothie Fruits (The Green One, The Purple One, The Red One, The Yellow One)
Hansen's Smoothie Nectar - Energy Island Blast, Guava Strawberry, Mango Pineapple, Peach Berry, Pineapple Coconut, Strawberry Banana

snacks

S

Pure Market Express▲ - Athena●, Blueberry Buzz●, Classic Green●, Creamy Strawberry●, Easy Like Sunday Morning●, Greenberry Heaven●, Happy Green●, Hemp Love●, Jolly Green●, Life's A Peach●, Mud Slide Pie●, Om●, Pandora's Peach●, Perfect Pear●, Pina Colada Song●, Power Ranger●, Purple Power●, Razzle●, Thin Mint●, Tropical Peach●, Vanilla Nut●

Snacks

AllerEnergy▲ - Soft Pretzels

Annie's - Organic Bunny Fruit Snacks (Berry Patch**!!**, Summer Strawberry**!!**, Sunny Citrus**!!**, Tropical Treat**!!**)

Baken-Ets - Pork Skins (Sweet 'N Tangy**!!**, Traditional**!!**)

Betty Lou's - Krispy Bites, Nut Butter Balls (Almond, Cashew Pecan, Chocolate Walnut, Spirulina Ginseng)

CheeCha▲ - Potato Puffs (Luscious Lime, Mediterranean Ginger, Original, Sea Salt & Spiced Pepper, Sea Salt & Vinegar)

Cheeky Monkey▲ - Peanut Butter Puffs●

Crunchies -
  Freeze Dried (Blueberries, Mango, Mixed Fruit, Pears, Pineapple, Raspberries, Roasted Veggies, Strawberries, Tropical Fruit, Very Berry)
  Organic (100% Bananas, 100% Peas, 100% Strawberries)

Eat Smart - Naturals (Garden Veggie Crisps●, Garden Veggie Stix)

Eden Organic - All Mixed Up Regular, Wild Berry Mix

Edward & Sons - Brown Rice Snaps (Onion Garlic, Plain Unsalted, Sesame Unsalted, Toasted Onion, Vegetable)

Gerbs Pumpkin Seeds -
  Baked Kernel Pumpkin Seeds (Roasted Red Pepper●, Toasted Onion & Garlic●, Touch Of Sea Salt●)
  Whole Roasted Pumpkin Seeds (Homestyle Red Pepper●, Lightly Salted●, Sea Salt N' Cracked Pepper Pumpkin Seeds In Shell●)

Glenny's - Brown Rice Marshmallow Treat (Chocolate ●, Peanut Caramel ●, Raspberry Jubilee ●, Vanilla ●)

S

Goraw▲ -
Flax Snax (Pizza●, Simple●, Spicy●)
Ginger Snaps●
Granola (Apple Cinnamon●, Live●, Live Chocolate●, Simple●)
Seed Mix (Simple●, Spicy●)
Seeds (Sprouted Pumpkin●, Sprouted Sunflower●)
Super Chips (Pumpkin●, Spirulina●)
Herr's - Pork Rinds (BBQ Flavored, Original)
Johnsonville - Summer Sausage Deli Bites (Beef, Original, Salami)
Kroger Brand - Popcorn Salted, Pork Rinds (Barbecue, Hot & Spicy)
Kroger Value - Gummi (Bears, Sour Neon Bears, Sour Neon Worms, Worms)
Lowes Foods Brand - Pork Rinds (BBQ, Regular)
Mareblu Naturals▲ -
Crunch Bags (Almond●, Cashew●, Cashew Coconut●, CranMango Cashew●, Pecan Cinnamon●, Pecan Cranberry Cinnamon●)
Crunch Bars (Almond●, Cashew●)
Trail Mix Crunch Bags (Blueberry Pomegranate●, Cranberry Pomegranate●, Cranblueberry●, Cranstrawberry●, Pecan●, Pistachio●)
Trail Mix Crunch Bars (BlueCran Pomegranate●, Mango Pomegranate●, Pistachio●, Strawberry Pomegranate●)
Mary's Gone Crackers▲ - Sticks & Twigs (Chipotle Tomato●, Curry●)
Meijer Brand -
Fruit Rolls
Justice League Galactic Berry
Rescue Heroes
Strawberry (Garfield, Regular)
Wildberry Rush
Fruit Snacks
African Safari
Curious George

Jungle Adventure
Justice League (Big Box, Regular)
Mixed Fruit
Rescue Heroes Big Box
Underwater World
Variety Pack (Big Boy, Regular)

Mini Pops▲ - Popped Sorghum (Hot N' Chilly Chili●, Little Lemon Pepper●, Petite Plain●, Subatomic Sea Salt●)

Mrs. Crimble's - Slightly Salted Corn Cakes

Mrs. May's Naturals - Crunch (Almond●, Black Sesame●, Cashew●, Coconut Almond●, Cran Blueberry●, Cran Tropical●, Pom Raspberry●, Pumpkin●, Strawberry Pineapple●, Sunflower●, Ultimate●, Walnut●, White Sesame●)

Nutland - Almond Crunch●, Berries & Cherries Crunch●, Cashew Crunch●, Pecan Crunch●, Pistachio Crunch●, Trail Mix Crunch●

Nuts Online - Organic Pecan Date Rolls●, Organic Walnut Date Rolls●, Raw Organic Cacao Beans●, Turkish Delight (Almond●, Mixed Nut●, Pistachio●)

Nu-World Foods▲ - Snackers (BBQ Sweet & Sassy●, Chili Lime●, French Onion●)

Old Dutch - Bac'N Puffs

Original Tings - Crunchy Corn Sticks

Oskri Organics - Honey Crunch (Almond, Cashew w/Cranberries, Pecan w/Cinnamon)

Pirate's Booty - Popcorn Barbeque**!**

Planters - Harvest (Almond Orchard Blend, California Almonds, Jumbo Cashews, Pistachio Grove Blend), On The Go (Cocktail Peanuts Stadium Roasted In Shell Salted, Kettle Roasted Extra Crunchy Classic Salt, Peanuts (Dry Roasted, Honey Roasted, Salted), Sunflower Kernels), Trail Mix (Fruit & Nut, Mixed Nuts & Raisins, Nuts Seeds & Raisins)

Publix - Deli Snacks Popcorn**!!**

Pure Market Express▲ - Bacon Jalapeno Poppers●, MexiWraps●, Pepperoni Bites●, Spicy Pepitos●

S

Sensible Foods - Organic Crunch Dried Sweet Corn

Sharkies▲ - Kids Sports Chews (Berry Blasters, Tropical Splash), Organic Energy Sports Chews (Berry Blasters, Citrus Squeeze, Fruit Splash, Watermelon Scream)

Sunbelt - Fruit Jammers, Gummy Bears

Trader Joe's - Green Bean Snacks‼, Sea Salt & Pepper Rice Crisps‼

Woodstock Farms - Organic Snack Mixes (Campfire, Cranberry Walnut Cashew, Goji Berry Power, Trail Mix, Tropical Delight, Tropical Fruit), Snack Mixes (California Supreme, Cape Cod Cranberry, Cascade, Cranberrys Cove, Gourmet Trail, In The Raw)

Soda Pop/Carbonated Beverages

7up - All Varieties

A & W - Root Beer

Aquafina - FlavorSplash (Grape, Lemon, Peach Mango, Raspberry, Strawberry Kiwi, Wild Berry)

Barq's Root Beer - Diet, Diet Red Crème Soda, Regular

Blue Sky - All Soda Varieties

Boylan Bottleworks -
    Birch Beer (Creamy Red, Diet, Regular)
    Black Cherry
    Creme
    Diet (Black Cherry, Cane Cola, Creme, Root Beer)
    Ginger Ale
    Grape
    Natural (Black Cherry, Cane Cola, Root Beer)
    Orange (Creme, Regular)
    Root Beer
    Seltzer (Lemon, Orange, Pure)
    Sugar Cane Cola

Bunch - Grape Soda

Calistoga - Sparkling Juice Beverages (All Flavors)

Canada Dry - Club Soda (All Varieties), Ginger Ale (Cranberry, Diet, Regular), Seltzer (All Varieties), Tonic Water (All Varieties)

soda pop/carbonated beverages

S

Clear American (Wal-Mart) - Sparkling Water (Black Cherry, Golden Peach, Key Lime, Lemon, Mandarin Orange, Pomegranate Blueberry Acai, Raspberry Apple, Strawberry, White Grape, Wild Cherry)

Coca-Cola -
Cherry Coke (Diet, Regular, Zero)
Classic Coke (Caffeine Free, Regular, Zero)
Diet Coke (Caffeine Free, Plus, Regular, w/Lime, w/Splenda)
Vanilla Coke (Regular, Zero)

Crush - Cherry, Grape, Strawberry

Diet Rite

Dr. Pepper - All Varieties

Fanta - Grape

Fiesta Mirinda - Mango, Pina

Great Value Brand (Wal-Mart) - Low Sodium Club Soda, Sodium Free Seltzer, Tonic Water (Calorie Free, Regular)

Hannaford Brand - All Soda Flavors, Seltzer Water

Hansen's - All Sodas

Hires - Root Beer

Hy-Vee -
Black Cherry
Cherry Cola
Club Soda
Cola (Diet, Regular)
Cream Soda
Diet (Dr. Hy-Vee, Tonic)
Dr. Hy-Vee
Fruit Punch (Coolers, Regular)
Gingerale
Grape
Hee Haw (Diet, Regular)
Lemon Lime
Root Beer (Diet, Regular)
Seltzer Water

S

Sour
Strawberry
Tonic Water
Tropical Punch Coolers
Water Cooler (Black Cherry, Key Lime, Kiwi Strawberry, Mixed
    Berry, Peach, Peach Melba, Raspberry, Strawberry, White Grape)

I.B.C. - Root Beer
Juicy Juice - Sparkling Fruit Juice (All Flavors)
Kas Mas
Kroger Brand - Big K Soft Drinks
Lowes Foods Brand -
Cola (Diet, Regular)
Dr. Sparkle
Ginger Ale
Grape
Kiwi Strawberry
Lemonade
Mountain Breeze
Root Beer
Sparkle Up
Manzanita Sol
Meijer Brand - Encore (Cherry Red, Diet (Blue, Red)), Red Pop
Mr. Pibb - Xtra, Zero
Mug - Cream Soda (Diet, Regular), Root Beer (Diet, Regular)
O Organics - Italian Soda (Cranberry Acai, Lemon, Pink Grapefruit,
    Pomegranate)
Orangina - Sparkling Citrus Beverage
Patch - Strawberry Soda
Patio - Gingerale, Quinine Tonic
Pepsi -
Caffeine Free Pepsi (Diet, Regular)
Cherry Vanilla
Lime (Diet, Regular)

soda pop/carbonated beverages

Max
Natural
One
Pepsi (Diet, Regular)
Throwback
Vanilla Diet
Wild Cherry (Diet, Regular)

Publix -
Black Cherry Soda
Cherry Cola
Club Soda
Cola Regular
Diet (Cola, Ginger Ale, Tonic Water)
Ginger Ale
Grape Soda
Lemon Lime (Seltzer, Soda)
Root Beer
Tonic Water

RC Cola - All Varieties

Reed's - Ginger Brew (Cherry, Extra, Original, Premium, Raspberry, Spiced Apple Cider)

Safeway Brand - Blackberry, Cherry Go2 Soda, Cream Soda, Ditto (Diet, Regular), Dr. Skipper, Ginger Ale, Go2 Cola (Diet, Regular), Grape, Grapefruit, Mountain Breeze Punch, Root Beer (Diet, Regular), Strawberry

Safeway Select - Clear Sparkling Water (Cranberry Raspberry, Grapefruit Tangerine, Key Lime, Raspberry Black Cherry, Strawberry Kiwi, Strawberry Watermelon, Tangerine Lime, Wild Cherry), Sodas (All Varieties)

Santa Cruz - Champagne Style Sparkling Juice (All Varieties), **Organic Sparkling Beverages (All Varieties)**

Schweppes - All Varieties

Sierra Mist - Cranberry Splash (Diet, Regular), Free, Regular, Ruby Splash (Diet, Regular)

S

Slice - Grape, Red

Sprite - Regular, Zero

Sunkist - Cherry Limeade, Citrus Fusion, Grape, Lemonade (Diet Sparkling, Sparkling), Solar Fusion, Strawberry

Trader Joe's - French Market Sparkling Beverages, Sparkling Juice Beverages (Apple Cider, Blueberry, Cranberry, Pomegranate), Sparkling Water (All Flavors)

Tropicana Twister Soda -
    Grape
    Orange (Diet, Regular)
    Strawberry

Tubz - Diet Root Beer, Root Beer

Vernors - Diet, Regular

Virgil's - Cream Soda, Diet Root Beer, Root Beer

Wegmans Brand -
    Aqua Mineral Water
        Lemon
        Lemongrass
        Lime
        Mixed Berry
    Black Cherry Diet
    Frizzante European Soda
        Blood Orange
        Cranberry Lime
        Sicilian
        Lemon
        Sour Cherry Lemon
    Soda
        Cherry (Black, Diet Wedge)
        Club Soda
        Cola (Caffeine Free, Caffeine Free Diet, Diet, Regular)
        Cream Soda
        Diet Lime
        Diet Wedge (Cherry Grapefruit, Grapefruit, Peach)
        Dr. W Cola (Diet, Regular)

Fountain Root Beer (Diet, Regular)
Ginger Ale (Diet, Regular)
Grape Soda
Green Apple Sparkling Soda (Diet, Regular)
Mango
Tonic (Diet, Regular)
W-up (Diet, Regular)
Sparkling Beverage
Black Cherry Regular
Cranberry (Blend, Raspberry Diet)
Key Lime (Diet, Regular)
Kiwi Strawberry Diet
Lemonade
Mineral Water
Mixed Berry (Diet, Regular)
Peach (Diet, Grapefruit Diet)
Sparkling Beverage w/Sweeteners (Black Cherry, Key Lime)
Sparkling Juice (Niagara Grape)
Welch's - All Varieties

Soup

Amy's -
Indian Dal Golden Lentil!
Lentil Curried!
Organic
Black Bean Vegetable!
Chunky Vegetable!
Fire Roasted Southwestern Vegetable!
Hearty
French Country Vegetable!
Rustic Italian Vegetable!
Lentil (Light In Sodium!, Regular!)
Lentil Vegetable (Light In Sodium!, Regular!)
Spanish Rice & Red Bean!
Split Pea (Light In Sodium!, Regular!)
Tuscan Bean & Rice!

S

Baxters -
Favourites (Chicken Broth, Cock A Leekie, Lentil & Bacon, Pea & Ham, Scotch Vegetable)
Healthy Choice
Chicken & Vegetable
Chunky (Chicken & Vegetable Casserole, Country Vegetable)
Tomato & Brown Lentil
Luxury Beef Consomme
Vegetarian Tomato & Butterbean
Caskey's - Onion Soup Mix
Cuisine Sante▲ - Soup Mix (Sweet Corn●, Tomato●), Soup/Sauce Base White Roux●
Dinty Moore - Beef Stew
Dr. McDougall's - Black Bean & Lime, Light Sodium Split Pea, Ready To Serve Soups (Black Bean, Chunky Tomato, Roasted Pepper Tomato, Vegetable), Tamale w/Baked Chips, Tortilla w/Baked Chips
Fantastic World Foods - Simmer Soups Split Pea Soup
Frontera - Black Bean Tomato, Classic Tortilla, Roasted Tomato, Roasted Vegetable
Full Flavor Foods▲ - Soup Mix ()Chicken●)
Fungus Among Us - Organic Soup Mix (Moroccan Porcini & Green Lentil!, Spicy Shiitake & Vegetable!)
Gluten Free Cafe - Black Bean●, Chicken Noodle●, Veggie Noodle●
Grandma Ferdon's▲ - Soup Mix Onion●
Hormel - Microwave Chicken w/Vegetable & Rice
Imagine -
Organic Creamy
Acorn Squash & Mango
Butternut Squash
Light In Sodium (Garden Broccoli, Garden Tomato & Basil, Harvest Corn, Red Bliss Potato & Roasted Garlic, Sweet Potato)
Potato Leek

S

Sweet Potato

Tomato

Kettle Cuisine - Chicken w/Rice Noodles●, Roasted Vegetable●, Thai Curry Chicken●, Tomato w/Garden Vegetables●

Mixes From The Heartland▲ - Soup Mix (Cajun Bean●, Cajun Pastalaya●, Cheeseburger Chowder●, Chicken Veggie●, Cowboy●, Green Chili Hamburger●, Green Chili Stew●, Hamburger Pasta●, Harvest Chicken & Rice●, Italian Bean●, Minestrone●, Navy Bean●, Pasta Veggie●, Southwest Chicken Stew●, Tex Mex Pasta●, Texas Sausage & Bean●, Tortilla Pasta●)

O Organics - Butternut Squash, Lentil, Southwest Black Bean

Orgran▲ - Garden Vegetable, Tomato

Pacific Natural Foods - Cashew Carrot Ginger, Curried Red Lentil, Organic Savory Chicken & Wild Rice, Organic Spicy (Black Bean w/Chicken Sausage, Chicken Fajita), Spicy Black Bean

Progresso - Vegetable Classics Garden Vegetable

Publix - Deli (Chili w/Beans, Spring Vegetable)

Pure Market Express▲ - Corn Chowder●, Emerald City●, French Onion●, Spicy Cilantro●, Tomato Herb●, Tzatziki●, Watermelon●

Really Great Food Company▲ - Black Bean, Curry Lentil, Golden Pea, Split Pea, Sweet Corn Chowder

Spartan Brand - Chicken & Rice, Onion Soup & Dip

Thai Kitchen - Coconut Ginger, Hot & Sour

Trader Joe's - Organic (Black Bean!!, Split Pea!!), Regular (Carrot Ginger!!, Corn & Roasted Red Pepper!!, Instant Rice Noodle Soup (Mushroom, Roasted Garlic, Spring Onion), Latin Black Bean!!, Organic Lentil Soup w/Vegetables!!, Sweet Potato Bisque!!)

Wegmans Brand - Chili Soup Vegetarian, Gazpacho, Moroccan Lentil w/Chick Pea

Sour Cream

Pure Market Express▲ - Vegan●

Wayfare - We Can't Say It's Sour Cream Original●

S Soy Sauce
   Yin - Soy Free Sauce
Spaghetti Sauce...see Sauces
Spaghetti...see Pasta
Spices...see Seasonings
Spinach
   *... *All Fresh Spinach Is Gluten/Casein/Soy Free*
   Albertsons - Canned Cut Leaf
   Birds Eye - All Plain Frozen Spinach
   C & W - All Plain Frozen Spinach
   Del Monte - All Canned Spinach
   Dr. Praeger's - Spinach Littles!
   Great Value Brand (Wal-Mart) - Canned Whole Leaf Spinach
   Hannaford Brand - Whole Leaf
   Hy-Vee - Canned, Frozen (Chopped, Leaf)
   Lowes Foods Brand - Frozen (Chopped, Leaf)
   Meijer Brand - Canned (Cut Leaf, No Salt, Regular), Frozen Spinach
      Chopped, Leaf)
   Nuts Online - Simply Spinach Freeze Dried Vegetables●
   O Organics - Chopped Frozen
   Pictsweet - All Plain Frozen Spinach
   Publix - Canned, Frozen (Chopped, Cut Leaf, Leaf)
   Publix GreenWise Market - Organic (Baby Spinach Salad, Spinach)
   S&W - All Canned Spinach
   Safeway Brand - Canned Leaf, Frozen Chopped
   Spartan Brand - Canned Cut Leaf, Frozen (Chopped, Cut, Leaf)
   Stop & Shop Brand - Chopped, Cut, Leaf, No Salt Added, Regular
   Tasty Bite - Spinach Dal!
   Trader Joe's - Frozen Organic Chopped
   Wegmans Brand - Frozen (Chopped, Cut Leaf)
   Winn Dixie - Canned (No Salt Added, Regular), Frozen (Chopped,
      Cut Leaf)
   Woodstock Farms - Organic Frozen Cut Spinach

Sports Drinks

Gatorade -
G Series Perform 02 (G Powder (Fruit Punch, Lemon Lime)
G2 Lo-Cal (Blueberry Pomegranate, Fruit Punch, Glacier Freeze,
Grape, Lemon Lime)
G2 Powder Packets (Fruit Punch, Grape)
Original G (Citrus Cooler, Cool Blue, Fruit Punch, Glacier Freeze,
Grape, Lemon Lime, Riptide Rush, Strawberry)
G Series Prime 01 (Berry, Fruit Punch, Orange)
Hy-Vee - Thunder Sport Drink (Berry, Fruit Punch, Glaciar Ice, Lemon
Lime, Orange)
Meijer Brand -
Drink Thirst Quencher
Fruit Punch
Lemon Lime
Orange
Powerade - Ion 4 (Grape, Lemon Lime, Mountain Berry Blast, Sour
Lemon, White Cherry Zero, Zero)
Wegmans Brand - MVP Sport Drink (Blue Freeze, Fruit Punch, Grape,
Green Apple, Lemon Lime, Raspberry Lemonade)

Spread

Bionaturae - Organic Fruit Spread (All Varieties)
Cantare - Olive Tapenade Traditional
Dietz & Watson▲ - Jalapeno●
Earth Balance▲ - Natural Buttery Spread Soy Free
Eden Organic - Butter (Apple, Cherry)
Malone's - Ham Spread
Maple Grove Farms Of Vermont -
Blended Maple
Honey Maple
Pure Maple
Peloponnese - Baba Ganoush, Eggplant Meze, Eggplant Spread,
Kalamata Olive Spread
Polaner▲ - All Varieties

S

Santa Barbara Olive Co. - Olive Muffalette

Tartex -

Cremisso (Champignon, Chardonnay Cote D'or, Delicacy, Exquisite, Green Pepper, Herbs, Horseradish Apple, Hungarian, Mediterrana, Mexicana, Olivera, Peppers Chili, Pesto, Pomodoro d'Italia, Provence Herbs, Ratatouille, Shiitake, Tomato Basil, Truffle Champagne, Zucchini Curry)

Organic Pate In Tubes (Classic, Green Olive, Herb, Herb & Garlic, Mushroom, Roasted Onion & Pink Peppercorn)

Pate Creme (Basil, Italian Olives, Rocket & Mustard, Sundried Tomato & VanDouvan)

The Ginger People - Ginger Spread!

Trader Joe's - Artichoke Red Pepper Tapenade!!, Eggplant Garlic Spread, Olive Green Tapenade!!, Red Pepper Spread w/Garlic & Eggplant

Underwood - Deviled Ham Spread

Walden Farms - Spreads (Apple Butter, Apricot, Blueberry, Grape, Orange, Raspberry, Strawberry)

Sprinkles... see Baking Decorations & Frostings

Squash

... *All Fresh Squash Is Gluten/Casein/Soy Free*

C & W - All Plain Frozen Squash

Meijer Brand - Frozen Squash Cooked

Pictsweet - All Plain Frozen Squash, Cracked Pepper Seasoned Okra & Squash

Publix - Frozen (Cooked Squash, Yellow Sliced)

Spartan Brand - Frozen Yellow

Stop & Shop Brand

Winn Dixie - Frozen Yellow

Starch

AgVantage Naturals▲ - Tapioca●

Argo - Corn

Augason Farms▲ - Gluten Free (Potato Starch●, Tapioca Flour/ Starch●)

Authentic Foods▲ - Corn, Potato
Bob's Red Mill▲ - Arrowroot, Corn, Potato
Cause You're Special▲ - Corn Starch, Potato Starch
Clabber Girl - Corn!
EasyGlut - Rice
El Peto▲ - Arrowroot, Corn, Potato, Tapioca
Ener-G▲ - Potato
Expandex▲ - Modified Tapioca Starch●
Gifts Of Nature▲ - Potato
Ginger Evans - Corn Starch
Gluty Free - Potato●
Grandma Ferdon's▲ - Corn Starch●, Potato●, Tapioca●
Hannaford Brand - Corn
Hearth Club - Corn
Hodgson Mill - Pure
Hy-Vee - Corn
Kingsford - Corn
Kinnikinnick▲ - Corn, Potato, Tapioca
Kroger Brand - Corn
Let's Do...Organic - Corn
Meijer Brand - Corn
Nuts Online - Gluten Free Corn Starch●, Potato Starch●
Really Great Food Company▲ - Potato
Rumford - Corn
Safeway Brand - Corn
Spartan Brand - Corn

Steak

... *All Fresh Cut Meat Is Gluten/Casein/Soy Free (Non-Marinated, Unseasoned)*

Steak Sauce

A.I. - Bold & Spicy, Cracked Peppercorn, Regular Steak Sauce, Sweet Hickory, Thick & Hearty
Albertsons
Hannaford Brand
Hy-Vee - Classic, Vidalia Onion

S

Kroger Brand - Bold & Spicy, Original, Sweet & Spicy
Kurtz - Original
Meijer Brand
Publix
Safeway Brand - Original
Spartan Brand - Original
Wegmans Brand - Bold, Regular

Stew... see also Soup
Dinty Moore - Beef, Microwave Meals Beef
Kroger Brand - Beef

Stir Fry Sauce
Mr. Spice Organic - Ginger Stir Fry Sauce & Marinade

Stir Fry Vegetables... see also Mixed Vegetables
Albertsons - Stir Fry Vegetables
C & W - The Ultimate Southwest Blend, The Ultimate Stir Fry
Meijer Brand - Frozen Vegetable Stir Fry
Wegmans Brand - Asian, Cleaned & Cut Vegetable Medley, Far East, Hong Kong

Stock
Cuisine Sante▲ - Beef Flavored●, Chicken Flavored●, Vegetable●
Emeril's - Beef, Chicken, Organic Vegetable
Full Flavor Foods▲ - Soup Stock Mix (Chicken●)
Imagine - Organic Cooking Stock (Beef, Chicken, Low Sodium Beef, Vegetable)
Kirkland Signature - Chicken (Organic, Regular)
Kitchen Basics▲ - Original (Beef, Chicken, Clam, Ham, Pork, Seafood, Turkey, Veal), Unsalted (Beef, Chicken, Vegetable)
Swanson - Beef Carton, Chicken Carton
Wegmans Brand - Culinary Stock (Chicken, Thai, Vegetable)

Strawberries
... *All Fresh Strawberries Are Gluten/Casein/Soy Free*
Albertsons - Frozen (Sliced w/Sugar, Whole)

Bramley's - Frozen
C & W - All Plain Frozen Fruits
Full Circle - Organic Whole Strawberries
Gluty Free - Dried Organic●, Dried●, Freeze Dried●
Great Value Brand (Wal-Mart) - Frozen (Sliced w/Sugar, Whole)
Hy-Vee - Frozen (Sliced, w/Sugar, Whole)
Kirkland Signature - Frozen
Kroger Brand - Plain Frozen Fruit
Meijer Brand - Frozen (Organic, Sliced), Whole Individually Quick
    Frozen
Nuts Online - Dried●, Natural Dried Juice Infused●, Organic
    Simply●, Organic●, Simply Whole●, Simply●
Publix - Frozen (Sliced, Sweetened, Whole)
Safeway Brand - Frozen (Sliced w/Sugar, Sliced w/Sweetener, Whole)
Spartan Brand - Frozen (Sliced, Whole)
Stop & Shop Brand - Sliced Strawberries (In Sugar, Regular),
    Strawberries
Trader Joe's - Frozen (Grade A Fancy, Organic)
Wegmans Brand - Frozen Sliced w/Sugar
Winn Dixie - Frozen (Sugar Whole, Sweetener, Whole)
Woodstock Farms - Organic Frozen Whole Strawberries

Stuffing
El Peto▲ - Stuffing
Mixes From The Heartland▲ - Cornbread Stuffing Mix●
Mrs. Crimble's - Stuffing Mix

Succotash
...*All Fresh Succotash Is Gluten/Casein/Soy Free
Publix - Frozen Vegetable Blend
Spartan Brand - Frozen

Sugar
Albertsons - Dark Brown, Granulated, Light Brown, Powdered
Bakers & Chefs - Light Brown, Powdered
Dixie Crystals - All Varieties

S

Domino - Brown, Brownulated, Confectioners, Cubes, Demerara Washed Raw Cane, Granulated, Organic, Pure D'Lite, Sugar 'N Cinnamon, Superfine, Tablets

Full Circle - Light Brown, Organic Cane Sugar

Gifts Of Nature▲ - Turbinado Sugar (Raw Sugar)

Ginger Evans - Sugar

Gluty Free - Organic (Evaporated Cane Juice●, Palm Sugar●)

Great Value Brand (Wal-Mart) - Confectioners Powdered, Extra Fine Granulated, Light Brown, Pure Cane

Hain Pure Foods - Organic (Light Brown, Powdered, Regular), Turbinado

Hannaford Brand - Dark Brown, Granulated, Light Brown, Powdered

Heavenly Sugar - Premium Organic Sugar

Hy-Vee - Confectioners Powdered, Dark Brown, Light Brown, Pure Cane

Imperial Sugar - All Varieties

Kinnikinnick▲ - Icing Sugar

Kroger Brand - Dark Brown, Granulated, Light Brown, Powdered

Kroger Value - Brown, Granulated

Lowes Foods Brand - Granulated, Light Brown, Powdered

Meijer Brand - Confectioners, Dark Brown, Granulated, Light Brown

Midwest Country Fare - Granulated, Light Brown, Powdered

Nielsen-Massey - Madagascar Bourbon Pure Vanilla Sugar●

Nuts Online - Organic Evaporated Cane Juice●, Organic Palm Sugar●

O Organics - Evaporated Cane Juice, Light Brown, Powdered, Turbinado

Phildesco - Coconut

Private Selections - Natural Cane Turbinado, Organic (Blue Agave, Light Brown, Powdered, Regular)

Publix - Dark Brown, Granulated, Light Brown, Powdered

Rapunzel - Organic Whole Cane, Powdered

Safeway Brand - Brown (Dark, Light), Granulated, Powdered

Shiloh Farms - Organic Date

sugar substitute/sweetener

S

Spartan Brand - Confectioners Powdered, Dark Brown, Granulated, Light Brown

Stop & Shop Brand - Granulated

Tops - Confectioner's Powdered, Light Brown, Pure Granulated

Trader Joe's - All Varieties

United Sugar Products - Crystal Sugar Products

Wegmans Brand - Dark Brown, Granulated White, Light Brown Pure Cane

Wholesome Sweeteners - All Varieties

Winn Dixie - Granulated, Light Brown, Powdered

Woodstock Farms - Organic (Brown, Powdered, Pure Cane, Turbinado)

Sugar Substitute/Sweetener

Albertsons - Aspartame, Saccharin

Equal - Flavor For Water (Black Cherry, Lemon Lime, Mandarin Orange), Lemon, Packets, Peach, Spoonful, Sugar Lite, Vanilla

Great Value Brand (Wal-Mart) - Calorie Free Sweetener, w/ Aspartame

Hannaford Brand - Sweetener (Aspartame, Sweet Choice)

Hy-Vee - Aspartame Sweetener, Delecta Sugar Substitute

Kirkland Signature - Sweetener Made w/Sucralose

Krisda - Premium Stevia Extract

Kroger Brand - Apriva, Calorie Free (Liquid, Powdered)

NutraSweet

Publix - Aspartame

Spartan Brand

Splenda - Brown Sugar Blend, Flavors For Coffee (French Vanilla, Hazelnut, Mocha), No Calorie Sweetener (Granulated, Packets, w/ Fiber), Sugar Blend

Sweet And Low

Sweet Fiber - All Natural Sweetener●

Wegmans Brand - Sugar Substitute w/Saccharin

Wholesome Sweeteners - All Varieties

Winn Dixie - Sugar Sweetener Substitute

S Sunflower Seeds... see Seeds

Sweet & Sour Sauce

   Mr. Spice Organic - Sweet & Sour Sauce & Marinade

   Wegmans Brand - Sweet & Sour

Sweet Potatoes

   ... *All Fresh Sweet Potatoes Are Gluten/Casein/Soy Free*

   Dr. Praeger's - Sweet Potato Littles**!**, Sweet Potato Pancake**!**

   Pure Market Express▲ - Sweet Potatoe Pineapple Slaw●

Sweetener... see Sugar Substitute/Sweetener

Swiss Chard

   ... *All Fresh Swiss Chard Is Gluten/Casein/Soy Free*

Swordfish... see Fish

   ... *All Fresh Fish Is Gluten/Casein/Soy Free (Non-Marinated, Unseasoned)*

Syrup

   Albertsons - Chocolate, Light, Original, Strawberry

   Beehive - Corn Syrup

   Black Horse - Marionberry, Raspberry

   Brer Rabbit - Syrup (Full, Light)

   Cabot - Vermont Pure Maple Syrup

   Crown - Corn Syrup (Golden, Lily White)

   Full Circle - Organic Maple

   Golden Griddle - Pancake Syrup

   Grand Selections - 100% Pure Maple

   Hannaford Brand - Chocolate, Pancake (100% Pure Maple, Lite, Regular, Sugar Free), Strawberry

   Hershey's - Chocolate (Lite, Regular, Special Dark)

   Hy-Vee - Butter Flavor, Chocolate, Lite, Low Calorie Sugar Free, Pancake & Waffle, Strawberry

   Karo▲ - All Varieties

   Kirkland Signature - Maple

   Kroger Brand - Butter Flavor, Chocolate, Cinnamon Maple, Light Corn, Lite, Original, Strawberry, Sugar Free

   Kroger Value - Regular

Log Cabin - Lite, Original

Lowes Foods Brand - 2% Maple (Lite, Regular)

Lundberg▲ - Sweet Dreams Brown Rice Syrup (Eco Farmed, Organic)

Maple Grove Farms Of Vermont - Flavored Syrups (Apricot, Blueberry, Boysenberry, Red Raspberry, Strawberry), Pure & Organic Maple Syrup, Sugar Free Syrup (Maple Flavor, Vermont)

Maple Ridge - White Corn

Maple Valley - Organic Maple Syrup

Meijer Brand - Butter, Chocolate, Lite, Lite Butter, Lite Corn, Regular

Melissa's - Organic Blue Agave

Midwest Country Fare - Pancake & Waffle (Butter, Original)

Morning Delight - Original

Mrs. Renfro's - Cane, Country

Nesquik - All Flavors

Nestle - Nesquik Syrup (All Flavors)

O Organics - 100% Pure Maple

Old Tyme - All Varieties

Organic Nectars - Chocagave, Vanillagave

Oskri Organics - Date

Private Selections - Pure Maple

Publix - Chocolate (Regular, Sugar Free), Pancake (Lite, Original, Sugar Free)

Safeway Brand - Butter Light, Chocolate, Light, Original

Safeway Select - Pure Maple

Santa Cruz - Dessert Toppings (All Varieties)

Shiloh Farms - Maple (Agave Blend, Dark Amber Grade B, Grade A, Organic (Blueberry, Cranberry)

Smucker's▲ - All Fruit Syrup, Pure Maple Syrup, Sugar Free Breakfast Syrup

Spartan Brand - 2% Real Maple, Artificial Butter, Corn Syrup, Reduced Calorie (Butter, Lite)

Taste Of Inspiration - Red Raspberry!

The Ginger People - Ginger Syrup!

S
T

Trader Joe's - All Maple Syrup
Tropical Traditions - Brown Rice Syrup
Uncle Luke's - 100% Pure Maple Syrup
Vermont Maid - All Varieties
Walden Farms - Fruit Syrups (Blueberry, Strawberry), Single Serve
   Packets (Chocolate, Pancake), Syrup (Caramel, Chocolate,
   Pancake)
Wegmans Brand - Regular (Chocolate Flavored, Maraschino Cherry
   Flavored, Pancake (Light, Regular), Pure Maple (Organic Dark
   Amber, Regular), Sugar Free)
Winn & Lovett - Maple Syrup (All Varieties)
Winn Dixie - Butter Flavor, Chocolate, Lite, Regular, Strawberry

T

Taco Sauce
   Chi-Chi's - Taco Sauce
   Frontera - Taco Sauce (Chipotle Garlic, Roasted Tomato)
   Hannaford Brand
   Hy-Vee - Medium, Mild
   Kroger Brand - Hot, Mild
   La Victoria - Chipotle Medium, Green (Medium, Mild), Red
      (Medium, Mild)
   Lowes Foods Brand - Mild
   Old El Paso - Hot, Medium, Mild
   Ortega - Green, Green, Hot, Medium, Mild
   Pace - Medium, Mild
   Senora Verde - Medium, Mild
   Spartan Brand - Fat Free (Medium, Mild)
Taco Seasoning... see also Seasonings
   Chi-Chi's - Fiesta Restaurante Seasoning Mix
   Ortega - Chipotle Mix, Hot & Spicy Mix, Jalapeno & Onion Mix, Taco
      40% Less Sodium Mix, Taco Seasoning Mix

Taco Shells
- **Garden Of Eatin'** - Blue Corn Taco Shells, Yellow Corn Taco Shells
- **Kroger Brand** - Taco Shells
- **Old El Paso** - Stand N' Stuff Yellow Corn Taco Shells, Taco Shells (Super Stuffer, White Corn), Tostada Shells
- **Safeway Brand** - Taco Shells (Jumbo, White Corn)
- **Senora Verde** - Taco Shells
- **Taco Bell** - Taco Shells (12 ct., 18 ct.)

Tahini
- **Arrowhead Mills** - Organic Sesame Tahini
- **Gluty Free** - Organic●
- **Krinos** - Tahini
- **MaraNatha** - Natural w/Salt (Raw, Roasted)
- **Nuts Online** - Organic Sesame Tahini●
- **Oskri Organics** - Tahini (& Honey, & Molasses, Regular)
- **Peloponnese** - Tahini Paste

Tamales
- **Amy's** - Roasted Vegetables!, Verde Black Bean!
- **Hormel** - Beef

Tangerines
- ... *All Fresh Tangerines Are Gluten/Casein/Soy Free*

Tapioca... see also Flour
- **Let's Do...Organic** - Organic (Granules, Pearls, Starch)

Tartar Sauce
- **McCormick** - Fat Free
- **Simply Delicious** - Organic Tartare Sauce

Tarts
- **Crave Bakery▲** - Apple Frangipane, Apricot Frangipane, Lemon, Pumpkin
- **Pure Market Express▲** - Lemon●

Tater Tots... see Potatoes

Tea
- **Albertsons** - Bags (Decaf, Regular)

T Bigelow Tea -
    All Novus Varieties
    All Organic Varieties
    American Classic
        Pyramid Bags
            Charleston (Blended Loose, Breakfast)
            Governor Grey
            Plantation Peach
            Rockville Raspberry
        Regular
    Dajeerling
    Decaffeinated
        Constant Comment
        Earl Grey
        English Teatime
        Green Tea
    English Breakfast
    English Teatime
    Flavored Tea
        Cinnamon Stick
        Constant Comment
        Earl Grey
        Plantation Mint
        Raspberry Royale
        Vanilla (Almond, Hazelnut)
        White Chocolate Kisses
    Green Tea
        Constant Comment Green
        Earl Grey Green
        Jasmine Green
        Regular
    Green Tea w/Mint
    Herbal Tea
        Chinese Oolong

    Cozy Chamomile
    Hibiscus & Rose Hips
    Juice Tea
        Taste Of The Tropics
        Tasty Tangerine
    Mint Medley
    Peppermint
    Red Raspberry
    Sweet Dreams
  Iced Tea Red Raspberry
  Loose Tea
    Constant Comment
    Earl Grey
    English Breakfast
    Green

Caribou - All Flavors

Celestial Seasonings -

  Bottled Tea Kombucha (Antioxidant Superfruit, Digestion Meyer
    Lemon Ginger, Energy Pomelo Citrus, Metabolism Berry Guava,
    Super Green Tropical Blend)
  Chai India Spice (Decaf, Regular)
  Cool Brew Iced Tea Peach Ice
  Green Tea (Authentic, Decaf Green, Gen Mai Cha, Tropical
    Acai Berry)
  Herbal Tea (Acai Mango Zinger, Bengal Spice, Caffeine Free,
    Chamomile, Mint Magic, Morning Thunder, Peppermint, Red
    Zinger, Sleepytime, Sleepytime Vanilla, Sweet Clementine
    Chamomile Organic)
  Holiday Tea (Candy Cane Lane, Nutcracker Sweet)
  Rooibos Tea (Madagascar Vanilla, Moroccan Pomegranate Red)
  Wellness Tea All Natural Herbal (Sleepytime Extra, Sleepytime
    Sinus Soother)
  White Tea Decaf

T

Full Circle - Organic Tea (Chai, Chamomile, Earl Grey, English Breakfast, Green, Peppermint)

Fuze - Black & Green Tea, Diet Green Tea w/Orange Ginger, Diet White Tea w/Pomegranate, Green Tea w/Honey, White Tea Agave Gogi Berry

Garelick Farms - Diet Iced Tea w/Lemon Flavor, Sweetened Green Tea, Sweetened Iced Tea w/Lemon Flavor

Gluty Free - Hibiscus Flowers●

Gold Peak - Iced Tea Lemon

Great Value Brand (Wal-Mart) - Refrigerated (Green, Sugar Free Sweet Tea, Sweet Tea), Tea 100% Natural (Decaf, Regular)

Hannaford Brand - All (Bags, Instant)

Hansen's - All Varieties

Higgins & Burke - All Varieties

Honest - Assam Black, Black Forest Berry, Community Green, Green Dragon, Half & Half, Honey Green, Jasmine Green Energy, Just Black, Just Green, Lemon Black, Lori's Lemon, Mango Acai, Mango Green, Moroccan Mint Green, Passion Fruit Green Tea, Peach Oolalong, Peach White, Perfect White, Pomegranate Red w/Goji Berry

Hy-Vee -
Bottled (Diet Green Tea w/Citrus, Green Tea w/Citrus, Green Tea w/Pomegranate)
Chai Black
Chamomile Herbal
Cinnamon Apple Herbal
Decaf (Green, Tea Bags)
Dream Easy Herbal
Earl Grey Black
English Breakfast Black
Family Size Tea Bags
Green (Tea, Tea Bags, Tea w/Pomegranate)
Honey Lemon Ginseng
Instant

Jasmine Green
Orange & Spice Specialty
Peppermint Herbal
Rooibos Red Herbal
Strawberry Herbal Tea Bags
Inko's White Tea - Apricot, Blueberry, Cherry Vanilla, Energy,
   Honeydew, Lemon, Lychee, Original, Unsweetened Hint O'Mint,
   Unsweetened Honeysuckle, Unsweetened Original, White Peach
Kirkland Signature - Tea Bags
Kroger Brand - Tea (Bagged, Instant)
Lipton -
   Black Tea Bags
      Cold Brew
      Decaf (Cold Brew, Pitcher Sized, Regular)
      Pitcher Sized
      Regular
   Bottled Iced Tea
      Chilled (Green w/Peach & Mango, Iced w/Lemon)
      Diet
         Green w/(Citrus, Mixed Berry)
         Iced Green w/Lemon
         Sparkling Green w/Strawberry Kiwi
         White w/Raspberry
      Green w/Citrus
      Half & Half Tea Lemonade
      Iced Tea w/Lemon
      Pure Leaf
         Extra Sweet
         Green w/Honey
         Iced w/(Lemon, Peach, Raspberry)
         Sweetened
         Unsweetened
      Sparkling Green w/Berry
      Sweet Iced
      White w/Raspberry

T

Diet Iced Tea Mix
Lemon (Decaf, Regular)
Peach
Raspberry
Unsweetened
Flavored Tea Bags French Vanilla
Green Tea Bags
100% Natural (Decaf, Regular)
Mint
Herbal Tea Bags Peppermint
Iced Tea Mix
Lemon
Mango
Summer Peach
Unsweetened
Wild Raspberry
Iced Tea To Go
Green w/Blueberry & Pomegranate
Regular w/Natural Lemon
Pyramid Tea Bags
Bavarian Wild Berry
Bedtime Story Herbal
Black Pearl
Green w/Mandarin Orange
Red w/Strawberry & Passionfruit
Tuscan Lemon
Vanilla Caramel Truffle
White w/Blueberry & Pomegranate
White w/Mango & Peach
Meijer Brand - Iced Tea Mix, Instant, Tea Bags (Decaf, Green, Green Decaf, Regular)
Midwest Country Fare - Tea Bags 100 ct.
Minute Maid - Pomegranate Flavored Tea
Mother Parkers - All Tea (Black, Flavored, Green, Herbal)

Newman's Own - Lemon Aided Iced Tea
Numi - All Varieties
O Organics - Bags (Green, Mint Herbal)
Orient Emporium - All Varieties
Pacific Natural Foods -
>   Organic Iced Tea (Green, Lemon, Peach, Raspberry, Sweetened Black)
>   Organic Simply Mate Yerba Mate (Citrus Lychee, Lemon Ginger, Peach Passion, Traditional)
>   Organic Simply Tea (Kiwi Mango Green, Peach Green, Tangerine Green, Unsweetened Green, Wild Berry Green)

Prairie Farms - Sweetened Iced Tea
Private Selections - Organic (All Varieties), Regular (All Varieties)
Publix - Deli Iced Tea (Sweetened, Unsweetened), Instant (Lemon, Regular), Tea Bags (All Varieties)
Red Rose - All Varieties
Republic Of Tea -

>   Black (2010 Darjeeling First Flush●, All Day Breakfast●, Assam Breakfast●, Big Bold●, Bing Cherry Vanilla●, Blackberry Sage●, British Breakfast●, Calorie Free Naturally Sweet●, Cinnamon Plum●, Comfort & Joy●, Cranberry Blood Orange●, Decaf (Apricot●, Blackberry Sage●, British Breakfast●, Earl Greyer●, Ginger Peach●, Mango Ceylon●, Vanilla Almond●, Earl Greyer●, Eat Pray Love Blood Orange Cinnamon●, Ginger Peach●, Golden Yunnan●, Imperial Republic Lychee●, Imperial Republic Pu Erh●, Jerry Cherry●, Lapsang Souchon●, Lucky Irish Breakfast●, Mango Ceylon●, Margaret's Hope Rare Darjeeling●, Organic Ceylon Breakfast●, Passion Fruit Papaya●, Phoobsering Rare Darjeeling●, Raspberry Quince●, Republic Chai●, Republic Darjeeling●, Rohini Rare Pearl●, Rose Petal●, Tea Of Good Tidings●, Vanilla Almond●, Wild Blueberry●), Green (Acai●, Acerola Cherry●, Apple Blossom●, Big Hojicha●, Black Raspberry●, Blood Orange●, Blueberry Lemon●, Blueberry●, Decaf (Honey Ginseng●, Kiwi Pear●, Pomegranate●, The People's Green●, Wild Berry Plum●),

T

Dragon Well●, Flower Of Prosperity●, Flowering (Dancing Blossom●, Lychee Blossom●), Ginger Lemon●, Ginger Peach●, Goji Raspberry●, Honey Ginseng●, Jasmine Jazz●, Kiwi Pear●, Moroccan Mint●, Orange Spice●, Organic (Dancing Leaves●, Earl Greyer●, Lemon w/Honey●, Turmeric Ginger●), Pineapple Ginger●, Pomegranate●, Republic Chai●, Sea Buckthorn●, Sky Between the Branches●, Spring Cherry●, Tangerine Orange●, Tea Of Inquiry●, The People's Green●, Wildberry Plum●), Herbal (Be Well Red (Get Charged No. 3●, Get Clean No. 7●, Get Gorgeous No. 1●, Get Happy No. 13●, Get Heart No. 12●, Get It Going No. 2●, Get Lost No. 6●, Get Maternal No. 10●, Get Passionate No. 17●, Get Relaxed No. 14●, Get Relief No. 9●, Get Smart No. 16●, Get Some Zzz's No. 5●), Cardamon Cinnamon●, Chamomile Lemon●, Desert Sage●, Double Dark Chocolate Mate●, Ginseng Peppermint●, Hot Apple Cider●, Imperial Republic Snow Rose●, Lemon Wintergreen●, Orange Ginger Mint●, Organic (Cedarburg Red●, Double Red Rooibos●, Flowering Fruit●, Mint Fields●, Temple Of Health●), Rainforest●, Red (Cherry Apple●, Cinnamon Orange●, Dream By The Fire●, Earl Greyer●, Ginger Peach●, Good Hope Vanilla●, PassionFruit Mango●, Republic Chai●, Safari Sunset●, Sip For The Cure Pomegranate Vanilla●, Strawberry Chocolate●, Tangerine●, Yak the Yak Strawberry Vanilla●), Year Of The Tiger●), Hibiscus Superflower (Blueberry●, Key Lime●, Natural●, Pineapple Lychee●, Vanilla Apple●), Oolong (All Day Breakfast●, Dragon●, Imperial Republic Monkey Picked●, Imperial Republic Orchid●, Old Bush Shui Xian Rare●, Osmanthus Rare Estate●, Peach Blossom●, Ti Kuan Yin●, Wuyi●), Organic Matcha Powder●, Raw Green Bush Tea (Black Currant Cardamon●, Mango Chili●, Natural Organic●, Plantain Coconut●), White (Asian Jasmine●, Emperor's●, Ginger Peach●, Honeydew Melon●, Honeysuckle●, Orange Blossom●, Persimmon●, Pineapple Guava●, Silver Rain●, Sip For The Cure Red Cherry●, Vanilla Coconut●)

Rishi Tea▲ - All Varieties

Safeway Brand - Black, Iced Tea Mix (All Flavors), Tea Bags (Chamomile, Decaffeinated, Earth Grey, English Breakfast, Green, Peppermint)

Salada Tea - Decaffeinated & Regular (Green, White)

Santa Cruz - Bottled Tea (All Varieties)

Snapple - All Varieties

SoBe - Green

Spartan Brand - Instant Tea Bags, Orange Pekoe Tea Bags (Decaf, Regular)

Stash Tea - All Varieties

Summer Set - Caffeinated Tea Bags, Decaffeinated Tea Bags, Sweetened Iced, Unsweetened Iced

Sweet Leaf -
Bottled (Citrus Green, Half & Half Tea Lemonade, Lemon, Lemon & Lime Unsweetened, Mint & Honey, Peach, Raspberry, Sweet Tea)
Diet Bottled (Citrus Green, Peach, Sweet)

Tazo Tea - All Varieties *(Except Green Ginger, Tazo Honeybush)*

Trader Joe's - Green Tea Unsweetened

Twinings Tea - All Varieties

Wegmans Brand -
Black Tea
Decaf (Black Tea, Green Tea)
Earl Grey (Black, Black Decaf, Green, Supreme, Supreme Decaf)
English Breakfast (Black, Organic)
Green Tea
Ice Tea Mix w/Natural Lemon Flavor & Sugar (Decaf, Regular)
Iced Tea Lemon
Organic (Chai, Chamomile, Earl Grey, English Breakfast, Jasmine Green, Peppermint, Rooibos Strawberry Cream)
Regular Bags
Sencha Pure Japanese Green

Winn Dixie - Regular & Family (Decaffeinated, Tea Bags)

T **Teff**

  Bob's Red Mill▲ - Flour, Whole Grain Teff

  Shiloh Farms - Brown , Ivory

Tequila

  ... *All Distilled Alcohol Is Gluten/Casein/Soy Free* [2]

Tilapia

  ... see *All Fresh Fish Is Gluten/Casein/Soy Free (Non-Marinated, Unseasoned)*

Tomatillos

  ... *All Fresh Tomatillos Are Gluten/Casein/Soy Free*

  Las Palmas - Crushed Tomatillos

Tomato Juice... see Drinks/Juice

Tomato Paste

  Albertsons - Regular

  Bionaturae - Organic

  Contadina - Regular

  Del Monte - All Tomato Products *(Except Spaghetti Sauce Flavored With Meat)*

  Full Circle - Organic

  Hannaford Brand

  Hy-Vee - Regular Tomato

  Lowes Foods Brand - Tomato

  Meijer Brand - Domestic, Organic

  Publix - Regular

  Publix GreenWise Market - Organic

  S&W - All Canned Vegetables

  Spartan Brand

  Wegmans Brand - Tomato

  Winn Dixie - Regular

Tomato Puree

  Contadina - Regular

  Dei Fratelli - Regular

  Full Circle - Organic

  Meijer Brand - Regular

S&W - All Canned Vegetables
Wegmans Brand - Regular
Winn Dixie - Regular
Tomato Sauce... see Sauces
Tomatoes
... *All Fresh Tomatoes Are Gluten/Casein/Soy Free*
Albertsons - Diced Tomatoes & Green Chilies, Stewed Italian, Whole
(No Salt, Regular)
Bionaturae - Organic (Strained, Whole Peeled & Diced, Whole
Peeled Diced & Crushed)
Contadina -
All Crushed
All Stewed
Diced (Petite Cut, Regular, w/Italian Herbs, w/Roasted Garlic, w/
Roasted Red Pepper, w/Zucchini Bell Pepper & Carrots)
Dei Fratelli -
Canned
Chopped (Italian, Mexican Tomatoes & Jalapenos, w/Onions
& Garlic)
Crushed (Regular, w/Basil & Herbs)
Diced (In Hearty Sauce, Low Sodium, Seasoned)
No Salt Whole
Petite Diced (Regular, w/Onion & Celery & Pepper)
Pizza Sauce
Stewed
Whole (In Puree, Regular)
Del Monte - All Tomato Products *(Except Spaghetti Sauce Flavor)*
Diane's Garden - Canned (Sliced Stewed, Tomato Juice, Tomato Paste,
Tomato Sauce, Whole Peeled)
Eden Organic -
Crushed (Regular, w/Basil, w/Onion & Garlic)
Diced (Regular, w/Basil, w/Green Chilies, w/Roasted Onion)
Whole Tomatoes (Regular, w/Basil)
Full Circle - Organic (Crushed Tomatoes w/Basil, Diced)

T

Gluty Free - Sun Dried●
Hannaford Brand -
  Diced (Crushed, Italian, Kitchen Ready Crushed In Heavy Puree,
    No Salt, Puree, Regular, w/Green Chilies, w/Roasted Garlic &
    Onion, Whole Peeled)
  Stewed (Italian, Mexican, No Salt, Regular)
Hy-Vee -
  Diced (Chili Ready, Regular, w/Chilies, w/Garlic & Onion)
  Italian Style (Crushed, Stewed)
  Original Diced & Green Chilies
  Petite Diced
  Stewed
  Whole Peeled
Kroger Value - Diced, Fire Roasted, Whole
Lowes Foods Brand - Crushed, Diced, Sauce, Stewed, Whole
Meijer Brand -
  Crushed In Puree
  Diced (Chili Ready, In Italian, In Juice, Organic, Petite, w/Green
    Chilies)
  Stewed (Italian, Mexican, Regular)
  Whole (Organic, Peeled, Peeled No Salt, w/Basil Organic)
Melissa's - Sun Dried **!**
Mezzetta - Sun Ripened Dried (In Olive Oil, Julienne Cut In Olive
  Oil, Regular)
Midwest Country Fare - Diced, Stewed, Whole Peeled
Nuts Online - Dried Tomatoes (Julienne●, Organic Sun Dried●, Sun
  Dried●, Sun Dried w/Olive Oil●)
O Organics - Diced (No Salt Added, Regular, w/Basil Garlic &
  Oregano), Whole Peeled
Pictsweet - All Plain Frozen Tomatoes
Private Selections - Organic Diced (No Salt, w/Salt), Sun Dried
Publix - Crushed, Diced (w/Green Chilies, w/Roasted Garlic &
  Onion), Peeled Whole, Sauce, Sliced & Stewed

Publix GreenWise Market - Organic (Crushed, Diced, Diced w/ Basil Garlic & Oregano, Sauce)

S&W - All Plain Canned Tomatoes

Safeway Brand -
Crushed
Diced (Fire Roasted, Peeled, Peeled No Salt, Petite)
Mexican Style Stewed (Whole Peeled)

Senora Verde - Diced Tomatoes

Spartan Brand - Crushed, Diced (For Chili, Mexican, No Salt Added, Regular, w/Green Chilies, w/Roasted Garlic & Onion), Italian Stewed, Stewed, Whole

Trader Joe's - Whole Peeled Tomatoes w/Basil

Wegmans Brand -
Crushed
Diced (Chili Style, Italian Style Stewed, Petite, Regular, Roasted Garlic & Onion)
Italian Classics (Coarse Ground, Kitchen Cut w/Basil, San Marzano Tomatoes Whole Peeled)
Italian Style (Diced Tomatoes, Stewed, Whole w/Basil)
Organic (Diced, Diced In Juice)
Peeled Whole
Petite Diced Tomatoes w/Garlic Olive Oil & Seasoning
Puree
Stewed
Whole Peeled

Winn Dixie - Canned (Crushed, Diced, Diced w/Chilies, Italian Style (Diced, Stewed), Petite Diced, Petite Diced w/Onion Celery Green Peppers, Puree, Sauce, Stewed, Whole Peeled)

Woodstock Farms - Organic Crushed (Original, w/Basil), Organic Diced (Basil & Garlic, Italian Herbs, No Salt, Original), Organic Sauce No Salt Added, Organic Tomato Paste, Organic Whole Peeled (In Juice, w/Basil)

Tonic... see Soda Pop/Carbonated Beverages

T Tortilla Chips... see Chips

Tortillas
- **Don Pancho** - Gluten Free Flour Tortillas
- **Food For Life** - Brown Rice
- **French Meadow Bakery** - Gluten Free Tortillas●
- **Maria & Ricardo's** - Gluten Free Tortillas●
- **Mission** - Corn Tortillas (Extra Thin!, Super Size White!, Super Size Yellow!, White!, Yellow!)
- **Nuevo Leon** - White Corn Tortillas
- **Que Pasa▲** - Corn Tortillas
- **San Carlos** - Masa Lista
- **Trader Joe's** - Corn Tortillas (Handmade!!, Original!!)

Trail Mix
- **Back To Nature** -
  - Harvest Blend
  - Nantucket Blend
  - Sonoma Blend
- **Eden Organic** - All Mixed Up
- **Enjoy Life▲** - Not Nuts (Beach Bash●, Mountain Mambo●)
- **FritoLay** - Nut & Fruit!!
- **Mareblu Naturals▲** -
  - Crunch Bags (Almond●, Cashew●, Cashew Coconut●, CranMango Cashew●, Pecan Cinnamon●, Pecan Cranberry Cinnamon●)
  - Trail Mix Crunch Bags (Blueberry Pomegranate●, Cranberry Pomegranate●, Cranblueberry●, Cranstrawberry●, Pecan●, Pistachio●)
- **Nuts Online** - Mango Goji Fire Sprouted●, Wild Berry Sprouted●
- **Oskri Organics** - Honey Crunch (Almond, Cashew w/Cranberries, Pecan w/Cinnamon)
- **Pure Market Express▲** - The Goji Trail●
- **Trader Joe's** - Go Raw Trek Mix, Simply Almonds Cashews & Cranberries Trek Mix, Simply The Best Trek Mix
- **Wild Garden** - Tropical Mix

Trek Mix... see Trail Mix
Tuna... see also Fish
 ... *All Fresh Fish Is Gluten/Casein/Soy Free (Non-Marinated, Unseasoned)
 Bumble Bee - Tonno In Olive Oil
 Crown Prince - Natural Solid White Albacore (No Salt, Regular)
 Great Value Brand (Wal-Mart) - Pouch w/Water
 Henry & Lisa's - Canned Solid White Albacore
 Kirkland Signature - Albacore, Fresh Ahi
 Lowes Foods Brand - Chunk Lite
 Member's Mark - Highest Quality Solid White Albacore Tuna In Water
 Publix - Tuna Fillets
 Starkist -
  Gourmet Choice (Albacore Tuna Fillet, Low Sodium, Solid Light Tuna Fillet In Olive Oil, Solid Light Tuna Fillet In Water, Very Low Sodium, Yellowfin Marinated Tuna Fillet w/Roasted Garlic)
  Pouch Yellowfin Tuna In Extra Virgin Olive Oil
 Trader Joe's - Marinated Ahi Tuna Steaks
Turkey... see also Deli Meat
 ... *All Fresh Poultry Is Gluten/Casein/Soy Free (Non-Marinated, Unseasoned)
 Applegate Farms -
  Natural (Herb Turkey Breast, Honey & Maple Turkey Breast, Roasted Turkey Breast, Smoked Turkey Breast, Turkey Bologna, Turkey Salami, Uncured Turkey Hot Dogs)
  Organic (Herb Turkey Breast, Smoked Turkey Breast)
  Organic Turkey Burgers
  Organic ncured Turkey Hot Dogs
  Turkey Salami
 Armour - Deli (Oven Roasted, Oven Roasted w/Broth, Smoked)
 Boar's Head - All Varieties
 Bowman & Landes - All Turkeys

T

Butcher's Cut - Ground Turkey, Jumbo Turkey Franks, Oven Roasted Turkey Breast (97% Fat Free, Deli Style 98% Fat Free)

Butterball -

All Natural Turkey (Cutlets, Filets, Strips, Tenders)

Burgers Fresh (All Natural, Seasoned)

Fresh Fully Cooked Turkey (Oven Baked, Smoked)

Fresh Turkey (Li'l Butterball, Whole)

Frozen

   Boneless Roast (Ready To Roast Classic, Turkey)

   Fully Cooked Turkey (Baked, Li'l Butterball Baked, Smoked)

   Turkey (Li'l Butterball, Whole *(Except Stuffed Turkeys)*)

Fully Cooked Turkey Breast Roast (Cherrywood Smoked, Honey Smoked, Oven Roasted)

Ground Turkey (Italian Style, Regular, Seasoned, Turkey Breast, White)

Ground Turkey Chub (All Natural (85/15, 93/7), Seasoned)

Lunch Meat (Extra Thin Turkey Breast (Honey Roasted, Oven Roasted, Smoked), Lean Family Size (Honey Roasted Turkey Breast, Oven Roasted Turkey Breast, Smoked Turkey Breast, Turkey Bologna, Turkey Ham), Thick Sliced (Honey Roasted, Oven Roasted, Smoked), Thin Sliced (Honey Roasted, Oven Roasted, Smoked)

Tenderloins Herb Roasted

Turkey

   Bacon (Lower Sodium, Regular, Thin & Crispy)

   Breast (Fully Cooked Whole (Baked, Smoked), Ready To Roast Classic Bone In)

   Breasts Fresh Whole

   Drumsticks

   Sausage (Fresh Bratwurst, Fresh Breakfast, Fresh Hot Italian, Fresh Sweet Italian, Polska Kielbasa Dinner, Smoked, Smoked Dinner, Smoked Hot)

   Thighs

   Wings

Carl Buddig -
  Deli Cuts (Honey Roasted Turkey, Oven Roasted Turkey,
    Smoked Turkey)
  Extra Thin Original (Honey Roasted Turkey, Oven Roasted
    Turkey, Regular)
  Fix Quix Turkey
  Original (Honey Roasted Turkey, Oven Roasted Turkey, Regular)
Carolina Turkey - Ground Turkey
Castle Wood Reserve - Deli Meat (Herb Roasted Turkey Breast,
  Hickory Smoked Turkey, Oven Roasted Turkey, Turkey Pastrami)
Dietz & Watson▲ -
  Applewood Smoked●
  Black Forest Chef Carved Smoked●
  Black Forest Turkey●
  Carving Ready●
  Chipotle Pepper●
  Fire Roasted Breast Of Turkey●
  Glazed Honey Cured Turkey Breast●
  Herbed●
  Honey Mustard●
  Italian Style●
  Maple & Honey Cured●
  Mesquite Smoked●
  Oven Classic●
  Roasted●
  Slow Roasted●
  Smoked (Breast Fillets●, Julienne Strips●, Peppercorn●)
  Turkey Ham●
Eckrich - Deli Meat (Mesquite Smoked, Oven Roasted, Smoked)
Empire Kosher -
  Fresh Chill Pack Turkey
  Frozen Whole Turkey & Turkey Breasts
  Fully Cooked Barbecue Turkey (Fresh, Frozen)

T

Ground Turkey (Fresh, Frozen)
Premier Signature Edition
    All Natural Turkey Breast (Skinless, w/Skin)
    Breast Pastrami Skinless
    Pastrami Skinless
    Smoked Turkey Breast Skinless
Roll
    Turkey (Bologna, Salami)
    White Turkey
Signature Edition Turkey Breast (Oven Prepared, Smoked)
Skinless Honey Smoked Turkey Breast
Slices
    Smoked Turkey Breast
    Turkey (Bologna, Breast, Pastrami)
Turkey Franks
Farmer John - Lunch Meat Premium Oven Roasted Turkey Breast
Garrett County Farms -
    Frozen Turkey Maple Breakfast Links **!**
    Turkey Andouille **!**
    Turkey Breast Sliced (Roasted **!**, Smoked **!**, Turkey Ham **!**, Turkey Ham
        Steak **!**)
    Turkey Franks **!**
    Turkey Kielbasa **!**
    Turkey Tom Tom Snack Sticks **!**
Hillshire Farms - Deli Select Thin Sliced Turkey Breast (Honey
    Roasted, Oven Roasted, Smoked), Deli Select Ultra Thin Turkey Breast
    (Honey Roasted, Oven Roasted)
Honeysuckle White -
    Estate Recipe Turkey Deli Meat
        Canadian Brand Maple
        Dry Roasted
        Hickory Smoked (Honey Pepper, Original)
        Honey Smoked
        Mesquite Smoked

Fresh
  Bone In Turkey Breast
  Breast
    Boneless Skinless
    Cutlets
    Roast
    Strips
    Tenderloins
    Thin Cut Slices (Scallopini & Milanesa)
  Drumsticks
  Neck Pieces
  Split Breast
  Thighs
  Wing (Drumettes, Portions)
  Wings
Frozen
  Bone In Turkey Breast
  Boneless (Turkey, Turkey Breast w/Gravy Packet)
  Turkey Burgers
Fully Cooked Hickory Smoked Bone In Turkey Breast
Ground Turkey (85/15, 93/7, 97/99% Fat Free)
  Italian Style Seasoned
  Patties
  Roll (93/7, 99% Fat Free)
  Taco Seasoned
Hardwood Smoked (Bacon, Franks)
Hickory Smoked Deli Meat
  Cooked Turkey Salami
  Turkey (Ham, Pastrami)
Lunch Meat Deli Sliced
  Hickory Smoked (Honey Turkey Breast, Turkey Breast)
  Oven Roasted Turkey Breast
  Turkey Pastrami
Marinated Turkey Selections
  Balsamic Rosemary Turkey Breast Tenderloins

T

Creamy Dijon Mustard Breast Tenderloins
Lemon Garlic Breast Tenderloins
Rotisserie Turkey Breast Tenderloins
Zesty Italian Herb Breast Tenderloins
Ready To Roast Turkey Breast
Sausage
  Links
    Breakfast
    Hot Italian
    Original Smoked
    Poblano Pepper
    Sweet Italian
  Patties (Breakfast)
  Roll (Breakfast, Mild Italian)
  Traditional Bratwurst
Turkey Bologna
Turkey Breast Deli Meats
  Cajun Style Hickory Smoked
  Hickory Smoked (Peppered, Regular)
  Honey Mesquite Smoked
  Oven Prepared
Turkey Sausage Breakfast Roll
Whole Young Turkey
  Fresh
  Fresh All Natural
  Frozen
  Frozen All Natural
  Fully Cooked (Hickory Smoked, Oven Roasted)
Hormel -
  Bread Ready (Oven Roasted, Smoked)
  Chunk Meats Turkey
  Deli Meat Natural Choice (Honey, Oven Roasted, Smoked)
  Natural Choice Deli Counter (Honey Mesquite, Oven Roasted)
  Turkey Pepperoni

Hy-Vee - All Natural (Fresh, Frozen), Cubed, Deli Thin Slices Turkey Breast (Honey Roasted, Oven Roasted), Thin Sliced (Honey Turkey, Turkey)

Isaly's - All Deli Meat

Jennie-O Turkey Store -
Breakfast Lover's Turkey Sausage
Deli Meat Hickory Smoked Turkey Breast Cracked Pepper
Extra Lean Smoked Turkey Sausage (Kielbasa, Regular)
Flavored Tenderloins (Lemon Garlic, Roast Turkey Flavor)
Fresh
Breakfast Sausage Mild Patties
Dinner Sausage (Hot Italian, Lean Turkey Bratwurst, Sweet Italian)
Ground Turkey (Extra Lean, Italian, Lean, Taco Seasoned)
Frozen Ground Turkey Regular
Refrigerated (Turkey Ham, Quarter Turkey Breasts Sun Dried Tomato)
Turkey Franks

Johnsonville - Tenderloins Lemon Pepper

Jones Dairy Farm - Golden Brown All Natural Fully Cooked Turkey Sausage Links●

Kayem - Turkey Breast (Homestyle, Homestyle w/Skin On)

Manor House - Frozen Enhanced Turkey

Meijer Brand -
Frozen (Breast Tenders, Duckling, Split Breast, Young)
Gold Turkey (Hen, Tom)
Hen Turkey
Regular Turkey Breast
Tom Turkey
Turkey Basted w/Timer
Turkey Breast (Fresh, Fresh Natural, Hickory Smoked, Honey Roasted, Zipper 97% Fat Free)

Member's Mark - Premium Chunk Turkey Breast In Water

T

Organic Prairie -
Fresh Organic
Hardwood Smoked Turkey Bacon**!!**
Sliced Roast Turkey Breast**!!**
Sliced Smoked Turkey Breast**!!**
Frozen Organic
Ground Turkey 12 oz.**!!**
Whole Young Turkey (10-14 lbs., 14-18 lbs.)
Oscar Mayer -
Deli Fresh Meats (Oven Roasted, Smoked Turkey Breast)
Deli Meat (Lean White Honey Smoked, Oven Roasted White
Turkey, Smoked White Turkey)
Shaved Deli Fresh Meats (Cracked Black Peppered Turkey Breast,
Honey Smoked Turkey Breast, Oven Roasted Turkey Breast,
Smoked Turkey Breast)
Thin Sliced Deli Fresh (Honey Smoked Turkey Breast, Oven
Roasted Turkey Breast, Smoked Turkey Breast)
Perdue - Ground Turkey Burgers, Ground Turkey (Fresh Breast,
Fresh Lean)
Primo Taglio - Turkey Breast (Dinner Roast, Honey Maple, Mesquite
Smoked, Natural Hickory Smoked, Natural Hickory Smoked
Peppered, Pan Roasted)
Private Selections - Frozen Seasoned Burgers (Lean, Regular)
Publix -
Deli Fully Cooked Turkey Breast
Deli Pre Pack Lunch Meats (Extra Thin Sliced Oven Roasted
Turkey Breast, Extra Thin Sliced Smoked Turkey Breast,
Smoked Turkey, Turkey Breast)
Fully Cooked Breast
Ground Turkey (Breast, Regular)
Sara Lee - Deli Meat Slices (Cracked Pepper Turkey Breast,
Hardwood Smoked Turkey Breast, Honey Roasted Turkey Breast,
Oven Roasted Turkey Breast)

Shelton's -
 Free Range Ground
   Turkey (#1 Chub Pack, #3 Chub Pack)
   White Turkey #1 Chub Pack
 Free Range Whole Turkey (8-15 lbs., 16-26 lbs.)
 Organic (Large, Whole Small)
 Turkey Burgers
SPAM - Oven Roasted Turkey
Trader Joe's - Deli Meat (Oven Roasted Turkey Breast, Smoked
 Turkey Breast Sliced)
Tropical Traditions - Pastured Whole Turkey
Valley Fresh - All Varieties
Wegmans Brand -
 Lean Ground Turkey (94%, 99%)
 Organic Turkey Breast (Honey Roasted, Oven Roasted)
 Sliced Turkey Breast (Oven Browned, Smoked)
 Split Turkey Breast
 Turkey (Drumsticks, London Broil, Thighs, Wings)
Wellshire Farms -
 Morning Maple Turkey Breakfast Link Sausage**!!**
 Sliced (Oven Roasted Turkey Breast**!!**, Smoked Turkey Breast**!!**,
   Turkey Bologna**!!**, Turkey Ham**!!**)
 Turkey (Andouille Sausage**!!**, Franks**!!**, Kielbasa**!!**)
 Turkey Dinner Link Sausage (Mild Italian Style**!!**)
 Turkey Ham (Ham Steak**!!**, Nuggets**!!**, Whole**!!**)
 Turkey Tom Toms (Hot & Spicy**!!**, Original**!!**)
 Wellshire Organic - Organic Turkey Bacon
 Winn Dixie - Frozen Whole
Turkey Bacon... see Bacon
Turkey Breast... see Turkey
Turkey Burgers... see Burgers... see Turkey
Turkey Ham... see also Ham... see also Turkey
 Honeysuckle White - Hickory Smoked Turkey Ham
Turkey Jerky... see Jerky/Beef Sticks

T
U
V

Turnips
> ... *All Fresh Turnips Are Gluten/Casein/Soy Free*

Lowes Foods Brand - Turnip Greens w/Diced Turnips
Pictsweet - All Plain Frozen Turnips
Safeway Brand - Frozen Chopped
Winn Dixie - Frozen (Chopped, w/Turnips)

U
V

Vanilla Extract... see Extract
Vanilla Powder
    Authentic Foods▲
    Gifts Of Nature▲ - Cooks Vanilla Powder
    Mixes From The Heartland▲ - Powdered Vanilla●
    Really Great Food Company▲
Vegetable Juice... see Drinks/Juice
Vinegar
    Albertsons - Apple Cider, Red Wine, White Distilled
    Bakers & Chefs - White Distilled
    Bionaturae - Organic Balsamic
    Bragg - Apple Cider
    Dave's Gourmet - Precocious Pepper
    Eden Organic - Organic (Apple Cider, Brown Rice, Red Wine, Ume Plum)
    Grand Selections - Balsamic Of Modena, Red Wine, White Wine
    Great Value Brand (Wal-Mart) - Apple Cider, Balsamic, Distilled White, Premium (Garlic Flavored Red Wine, Red Wine)
    Hannaford Brand - Apple Cider, Balsamic, Red Wine, White
    Heinz - Apple Cider, Distilled White, Garlic Wine, Red Wine
    Holland House - All Vinegars *(Except Malt Vinegar)*
    Hy-Vee - Apple Cider Flavored Distilled, White Distilled
    Kirkland Signature - Balsamic

V

W

Kroger Brand - All Varieties *(Except Malt Vinegar)*
Kurtz - Apple Cider, Distilled White
Meijer Brand - Balsamic Aged (4 Yr., 12 Yr.), Cider, Red Wine, White Distilled, White Wine
Musselman's - Apple Cider, White Distilled
Newman's Own Organics - Balsamic
O Organics - Balsamic
Publix - Red Wine, White Distilled
Regina - All Varieties *(Except Malt Vinegar)*
Safeway Select - Balsamic, Red Wine, Rice, White Wine
Santa Barbara Olive Co. - Basil, Garlic & Pepper, Oregano, Tarragon
Spartan Brand - Apple Cider, White
Spectrum - Balsamic, Organic (Balsamic, Brown Rice, Distilled White, Filtered Apple Cider, Golden Balsamic, Red Wine, Seasoned Brown Rice, Unfiltered Apple Cider, White Wine)
Stop & Shop Brand - Cider, White, Wine
Trader Joe's - Orange Muscat Champagne
Tropical Traditions - Coconut Water Vinegar
Wegmans Brand - Apple Cider, Asian Classic Rice, Balsamic, Chianti Red Wine, Red Wine, Tuscan White Wine, White Distilled
Winn Dixie - Apple Cider, White
Vitamins... see Gluten/Casein/Soy Free OTC Pharmacy Section
Vodka

... *All Distilled Alcohol Is Gluten/Casein/Soy Free[2]*

W

Waffles/Waffle Mix... see Pancakes/Pancake Mix
Walnuts... see Nuts
Wasabi
   Eden Organic - Wasabi Powder
   Hime - Powdered Sushi Wasabi
   Sushi Sonic - Real Wasabi

W Water

Acqua Panna - Natural Spring

Albertsons - All Varieties

Aquafina -

    Flavor Splash (Grape, Lemon, Peach Mango, Raspberry, Strawberry Kiwi, Wild Berry)

    Purified Drinking Water

    Sparkling Water (Berry Burst, Citrus Twist)

Aquarius Spring - Natural Spring Water

Arrowhead - Mountain Spring

Calistoga - Sparkling Mineral Water (All Flavors)

Crystal Geyser - Alpine Spring, Sparkling Mineral Water

Dasani - Essence (Black Cherry, Lime, Strawberry Kiwi), Lemon, Purified

Deer Park - Natural Spring

Deja Blue - Purified Drinking Water

Evian

Fiji - Natural Artesian

Fruit2O - All Varieties

Hannaford Brand - Natural Spring, Seltzer Water, Sparkling (Black Cherry, Key Lime, Kiwi Strawberry, Peach, Raspberry, Tropical Punch, White Grape)

Hy-Vee -

    10 oz. Fun Pack (Flavored, Regular)

    10 oz. Kids Size Purified Water w/Fluoride

    Mother's Choice Infant Water (Regular, w/Fluoride)

    Natural Spring

    Premium Distilled

    Purified

    Spring

    Tonic

Ice Mountain - Spring Water

Kirkland Signature - Vita Rain

Kroger Brand - Crystal Clear Flavored Water

Lowes Foods Brand - Drinking, Spring

water

Meijer Brand - Calcium, Distilled, Flavored (Crystal Quencher
  (Black Cherry, Key Lime, Kiwi Strawberry, Peach, Raspberry,
  Tangerine Lime), White Grape), Natural Calcium, Spring
Nestle Pure Life - Purified
Ozarka - Natural Spring
Perrier - Carbonated Natural Spring
Poland Spring - Natural Spring
Publix - Spring Water
Safeway Brand - Drinking, Purified Drinking, Spring
San Pellegrino - Sparkling Mineral
Snapple - All Varieties
SoBe -
  Lifewater
    Agave Lemonade
    Blackberry Grape
    Orange
    Tangerine
    Pomegranate Cherry
    Strawberry Kiwi
    w/Purevia
      Acai Fruit Punch
      B Energy Black Cherry Dragonfruit
      B Energy Strawberry Apricot
      Black & Blue Berry
      Cherimoya Punch
      Fuji Apple Pear
      Mango Melon
      Strawberry Dragonfruit
      Strawberry Kiwi Lemonade
      Syrah Grape Berry
      Yumberry Pomegranate
Spartan Brand - Water (Distilled, Drinking, Natural Spring, Spring)
Trader Joe's - All Sparkling

W Vitaminwater (Glaceau) - Defense Connect, Dwnld, Energy,
    Essential, Fruit Punch, Multi-V, Power-C, Revive, Spark, Stur-D, XXX
WaterPlus
Wegmans Brand -
    Aqua Mineral Water (Italian, Lemon, Lemongrass, Lime,
      Mixed Berry)
    Sparkling Water (Lemon, Lime, Mandarin Orange, Mineral, Mixed
      Berry, Natural, Raspberry, Tangerine Lime)
Winn Dixie - Distilled, Drinking, Purified, Sparkling (All Flavors), Spring
Zephyrhills - Natural Spring

Water Chestnuts
    ... *All Fresh Water Chestnuts Are Gluten/Casein/Soy Free*
Ka-Me - Sliced & Peeled **!**, Whole & Peeled **!**
Reese - Diced, Sliced, Whole
Spartan Brand - Canned (Sliced, Whole)

Watermelon
    ... *All Fresh Watermelon Is Gluten/Casein/Soy Free*

Whipping Cream
MimicCreme - Almond & Cashew Cream (Sugar Free Sweetened,
    Sweetened, Unsweetened), Healthy Top Whipping Cream
Soyatoo - Rice Whip

Whiskey
    ... *All Distilled Alcohol Is Gluten/Casein/Soy Free* [2]

Wine
    ... *All Wine Made In The USA Is Gluten/Casein/Soy Free* [2]

Wing Sauce
Moore's Marinade - Honey BBQ Wing

Wings
    ... *All Fresh Chicken Is Gluten/Casein/Soy Free*
Great Value Brand (Wal-Mart) - Frozen Wing Sections
Wegmans Brand - Chicken Wings

Worcestershire Sauce
Great Value Brand (Wal-Mart) - Worcestershire Sauce
Hannaford Brand

Hy-Vee - Light
Kurtz
Lea & Perrins - Low Sodium, Original, Thick Original
Meijer Brand
Publix

W

X

Y

X

Xanthan Gum
   Augason Farms▲ - ●
   Authentic Foods▲
   Bob's Red Mill▲
   Cause You're Special▲
   Ener-G▲
   Gifts Of Nature▲
   Gluten-Free Essentials▲ - ●
   Hodgson Mill▲
   Kinnikinnick▲
   Mixes From The Heartland▲ - ●
   Nuts Online - ●
   Really Great Food Company▲

Y

Yams
   ... *All Fresh Yams Are Gluten/Casein/Soy Free
   S&W - All Canned Vegetables
   Spartan Brand - Yams Cut
Yeast
   Bakipan - Active Dry, Bread Machine, Fast Rising Instant
   Bob's Red Mill▲ - Active Dry
   Gayelord Hauser - 100% Natural Brewer's Yeast (Flake Form,
      Tablet Form)
   Hodgson Mill▲ - Active Dry, Fast Rise

Y
Z

Kroger Brand - Yeast Packets
Nuts Online - Gluten Free (Nutritional Yeast●, Yeast●)
Really Great Food Company▲ - Yeast
Red Star - Active Dry, Bread Machine, Cake, Quick Rise
SAF - Bread Machine, Gold Instant, Gourmet Perfect Rise, Red
   Instant, Traditional Active Dry

Yogurt

Nogurt - Organic (Banana Cinnamon●, Blueberry●, Chocolate●,
   Orange●, Pomegranate●)
Pure Market Express▲ - Cocogurt●, Strawberry Cocogurt Parfait●
Ricera - All Varieties
So Delicious - Coconut Milk (Blueberry●, Chocolate●, Passionate
   Mango●, Pina Colada●, Plain●, Raspberry●, Strawberry●,
   Strawberry Banana●, Vanilla●)

Z

Zucchini

   *... *All Fresh Zucchini Is Gluten/Casein/Soy Free*
C & W - All Plain Frozen Vegetables
Nuts Online - Simply Zucchini Freeze Dried Vegetables●
Trader Joe's - Frozen Misto Alla Grigio ! !

Gluten/Casein/Soy Free
Over The Counter (OTC)
Pharmacy Guide

Rx Allergy/Sinus/Cold/Flu Relief

Afrin - Nasal Spray (All Varieties)
Airborne -
  Lemon Lime
  On The Go Lemon Lime
  Original
  Pink Grapefruit
  Very Berry
California Baby - Colds & Flu Massage Oil
Claritin - Childrens Grape Chewables, Childrens Grape Syrup, D24
Cold-Eeze - Cold Remedy Lozenges (All Flavors)
Dayquil -
  Cold & Flu Plus Vitamin C Caplets
  Cough Liquid
  Mucus Control Expectorant Liquid
  Mucus Control Expectorant Cough Suppressant Liquid
Halls -
  Cough Drops Regular (Cherry, Ice Blue, Mentho Lyptus,
    Strawberry, Tropical Fruit)
  Halls Breezers (Cool Berry, Sugar Free Cool Berry)
  Halls Defense (Harvest Cherry, Strawberry, Watermelon)
  Halls Naturals (Honey Lemon Chamomile, Wild Cherry)
  Halls Refresh (Juicy Strawberry)
Meijer -
  Cough Cold (Infant Drops Cherry)
  PE Allergy Sinus Caplets
  PE Cold Flu Day Cool Caplets
  PE Cold Severe Congestion Caplets
  Diphedryl (Tablets)
  Loratadine (D 24hr Tablets)
  Nasal Spray (Liquid, No Drip Pump Liquid)
  Nitetime 6 hr (Cherry Liquid, Liquid Gels, Original Liquid)

Rx

Nitetime Cough 6 hr (Cherry Liquid)
Triacting Nitetime Grape Liquid
Tussin (Cough Cold Softgels)
Nyquil -
Cold & Flu Liquid (Alcohol Free, Cherry, Childrens, Original)
Cough Liquid (Cherry)
Nightime Relief LiquiCaps
Plus Vitamin C Cold & Flu Caplets
Olbas - Aromatherapy Massage Oil & Inhalant, Cough Syrup, Inhaler
Organix - Organic Cough & Sore Throat Drops (Dark Chocolate Mint, Golden Honey Lemon, Orchard Cherry)
Primatene - Mist
Publix - Adult Cold Relief, Children's Cough Cold Allergy
Sinex - Nasal Spray (Moisturizing Ultra Fine Mist, Regular, Ultra Fine Mist)
Theraflu - Warming Relief Syrups (Cold & Chest Congestion, Flu & Sore Throat)
Vicks -
44 Custom Care Liquid
Chesty Cough
Cough & Cold
Dry Cough
Baby Rub
Vapo Rub Ointment (Lemon, Regular)
Vapo Steam

Antacids

Lactaid - Dietary Supplement (Fast Act Caplets, Fast Act Chewables, Original Strength Caplets)
Meijer -
Antacid Calcium (Peppermint Chewables, XS Berry Chewables, XS Chewables, XS Tropical Chewables, XS Wintergreen Chewables)

Rx
    Cimetidine Tablets
    Effervescent Antacid Pain Tablets
    Milk Of Magnesia (Mint Liquid, Original Liquid)
    Pink Bismuth (Chewables, Maximum Strength Liquid, Regular
      Strength Liquid)
    Ranitidine
Pepto Bismol - All Varieties
Prilosec OTC
Tagamet - HB

Antibiotic/Analgesic Ointment & Spray

Cortaid - Poison Ivy Removal Cloths

Anti-Diarrhea

Lactaid - Dietary Supplement (Fast Act Caplets, Fast Act Chewables,
    Original Strength Caplets)
Meijer - Pink Bismuth (Chewables, Maximum Strength Liquid, Regular
    Strength Liquid)
Pepto Bismol - All Varieties

Anti-Fungal

AZO - Yeast Tablet (Maximum Strength, Standard)
Meijer -
    Miconazole Cream (3 Day Preapp. Combo, 3 Day Dissap. Combo, 7
      Day Dissap, 7 Day Reapp)
    Tioconazole 1 Day Ointment (Disapp.)

Anti-Gas

Rx

Lactaid - Dietary Supplement (Fast Act Caplets, Fast Act Chewables, Original Strength Caplets)

Cosmetics

Afterglow Cosmetics▲ - All Products
Arbonne -
    Kelp
        Blusher
        Cream Concealer
        Eye Liner
        Eye Shadow
        Lip Liner
        Loose Translucent Powder
        Mineral Powder Foundation SPF 15
        Wipe Out Eye Makeup Remover

Cough Drops/Sore Throat Spray/Lozenges

Albertsons - Sore Throat Spray
Cold-Eeze - Cold Remedy Lozenges (All Flavors)
Halls -
    Cough Drops Regular (Cherry, Ice Blue, Mentho Lyptus, Strawberry, Tropical Fruit)
    Halls Breezers (Cool Berry, Sugar Free Cool Berry)
    Halls Defense (Harvest Cherry, Strawberry, Watermelon)
    Halls Naturals (Honey Lemon Chamomile, Wild Cherry)
    Halls Refresh (Juicy Strawberry)
Olbas - Pastilles, Sugar Free Lozenges
Organix - Organic Cough & Sore Throat Drops (Dark Chocolate Mint, Golden Honey Lemon, Orchard Cherry)

Rx

Deodorant

Crystal -
  All Deodorants
  All Crystal Essence
Naturally Fresh Deodorant Crystal -
  Roll On
  Clear Twist Up Stick w/Aloe Vera
Tom's Of Maine - Natural Body Bar Deodorant

Hair Care

California Baby -
  Calming Hair (Conditioner, Detangler)
  Calming Shampoo & Body Wash
  Super Sensitive Hair Conditioner
  Super Sensitive Shampoo & Body Wash
  Swimmer's Defense (Conditioner, Shampoo & Body Wash)
  Tea Tree & Lavender (Hair Conditioner, Shampoo & Body Wash)
  Calendula Hair Conditioner
  Calendula Shampoo & Body Wash
Desert Essence Organics - Conditioner (Fragrance Free, Green
  Apple & Ginger, Italian Red Grape, Red Raspberry)
EO -
  Conditioner (Rose Geranium & Citrus●, Rosemary & Mint●)
  French Lavender Detangler Spray Rosemary & Cedarwood Pre
      Shampoo Treatment●
  Shampoo (Chamomile & Honey●, French Lavender●, Rose &
      Chamomile●, Rosemary & Mint●, Sweet Orange●)
  Wild Lime & Ginger Hair Repair●
  Wild Rose & Coconut Conditioning Serum●
Gluten-Free Savonnerie▲ - All Products

Head & Shoulders - All Shampoo & Conditioner   **Rx**
Johnson's - Baby Shampoo
Keys▲ - All Products
Kroger Brand - Comforts For Baby (Baby Wash, Shampoo)
Meijer - Minoxidil 5% Liquid (30 Day, 90 Day)

Laxatives/Hemorrhoidal Relief

Citrucel -
    Caplets
    Fiber Therapy Powder (Orange Regular, Orange Sugar Free)
Fleet - Fiber Gummies
Konsyl - All Fiber Products
Meijer -
    Fiber Therapy Caplets
    Hemorrhoidal (Suppository)
    Laxative Tablets (Natural MS, Senna)
    NVP (Capsules, Original Orange Powder, Original Regular Powder,
        Smooth Orange Powder, Sugar Free Smooth Orange Powder)
Metamucil ▬
    Capsules (Plus Calcium, Regular)
    Powder Coarse Milled Original Texture (Orange, Unflavored)
    Powder Smooth Texture (Orange)
Pedia-Lax -
    Chewable Tablets (Watermelon)
    Enema
    Fiber Gummies
    Liquid Stool Softener (Fruit Punch)
    Quick Dissolve Strips
Tucks - Medicated Pads, Take Along Medicated Pads

Rx
Lip Care

Arbonne -
Before Sun Lip Saver SPF 30
Bio Nutria Herbal Lip Ointment
Bio Nutria Lip Service Dietary Supplement
Blistex -
Deep Renewal
Raspberry Lemonade Blast
Desert Essence Organics -
Lip Tints
Coconut
Italian Red Grape
Red Raspberry
Vanilla Chai

Miscellaneous Products

Band-Aid - Flexible Fabric
Nature's Baby Organics - All Purpose Deodorizer (Lovely Lavender, Vanilla Tangerine)

Oral Hygiene

Albertsons - Mouth Rinse
Aquafresh -
Toothpaste
Cavity Protection
Extra Fresh
Sensitive
Crest - All Mouthrinses, All Toothpaste Varieties, All Whitestrips
Glide - Floss
Jason - All Toothpastes Varieties

Kolorz - Prophy Paste *(at the dentist)*
Listerine -
  Agent Cool Blue Tinting Rinse
  Antiseptic Mouthwash (All Varieties)
  Pocket Paks Oral Care Strips (All Varieties)
  Totalcare Anticavity Mouthwash (All Varieties)
  Whitening Pen
  Whitening Pre Brush Rinse
  Whitening Quick Dissolving Strips
  Whitening Vibrant White Rinse
  ZERO Mouthwash
Nupro -
  Fluoride
  Prophy Paste *(at the dentist)*
Oasis - Moisturizing (Mouthwash, Spray)
Plax -Advanced Formula Plaque Loosening Rinse (Original, Soft
  Mint)
Publix - Mouth Rinses
Sensodyne - Pronamel Toothpaste
Tom's Of Maine - Floss Antiplaque (Flat, Round)

Pain Relief

Meijer -
  Apap (Caplet, Cool Caplet, ER Caplet Red, ER Caplet White, ETS
    Tablet, Gelcap, Geltab, Tablet)
  Aspirin (Child Orange Chewables, Coated Tablets, Coated Yellow
    Tablets)
  Enteric Coated Yellow Tablets
  Headache Tablets
  Ibuprofen
    Caplets Brown
    Caplets Orange
    Junior Caplet

Rx
    Tablets Brown
    Tablets Orange
    Migraine Caplets
    Naproxen Sodium (Caplets, NCRC Caplets, Tablets)

Pet Food

IAMS –
    Healthy Naturals Dry Cat Food Adult (Weight Control)
    Premium Protection Dry Cat Food (Adult Cat, Kitten, Senior Cat)
    Premium Protection Dry Dog Food (Puppy)
    ProActive Health Canned Cat Food (Adult Filets w/Chicken In
        Gravy, Adult Filets w/Salmon In Sauce, Adult Filets w/Skipjack
        Tuna In Sauce, Adult Pate w/Chicken & Liver, Adult Pate w/
        Pacific Salmon, Adult Pate w/Seafood Sampler, Adult Premium
        w/(Country Style Turkey & Giblets, Gourmet Chicken, Lamb &
        Rice, Select Oceanfish, Tender Beef), Kitten Premium Pate w/
        Gourmet Chicken)
    ProActive Health Canned Dog Food (Adult Ground Dinner w/
        (Beef & Rice, Chicken & Rice, Lamb & Rice, Turkey & Rice),
        Adult Ground Mixed Grill w/Chicken & Beef, Puppy Ground
        Dinner w/Chicken & Rice)
    ProActive Health Dry Cat Food (Adult Active Maturity, Adult Active
        Maturity Hairball Care, Adult Digestive Care, Adult Hairball
        Care, Adult Indoor Weight & Hairball Care, Adult Multi Cat w/
        Chicken, Adult Original Chicken, Adult Original Ocean Fish
        w/Rice, Adult Original w/Lamb & Rice, Adult Original w/Tuna,
        Adult Weight Control, Kitten)
    ProActive Health Dry Dog Food (Adult Active Maturity Small &
        Toy Breed, Adult Chunks, Adult Mini Chunks, Smart Puppy
        Large Breed, Smart Puppy Original, Smart Puppy Small & Toy
        Breeds)
    Veterinary Formula Dry Dog Food (Intestinal Low Residue Puppy)
    Science Diet - Adult Cat Optimal Care (Oceanfish & Rice, Original)

Rx

Play Dough

Aroma Dough - All Natural Playing Dough
BlueDominoes - Organic Activity Dough●
Crayola - Air Dry Clay, Model Magic, Model Magic Fusion, Modeling Clay *(Crayola Dough Is Not Gluten/Casein/Soy Free)*
Max's Mud - Organic Sculpting Dough●

Skin Care

Arbonne -
  Aromassentials
    Awaken Sea Salt Scrub 16 oz.
    Unwind (Bath Salts, Massage Oil)
  Bio Nutria
    Herbal (Muscle Massage Gel, Vapor Rub)
    Leg Vein Formula
  Clear Advantage
    Acne Lotion
    Skin Support Supplement
    Spot Treatment
  FC5
    Moisturizing Night Crème
    Nurturing Day Lotion w/SPF 20
    Oil Absorbing Day Lotion w/SPF 20
    Purifying Cleanser + Toner
    Skin Conditioning Oil
    Ultra Hydrating Hand Crème
  NutriMinC RE9
    Retaliate Wrinkle Filler
  SeaSource Detox Spa
    5 In 1 Essential Massage Oil
    Foaming Sea Salt Scrub

Rx   Purifying Sea Soak
Remineralizing Body Lotion 24 Hr.
Renewing Body Gelée
Sea Mud Face and Body Mask

California Baby -
Aloe Vera Cream
Calendula (Cream, Everyday Lotion)
Calming (Bedtime Massage Oil, Botanical Moisturizing Cream,
   Diaper Rash Cream, Everyday Lotion, Massage Oil, Non Talc
   Powder, Soothing & Healing Spray)
Citronella (SPF 30+ Sunscreen Lotion, Summer Lotion)
Colds & Flu Massage Oil
Everyday/Year Round SPF 30 (Sunblock Stick, Sunscreen Lotion)
I Love You Aromatherapy Massage Oil
Overtired & Cranky Massage Oil
Resistance Builder Essential Oil
Sunblock Stick SPF 30 (No Fragrance)
Sunscreen Lotion SPF 18 (No Fragrance)
Sunscreen Lotion SPF 30 (Citronella, No Fragrance)
Super Sensitive (Everyday Lotion, Massage Oil)
Therapeutic (French Lavender Essential Oil, Tea Tree Pure
   Essential Oil)

Coppertone -
Sensitive Skin
Sport Lotion (All SPFs)
Sport Spray (All SPFs)
Water Babies (All SPFs)

Desert Essence Organics -
Age Reversal Pomegranate (Eye Serum, Face Serum)
Age Reversal SPF 30 Mineral Sunscreen
Almond Hand & Body Lotion
Bulgarian Lavender Hand & Body Lotion
Coconut Hand & Body Lotion
Frangrance Free Hand & Body Lotion
Pistachio Foot Repair Cream

Rx

Pumpkin Hand Repair Cream
Spicy Citrus Hand & Body Lotion
Vanilla Chai Hand & Body Lotion
Gluten-Free Savonnerie▲ - All Products
Johnson's - Baby Oil
Keys▲ - All Products
Lubriderm -
   Daily Moisture Lotion
      Fragrance Free
      Moisturizer w/Sunscreen SPF 15
      Original
      Sensitive Skin
      w/Shea & Cocoa Butter
Nature's Baby Organics -
   Baby Oil
   Silky Dusting Powder
   Soothing Stick
Olbas - Herbal Bath

Sleep Aids

Meijer - Sleep Aid Nitetime (Caplets, Tablets)

Soap

Arbonne -
   Aromassentials
      Awaken Sea Salt Scrub 16 oz.
      Unwind Bath Salts
   Bio Nutria Herbal Vapor Soak
   Clear Advantage Acne Wash
   FC5
      Purifying Cleanser + Toner

Rx SeaSource Detox Spa
  Foaming Sea Salt Scrub
  Purifying Sea Soak
California Baby -
  Bubble Bath (Calendula, Calming, Chamomile & Herbs, Colds
    & Flu, I Love You, Light & Happy, Overtired & Cranky, Party, Super
    Sensitive)
  Calendula Shampoo & Body Wash
  Calming Shampoo & Body Wash
  Diaper Area Wash
  Handwash (First Aid Moisturizing, Natural Antibacterial Blend
    Moisturizing, Super Sensitive)
  Swimmer's Defense Shampoo & Body Wash
  Tea Tree & Lavender Shampoo & Body Wash
Desert Essence Organics -
  Age Reversal Pomegranate Facial Cleansing Gel
  Almond Body Wash
  Bulgarian Lavender Body Wash
  Coconut (Body Wash, Hand Wash)
  Fragrance Free Body Wash
  Grapefruit Hand Wash
  Green Apple & Ginger Body Wash
  Italian Red Grape Body Wash
  Lavender Hand Wash
  Red Raspberry Body Wash
  Vanilla Chai (Body Wash, Hand Wash)
EO -
  Liquid Hand Soap (Chocolate & Mint●, French Lavender●,
    Lemon & Eucalyptus●, Peppermint & Tea Tree●, Rose
    Geranium & Citrus●, Rosemary & Mint●, Unscented
    w/Coconut Milk●)
  Shower Gel (Chocolate & Peppermint●, Grapefruit & Mint●,
    Lavender●, Orange Fusion●, Rose & Chamomile●)

supplements

Rx

Fleurish Beauty - Aloe & Shea Body Wash
Gluten-Free Savonnerie ▲ - All Products
Johnson's - Head To Toe Baby Wash
Keys ▲ - All Products
Kiss My Face -
  Peace Soap
    100% Natural All Purpose Castile Soap (Grassy Mint, Lavender
      Mandarin, Lemongrass Clary Sage, Pomegranate Acai)
    100% Natural Foaming Castile Soap (Grassy Mint, Lavender
      Mandarin, Lemongrass Clary Sage, Pomegranate Acai)
Tom's Of Maine - Body Bar (Natural Deodorant)

Stay Awake

Meijer - Stay Awake Tablets
Vivarin - Tablets

Supplements

Arbonne - Smart Nutritional Hybrids Daily Nutritional Chews For
  Teens, Smart Nutritional Hybrids Daily Power Punch For Kids
Country Life -
  Activated Charcoal Caplets●
  Bee Propolis Veg Caps●
  Bio Active Hyaluronic Acid●
  Celadrin●
  Cod Liver Oil●
  CoQ10●
  Daily Dophilus●
  Daily Fiber X Veg Caps●
  Easy Iron●
  Natural Acidophilus w/Pectin Veg Caps●
  Norwegian Kelp●
  Power Dophilus Veg Caps●

Rx
    RNA/DNA●
    Resveratrol Plus●
    Shark Cartilage Veg Caps●
    Shark Liver Oil●
    Stress Shield●
    Super Fiber Psyllium Seed Husk Powder●
    Super Omega 3●
    Ultra Omegas DHA/EPA●
    Zinc Picolinate●

Flex A Min - Complete

GlutaSolve - Powdered Glutamine Supplement (Packets)

Hy-Vee HealthMarket - Healthy Eyes Extra

Iceland Health -
    Advanced Memory Formula w/Omega 3
    Co Q10 Softgels
    Glucose Control Formula
    Immunity Plus
    Maximum Strength Omega 3 Softgels

Kirkman Labs -
    Acetyl L Carnitine
    Acidophilus Powder
    Alpha Ketoglutaric Acid
    Alpha Lipoic Acid
    Amino Support (Capsules, Powder)
    Beta Glucan
    Bifido Complex (Advanced Formula, Regular)
    Bio Core Dairy
    Buffered Magnesium (Glycinate Bio Max Series Powder, Oxide)
    Carb Digest w/Isogest
    Chromium
    Cod Liver Oil (Lemon Lime Liquid, Regular Liquid, w/Vitamins A
      & D)
    Coenzyme Q10 (Capsules, Chewable Tablets, Tablets)
    Colostrum Gold (Flavored, Unflavored)

supplements

Rx

Creatine (Capsules)

DMAE (Capsules, Chewable Wafers)

DMG (Capsules, Capsules w/Folic Acid & B12, Capsules w/Folinic Acid & B12, Liquid, Maximum Strength, w/B12 & Folinic Acid Liquid)

DPP IV Forte

Detox Aid Advanced Formula

Detoxification Aid Pro Support II

EFA Powder

EnZymAid Multi Enzyme Complex

EnZym Complete DPP IV II (Regular, w/Isogest)

Everyday Multi Vitamin (Regular, w/o Vitamins A & D)

Folic Acid (Chewable Tablets, w/B12 Capsules, w/B12 Liquid)

Folinic Acid (Capsules, w/B12 Liquid)

GABA (Plain, w/Niacinamide & Inositol)

Gastro Support

Gastromune AI Support

Ginkgo Biloba

Glucosamine Sulfate

Glycine

Grape Extract

Grapefruit Seed Extract

Idebenone

Immuno Aid

Inositol Pure Soluble Powder

Iron Bio Max Series (Capsules, Liquid)

L Glutamine

L Taurine

Lactobacillus Acidophilus

Lactobacillus Duo

Magnesium Citrate Soluble Powder

Magnesium Glycinate Bio Max Series

Magnesium Malate

Magnesium Sulfate Cream

Rx Maximum Spectrum Enzyme Complete/DPP IV Fruit Free
  w/Isogest
Melatonin (Chewables, Plus Magnesium, Slow Release Tablets)
Methylcobalamin Concentrated Powder
Milk Thistle
Mito Cell Support
Molybdenum
Multi Enzyme Formula
Multi Flora Spectrum
N Acetyl Cysteine
Nu Thera (Everyday, Everyday Companion, w/P5P, w/o Vitamins
  A & D)
P5P (Regular, w/Magnesium Glycinate)
Peptidase Complete
Phenol Assist (Companion, Regular)
Pro Bio (Chewable Wafers, Defense, Gold, Inulin Free)
Pro Culture Gold
Pro Immune Support
Reduced L Glatathione (Capsules, Lotion)
Saccharomyces Boulardii
Selenium
Spectrum Complete (Capsules, Powder Flavored, Powder
  Regular)
Super Cranberry Extract (Capsules, Chewables)
Super NuThera (Caplets, Capsules, Challenge Powders, Lemon
  Lime Liquid, New Improved Powder, Powder, Raspberry
  Flavored Concentrate, Tropical Fruit Liquid, w/P5P Caplets,
  w/P5P Lemon Lime Flavored Concentrate, w/P5P Liquid, w/
  P5P New Improved Powder, w/P5P Powder, w/Vitamins A & D
  (Cherry Liquid, Regular, Tropical Fruit Liquid))
Super Pro Bio (Bio Max Series)
TMG (Capsules, Capsules w/Folic Acid & B12, Liquid w/Folinic
  Acid & B12, Powder w/Folic Acid & B12, w/Folic Acid & B12,
  w/Folinic Acid & B12, w/Folinic Acid & Methyl B12)
Thera Response

supplements

Rx

    Threelac
    Vanadium
    Yeast Aid (Capsules, Powder)
Meijer -
    Antioxidant (Natural Caplets)
    Cinnamon Capsules
    Cranberry Caplets
    Echinacea
    Evening Primrose Oil Softgels
    Ferrous Gluconate Tablets
    Fish Oil Hi Potency Softgels
    Flax Seed Oil Softgels
    Folic Natural Tablets
    Garlic Hi Potency Odorless Tablets
    Gingko Biloba
    Glucosamine & Collagen & HA
    Glucosamine Chondroitin (3X, All Day Double Strength Tablets, Extra Strength, Plus MSM, Regular Strength Caplets, SOD Free Caplets, w/HA Tablets, w/MSM Double Strength Caplets, w/ MSM HLA Caplets)
    Glucosamine Complex Caplets
    Glucosamine Sulfate Caplets
    Green Tea
    Panax Ginseng
    Potassium Natural Caplets
    St. John's Wort Caplets
    Vision Formula w/Lutein
Member's Mark (Sam's Club) -
    Flaxseed Oil
    Glucosamine +MSM
    Glucosamine
    Probiotic Formula Acidophilus
    Red Yeast Rice
Osteo Bi-Flex - Double Strength Tablets, Strength Tablets

Rx Publix -

 Calcium (Citrate Caplets, Tablets)
 Cranberry Caplets
 Echinacea Caplets
 Evening Primrose Oil Softgels
 Fish Oil Softgels
 Folic 400mcg Natural Tablets
 Ginkgo Biloba Caplets
 Glucosamine Chondroitin
 L Lysine Natural Tablets
 Magnesium Natural Tablets
 Potassium Gluconate
 Saw Palmetto Softgels
 Selenium Tablets
 St. John's Wort

Schiff - Probiotics Acidophilus (Tablets)

Simplexity Health -

 Alpha Sun (Capsules, Tablets)
 ImmuSun
 Omega Sun (Capsules, Tablets)
 OsteoSun
 StemPlex

Vitamins & Minerals

Country Life -

 Action B Caps●
 Basic B Caps●
 Bio Rutin Complex●
 Biotin●
 Buffered Vitamin C●
 Cap C Veg Caps●
 Chewable Acerola C Complex●

Rx

Chewable Orange Juice●
Choline●
Choline Inositol Complex●
Citrus Bioflavonoids●
Coenzyme Active B6●
Dry Vitamin D●
Flush Free Niacin Veg Caps●
Folic Acid●
Grape Complete Caps●
Grape Seed Extract Veg Caps ●
Hi Potency Biotin●
Inositol Powder●
Lutein●
Maxi C Complex Vitamin C●
Niacin●
Niacinamide●
PABA●
Pantothenic Acid●
Rutin●
Stress M●
Sublingual Vitamin B12●
Super Potency Action B●
Super Potency Hi B●
Vitamin A Dry●
Vitamin B1●
Vitamin B2●
Vitamin B6●
Vitamin B6 Veg Caps●
Vitamin B12●
Vitamin C●
Vitamin C Crystals●
Vitamin D3●
Vitamin K1●

Rx Kirkman Labs -

Advanced Adult Multi Vitamin

Advanced Mineral Support

B Complex w/CoEnzymes Pro Support (Capsules, Powder)

Calcium Bio Max Series

Calcium Magnesium Liquid

Calcium w/Vitamin D (Chewable Tablets, Powder Unflavored)

Calcium w/o Vitamin D Bio Max Series

Children's Chewable Multi Vitamin/Mineral (Capsules, Wafers)

Buffered Vitamin C Powder

D Biotin

Multi Mineral Complex Pro Support

Multi Vitamin Pro Support

Mycellized Vitamin A Liquid

Perry Prenatal

Vitamin B6 (Magnesium Vitamin/Mineral Chewable Wafers, Regular)

Vitamin C (Bio Max Series Buffered Powder Flavored, Bio Max Series Buffered Powder Unflavored, Capsules, Chewables, Tablets)

Vitamin (D, D3, E)

Zinc (Bio Max Series, Liquid, Sulfate, w/Vitamin C & Slippery Elm Lozenges)

Meijer -

A Shaped (Gummy Chewables, w/Iron Chewables)

Advanced Formula w/Ester C

Calcium (All Day w/Vitamin D, Citrate w/Vitamin D Caplets, Coral, Magnesium Zinc Caplets, Natural Oyster Shell Tablets, Tablets, w/D Chewables, w/D Mineral Tablets)

Daily Energy Multi Caplets

Ester C

Ferrous Sulfate (TR Tablets)

Multi Vitamin (Century Advantage, Century Mature Tablets, Century Tablets, RDI Cholesterol Caplets)

Niacin Tablets

One Daily Plus Mens Tablets

Slow Release Iron

Rx

Teen Multi Caplets
Vitamin B (Complex w/Iron, Natural Tablets, Regular Tablets,
    Synthetic Tablets, Time Released Tablets)
Vitamin B12 Tablets
Vitamin C (Caplets, Natural w/Rose Hips Caplets, Synthetic
    Tablets)
Vitamin E Synthetic Softgels
Zinc Natural Caplets
Member's Mark (Sam's Club) -
Niacin
Slow Release Iron
Vitamin B Complex w/Vitamin C
Vitamin B12
Nutrition Now -
Rhino Gummy (Calci Bear, Chewy C, Multivitamin, Omega 3,
    Veggie Fruit, Vitamin D)
Rhino Chewable (C & Echinacea, Calcium & Vitamin D, FOS &
    Acidophilus, Zinc)
Adult Gummi Vitamins (B Complex, Calcium, Co Q10, Multi Vites,
    Omega 3, Vitmain B12, Vitamin C, Vitamin D, Vitamin E)
Ocuvite - Original
Publix -
Niacin Time Release Tablets Vitamin B (6, 12)
Vitamin C (Tablets, Time Release Tablets)
Zinc Natural Caplets
Schiff - Niacin Flush Free (Tablets)
Slice Of Life - Gummy Vitamins For Adults (All Varieties)
Yummi Bears - All Varieties (Organic, Regular)

Weight Loss

Country Life - 7 Ketotrim●, Genaslim●
Natrol - CitriMax Plus, Pure CitriMax

Index

index

index

index

index

Gluten-Free OTC Pharmacy

NOTES

NOTES

Making Gluten-Free Living Easy!

Cecelia's Marketplace
Kalamazoo, Michigan

www.CeceliasMarketplace.com

Mail In Order Form

Quick Order Form

Online Orders: www.CeceliasMarketplace.com

✉ Mail Orders: Kal-Haven Publishing
P.O. Box 20383
Kalamazoo, MI 49019
U.S.A.

Cecelia's Marketplace	Quantity	Price	Total
Gluten-Free Grocery Shopping Guide	_____	(x $24.95) =	_____
Gluten/Casein Free Grocery Shopping Guide	_____	(x $24.95) =	_____
Gluten/Casein/Soy Free Grocery Shopping Guide	_____	(x $24.95) =	_____
Gluten-Free Mexican Cookbook	_____	(x $14.95) =	_____

Sales Tax: Michigan residents please add 6% sales tax _____

Sub Total: _____

Shipping: (quantities 1-2 add $5.95)
(quantities 3-6 add $11.95) _____

Total: _____

*Please make check or money order payable to Kal-Haven Publishing

Name:_____

Address:_____

City:_____State:_____Zip:_____

Email address:_____

Making Gluten-Free Living Easy!

Cecelia's Marketplace
Kalamazoo, Michigan

www.CeceliasMarketplace.com

Mail In Order Form

Quick Order Form

Online Orders: www.CeceliasMarketplace.com

Mail Orders: Kal-Haven Publishing
P.O. Box 20383
Kalamazoo, MI 49019
U.S.A.

Cecelia's Marketplace	Quantity	Price	Total
Gluten-Free Grocery Shopping Guide	_____	(x $24.95) =	_____
Gluten/Casein Free Grocery Shopping Guide	_____	(x $24.95) =	_____
Gluten/Casein/Soy Free Grocery Shopping Guide	_____	(x $24.95) =	_____
Gluten-Free Mexican Cookbook	_____	(x $14.95) =	_____

Sales Tax: Michigan residents please add 6% sales tax _____

Sub Total: _____

Shipping: (quantities 1-2 add $5.95)
(quantities 3-6 add $11.95) _____

Total: _____

*Please make check or money order payable to Kal-Haven Publishing

Name: _____

Address: _____

City: _____ State: _____ Zip: _____

Email address: _____

Making Gluten-Free Living Easy!

Cecelia's Marketplace
Kalamazoo, Michigan

www.CeceliasMarketplace.com

Mail In Order Form

Quick Order Form

Online Orders: www.CeceliasMarketplace.com

✉ **Mail Orders:** Kal-Haven Publishing
P.O. Box 20383
Kalamazoo, MI 49019
U.S.A.

Cecelia's Marketplace	Quantity	Price	Total
Gluten-Free Grocery Shopping Guide	_____	(x $24.95) =	_____
Gluten/Casein Free Grocery Shopping Guide	_____	(x $24.95) =	_____
Gluten/Casein/Soy Free Grocery Shopping Guide	_____	(x $24.95) =	_____
Gluten-Free Mexican Cookbook	_____	(x $14.95) =	_____

Sales Tax: Michigan residents please add 6% sales tax _____

Sub Total: _____

Shipping: (quantities 1-2 add $5.95)
(quantities 3-6 add $11.95) _____

Total: _____

*Please make check or money order payable to Kal-Haven Publishing

Name:_____

Address:_____

City:_____State:_____Zip:_____

Email address:_____